Perspectives in
Forest Entomology

Proceedings of a Lockwood Conference on
Perspectives of Forest Pest Management held
at The Connecticut Agricultural Experiment Station,
New Haven, Connecticut, October 15-17, 1975

Perspectives in Forest Entomology

Edited by
John F. Anderson
Harry K. Kaya

Department of Entomology
The Connecticut Agricultural Experiment Station
New Haven, Connecticut

Academic Press   New York   San Francisco   London   1976

A Subsidiary of Harcourt Brace Jovanovich, Publishers

ACADEMIC PRESS, INC.
111 Fifth Avenue, New York, New York 10003

United Kingdom Edition published by
ACADEMIC PRESS, INC. (LONDON) LTD.
24/28 Oval Road, London NW1

Library of Congress Cataloging in Publication Data

Main entry under title:

Perspectives in forest entomology.

   "A Lockwood conference on perspectives of forest
pest management held at the Connecticut Agricultural
Experiment Station, New Haven, Connecticut, October
15-17, 1975."
      Bibliography: p.
      Includes indexes.
      1.   Forest insects–Control.   2.   Forest
insects.   I.   Anderson, John F.,   Date
II.   Kaya, Harry K.   III.   Connecticut.   Agricultural
Experiment Station, New Haven.
SB761.P47   634.9'6'7   76-14452
ISBN 0–12–056650–8

PRINTED IN THE UNITED STATES OF AMERICA

To Samuel William Johnson

1876 photo by William Notman—Montreal, Toronto, & Halifax.

Contents

SECTION II.   INSECT BIONOMICS

SECTION III.   INSECT BEHAVIOR

SECTION IV.   BIOLOGICAL AND INTEGRATED CONTROL

APPENDIX

Contributors

SANDRA L. ANAGNOSTAKIS, Department of Genetics, The Connecticut Agricultural Experiment Station, New Haven, Connecticut 06504.

JOHN F. ANDERSON, Department of Entomology, The Connecticut Agricultural Experiment Station, New Haven, Connecticut 06504.

DONALD E. AYLOR, Department of Ecology and Climatology, The Connecticut Agricultural Experiment Station, New Haven, Connecticut 06504.

T. C. BAKER, Pesticide Research Center, Michigan State University, East Lansing, Michigan 48824.

CHARLES C. DOANE, Department of Entomology, The Connecticut Agricultural Experiment Station, New Haven, Connecticut 06504.

DENNIS M. DUNBAR, Department of Entomology, The Connecticut Agricultural Experiment Station, New Haven, Connecticut 06504.

J. M. FRANZ, Biologische Bundesanstalt für Land- und Forstwirtschaft, Institut für biologische Schädlingsbekämpfung, Darmstadt, Federal Republic of Germany.

J. GRANETT, Department of Entomology, The Connecticut Agricultural Experiment Station, New Haven, Connecticut 06504.

G. H. HEICHEL, Department of Ecology and Climatology, The Connecticut Agricultural Experiment Station, New Haven, Connecticut 06504.

MARJORIE A. HOY, Department of Entomology, The Connecticut Agricultural Experiment Station, New Haven, Connecticut 06504; now with the U. S. Forest Service, Northeastern Forest Experiment Station, Hamden, Connecticut 06514.

RICHARD A. JAYNES, Department of Genetics, The Connecticut Agricultural Experiment Station, New Haven, Connecticut 06504.

HARRY K. KAYA, Department of Entomology, The Connecticut Agricultural Experiment Station, New Haven, Connecticut 06504.

FRED B. KNIGHT, School of Forest Resources, University of Maine, Orono Maine 04473.

KENNETH L. KNIGHT, Department of Entomology, North Carolina State University, Raleigh, North Carolina 27607.

G. N. LANIER, Department of Forest Entomology, State University of New York, College of Environmental Science and Forestry, Syracuse, New York 13210.

P. S. MESSENGER, Department of Entomological Sciences, University of California, Berkeley, California 94720

J. R. MILLER, Department of Entomology, New York State Agricultural Experiment Station, Geneva, New York 14456.

RICHARD C. MOORE, Department of Entomology, The Connecticut Agricultural Experiment Station, New Haven, Connecticut 06504.

J. W. PEACOCK, USDA Forest Service, Northeastern Forest Experiment Station, Delaware, Ohio 43015.

W. L. ROELOFS, Department of Entomology, New York State Agricultural Experiment Station, Geneva, New York 14456.

R. M. SILVERSTEIN, Department of Chemistry, State University of New York, College of Environmental Science and Forestry, Syracuse, New York 13210.

DAVID M. SMITH, Yale University School of Forestry and Environmental Studies, New Haven, Connecticut 06520.

GEORGE R. STEPHENS, Department of Ecology and Climatology, The Connecticut Agricultural Experiment Station, New Haven, Connecticut 06504.

Y. TANADA, Division of Entomology and Parasitology, University of California, Berkeley, California 94720.

NEIL C. TURNER, Department of Ecology and Climatology, The Connecticut Agricultural Experiment Station, New Haven, Connecticut 06504.

NEAL K. VAN ALFEN, Department of Plant Pathology, The Connecticut Agricultural Experiment Station, New Haven, Connecticut 06504.

PAUL E. WAGGONER, Director, The Connecticut Agricultural Experiment Station, New Haven, Connecticut 06504.

W. G. WELLINGTON, Institute of Animal Resource Ecology and Department of Plant Science, University of British Columbia, Vancouver, British Columbia, Canada.

RONALD M. WESELOH, Department of Entomology, The Connecticut Agricultural Experiment Station, New Haven, Connecticut 06504.

Preface

In recognition of the founding of the first state agricultural experiment station in the United States, a Lockwood conference entitled "Perspectives of Forest Pest Management" was held in New Haven at the Connecticut Agricultural Experiment Station in October 1975, 100 years to the month after its opening. The proceedings of the conference are published in this volume, *Perspectives in Forest Entomology*. We dedicate this book to Dr. Samuel W. Johnson, an outstanding scientist of his time and the leading figure in the founding of the first agricultural experiment station.

The recent extensive and well-publicized outbreaks of forest insects attest to the timeliness of this work. The growing need for wood and its products, the ever-increasing number of people who enjoy the tranquility of the forest, the extension of the suburb into forested area—"suburban forest," and the increased desire to manage forest pests with the minimal use of chemical pesticides make it imperative to develop methods of pest management that are effective and acceptable to society. Designed to bring current knowledge on forest pest management into perspective, *Perspectives in Forest Entomology* should be of value to all who are concerned and interested in the subject.

We extend our appreciation to everyone who made this book possible and the conference a success. We thank the authors for their presentations and their promptness in completing their manuscripts. The time they have taken to present their material and summarize their thoughts should accelerate research and discovery. We thank the moderators of the conference: Drs. Paul E. Waggoner, James B. Kring, Israel Zelitch, and Ronald M. Weseloh and acknowledge Mrs. Sandra Piontek for her efforts with the conference registration.

Special thanks are extended to Mr. Paul Gough for his editorial assistance and to Mrs. Carol Lemmon and Mr. Michael Fergione for their assistance in compiling the bibliography and the indices. We are grateful to the staff of Academic Press for their cooperation in the production of this book. Finally, we wish to acknowledge the encouragement given by our Director, Dr. Paul E. Waggoner, and the support of the Station's Board of Control which provided the funds out of the Lockwood Trust that helped make the conference a reality.

John F. Anderson
Harry K. Kaya

Foreword

WELCOME TO THE EXPERIMENT STATION

On the occasion of its Centennial and on behalf of its Board of Control, I welcome you to America's first Agricultural Experiment Station. In October 1875 Wilbur Olin Atwater and two assistants began the work of the Station, and in October 1975 you have come to help us begin the New Century of the Station.

The name Lockwood and the nouns Forest and Pest are in the title of this Conference, and thus three of the stars of the Station are brought into conjunction.

Subscribing to the theory that people dominate events and history, I begin with the name Lockwood. To introduce William Raymond Lockwood, however, I must first detour, introducing two of the extraordinary men who caused America's first station to be in Connecticut.

These men were Samuel William Johnson and William Henry Brewer, both born in New York State, one in 1828 and the other only two years later. In 1850 both were in New Haven, drawn here by John Pitkin Norton, Benjamin Silliman, Jr., and their "School of Applied Chemistry," which had an established position but little other encouragement from Yale College. Both Johnson and Brewer studied in Justus Liebig's chemistry laboratory in Munich. By 1865 both were professors in the Sheffield Scientific School. And both became members of the National Academy of Sciences.[1]

Johnson and Brewer must have been different sorts despite their friendship. Johnson could see only a few feet without powerful glasses, he wrote constantly and suffered "writer's cramp", he was always the chemist, and he was a retiring scholar.

Brewer must have been more of an extrovert. I have seen a photograph of a geological survey party in California in 1864. There in the center sits bearded, booted Brewer, dominating the group. Sometimes Brewer was a chemist, sometimes a geological explorer, sometimes a botanist, sometimes a professor of agriculture, and sometimes a sanitarian.

The singleminded Johnson campaigned for twenty years for a Landwirtsch-aftlich Versuchsstation in America as he had seen during his student days in Germany in 1854. He had written the specifications early: Near to, but not part of, an academy so that research could go on full-time in an intellectual community. Steady state support so that serious rather than quick inquiries could be pursued. "Practice and theory ought to go together ... Agriculture will flourish from that day when practical men shall be philosophical enough to appreciate the philosopher's thoughts; and the philosophers practical enough to calculate the farmer's profits."[2]

Finally, in 1875 Johnson's specifications were met when the Connecticut legislature established the first American station.

Friend Brewer was on hand. When the Station Director concluded his first report, Brewer was the first to speak in support of the new Station, and the next day Brewer led a committee that recommended liberal support for the Station. His friendship continued undiminished; 34 years later his last official act before his death was attending a meeting of the Station Board.[3]

On the evening back in 1876 when Brewer rose to support the Station, however, he was a vigorous 46 years old, and he did more that night than lobby. He lectured on "Woods and woodlands." He told the audience that there was an enormous European literature relating to woodlands, but "vastly less, however, in English than in the Continental languages." Nevertheless, the species that would succeed in any region could only be determined by actual experiment, and America lacked experiments. Thus Brewer could not offer much knowledge about the best trees to plant.

The Board of Agriculture was upset by this proclamation of ignorance, and a committee was proposed to gather practical information and fill the void. Brewer, however, warned them, "The information that you are after does not exist," and it did not. No one on that December night in 1876 mentioned pests, and Brewer even predicted, "The chestnut will some day become more popular than now."

Now we reach William Lockwood of Norwalk, who would provide the remedy for the lacking experiments. Lockwood was only 7 years older than Brewer. Lockwood's son had prepared himself for agriculture by attending Sheffield Scientific School, but he died the following year. Lockwood was particularly acquainted with Brewer, who had instructed his son and who was secretary and treasurer of the Station. It was quite natural, then, that when making his will, Lockwood would have assisted the new Station, which promised to advance agriculture when it was feeling the agricultural competition of the west and the industrial competition of the east.[4]

In 1900 Lockwood's bequest became available to the Station, and Lockwood Field was promptly purchased for experiments in forestry. Also forester Walter Mulford was employed in 1901.

In 1856 Johnson had said, "Observation is the eye that watches (nature's) voluntary movement ... Experiment [,however,] is a wise cunning that cross-examines her and pries out her secret counsels."[5] In 1876 Brewer had complained of our lack of experiments in woodlands, and in 1900 Brewer's friend Lockwood enabled the experiments to begin at last. Although it had been a long campaign, Johnson was still director of the Station, and Brewer was still secretary of the Board in 1900!

This introduces the name Lockwood and the noun Forest. That leaves Pest.

The three great pests that have come to our suburban forest are the fungus that causes chestnut blight, the fungus that causes Dutch elm disease, and the insect called gypsy moth. Other pests have nibbled away or even burst forth and declined, but the two great fungal pests have nearly eliminated two valuable trees that we still lament, missing the woodwork, poles and nuts of one and the cathedral shade of the other. And the gypsy moth has likely only ebbed in 1975 as it has before, waiting for the right time to break forth again. These three pests were unforeseen when Brewer lectured on woodlands in 1876, and yet they appeared in Connecticut within the next two generations, changing the suburban forest more than all the selection and introduction of species that concerned Brewer. The three pests have rightly occupied much of the Station's attention,[6] and they will occupy you at this conference.

The frustration of man has been a characteristic shared by these three pests. Consider student Wilton Everett Britton, who wrote in high hope in 1893 of the day "when Experiment Stations keep in stock fungous germs and parasitic insects ready to check any sudden outbreak." Britton came to the Station in 1894 as a horticulturalist, and by 1898 he had made himself "something of an economic entomologist."[7] Thus he was ready when the gypsy moth appeared in Connecticut in 1906. He and his colleagues waged war on the gypsy moth. Nevertheless, after four decades of war and expense the moth was still here, and in 1945 Britton's successor, Roger Boynton Friend, concluded in both defeat and hope, "The gypsy moth in Connecticut has attained the status of a native insect pest with natural factors of control."[6]

Friend's hope was dashed. Severe outbreaks occurred in 1957 and 1961–1964. I recall that in 1962 at the first Lockwood Conference,[8] the discussion of the gypsy moth was a gloomy one. If the Conference could have foreseen the future, the discussion would have been even gloomier because in 1972 the gypsy moth, aided by the elm spanworm, ate the foliage from a record acreage of our suburban forest.

At the darkest time, however, there was a glimmer. A parasitic wasp removed the elm spanworm as if by magic, and the mystery and fear of unknown numbers of oaks dying in the train of the defoliators was allayed by learning that a borer gives the coup de grace.[9] Learning to grow the gypsy moth in confinement smoothed the way for studying parasites, and knowledge grew.[10]

Meantime a glimmer has also appeared in the darkness of the two fungal diseases. After decades of faithful labor to prove chemotherapy of plant disease was at least a possibility, chemotherapy even seems possible now for Dutch elm disease.[11] And after two generations of faithful search for chestnuts that resist blight, it seems possible that a hypovirulent strain of the pathogen could debilitate its virulent relative.[12]

You have now met Lockwood, Forest, and Pest. In the first year of this Station, one of its patriarchs lectured on the ignorance of woods and woodlands, and by the end of the 19th Century Lockwood had enabled the first experiments here to remove that ignorance. Then pests came to frustrate us.

As the second century of American Agricultural Experiment Stations dawns, so too dawns new hope for solving the problems of forest pests that have perplexed this state and Station. This is a bright beginning for the Lockwood Conference and for the New Century.

Paul E. Waggoner, Director

The Connecticut Agricultural Experiment
Station, New Haven, Connecticut 06504

NOTES

[1] The histories of Johnson and Brewer can be found in the book by E. A. Osborne, 1913. From the letter files of S. W. Johnson. Yale University Press, New Haven, in the introduction to F. P. Farquhar (ed.) 1930. Up and down California in 1860–1864, the Journal of William H. Brewer, Yale University Press, New Haven, and in the book by M. W. Rossiter. 1975. The emergence of agricultural science. Justus Liebig and the Americans, 1840-1880. Yale University Press, New Haven.

[2] Johnson, S. W. 1855. Theory and practice. Country Gentleman 5:300–301.

[3] Brewer's support of the Station and his lecture on woodlands are published in the Tenth Annual Report of the Connecticut Board of Agriculture. 1877. Case, Lockwood and Brainard Co., Hartford. His attendance at the Board is described in a Minute of the Board of Control, December 22, 1910.

[4] Information about Lockwood is taken from an unknown author's summary of Board records and newspaper reports from Norwalk, Ct., 1896.

[5] Johnson, S. W. 1856. Relations which exist between science and agriculture. Address to the New York State Agricultural Society, Albany. See Osborne, footnote 1.

[6] The history of the Station and the gypsy moth is told by R. B. Friend, 1945. The gypsy moth in Connecticut. Ct. Acad. Arts Sci. Trans. 36:607–629, in a collection of histories by N. Turner, C. C. Doane, J. B. Kring, and S. W. Hitchcock, 1974. Ct. Ent. Soc. 25th Ann. Mem. p. 19–98, and by J. F. Anderson and S. W. Gould. 1974. Defoliation in Connecticut 1969–1974. Ct. Agri. Exp. Sta. Bull. 749. The battle with chestnut blight is described by R. A. Jaynes. 1964. Interspecific crosses in the genus *Castanea*. Silvae Genetica 13:125–164. Turner, op cit. mentions the arrival of Dutch elm disease in Connecticut in 1933.

[7] Britton's graduation eassay and his self-appraisal quoted by Turner, op cit.

[8] Waggoner, P. E. and J. D. Ovington. 1962. Proceedings of the Lockwood Conference on the suburban forest and ecology. Ct. Agr. Exp. Sta. Bull. 652.

[9] Anderson, J. F. and H. K. Kaya. 1973. Influence of elm spanworm oviposition sites on parasitism by *Ooencyrtus clisiocampae* and *Telenomus alsophilae*. Environ. Entomol. 2:705–711.

Dunbar, D. M. and G. R. Stephens. 1975. Association of twolined chestnut borer and shoestring fungus with mortality of defoliated oak in Connecticut. Forest Sci. 21:169-174.

[10] Leonard, D. E. and C. C. Doane. 1966. Artificial diet for the gypsy moth, *Porthetria dispar*. Ann. Ent. Soc. Amer. 59:462–464.

Weseloh, R. M. and J. F. Anderson. 1975. Release of *Apanteles melanoscelus* for control of the gypsy moth. Environ. Entomol. 4:33–36.

Hoy, M. A. 1975. Hybridization of the strains of the gypsy moth parasitoid, *Apanteles melanoscelus* (Hymenoptera: Braconidae), and its influence upon diapause. Ann. Ent. Soc. Amer. 68:261–264.

[11] Zentmyer, G. A., J. G. Horsfall and P. P. Wallace. 1946. Dutch elm disease and its chemotherapy. Ct. Agr. Exp. Sta. Bull. 498.

Biehn, W. L. and A. E. Dimond. 1971. Prophylatic action of benomyl against Dutch elm disease. Plant Disease Reptr. 55:179–182.

[12] Van Alfen, N. K., R. A. Jaynes, S. L. Anagnostakis and P. R. Day. 1975. Chestnut blight: biological control by transmissible hypovirulence in *Endothia parasitica*. Science 189:890–891.

I

THE FOREST

Chapter 1

Changes in Eastern Forests Since 1600 and Possible Effects

David M. Smith

Yale University School of Forestry and Environmental Studies
New Haven, Connecticut 06520

INTRODUCTION

Forestry is so steeped in ecological principles that we chronically suspect, at least subconsciously, that many problems with forest pests are of our own making. This notion is partly correct, but can too easily be carried to the absurd conclusion that the man-free forest had no pests at all. There is no need to belabor the point that there were plenty of damaging agencies, biotic and non-biotic, at work in forests before we came. Furthermore forest vegetation is, at any time and place, the product of the lethal but life-renewing agencies that have been at work upon it. The purpose of this discourse is to examine how people have altered the forests of eastern North America in the hope that this may shed some light on how the interactions between forests and their dependent pests have changed and are changing.

REDUCTION IN AVERAGE AGE

Most of eastern North America was covered with forests when European settlement started almost four centuries ago. The most important thing that has happened since is that virtually all of this vast forest has been cut over at least once, or, if not cut, as in some of the most remote parts of Canada, heavily burned at least once. The result is that the average age of present forests is younger, by an indeterminable amount, than that of the so-called "original" forest. Presumably we have, in general, reduced the biotic pests of old forests and increased those associated with young forests.

If we still had many old forests, as is the case in the West, we would now be more concerned than we are with heart-rotting fungi, certain *Dendroctonus* bark beetles, and other pests associated with old trees. Since younger forests were not absent, we may presume that the native pests of young forests were active four centuries ago and are merely more active now, along with those very bad actors which we have inadvertently introduced.

CLEARANCE OF FOREST FOR AGRICULTURE

The next most important effect has been the removal of a major part of the original forest for agriculture and other uses. This has made existing forests more discontinuous and created more of the subtle, dimly known effects on pest problems that may be associated with interface between forest and either field or urban influence. Of more obvious importance in forest pest management has been the development of somewhat unnatural forest composition on immense areas of land where agricultural use ceased after varying degrees of soil degradation.

As far as the eastern United States is concerned, it is possible only to approximate the areas of original forest, of maximum clearance, and of cleared land reverted to forest. The original forest area approached 700 million acres. Very roughly half of this has been cleared at one time or another; evidence on this point from the old census records (Hendrickson, 1933) is difficult to interpret because much forest land, especially in the South, went through cycles of clearing, abandonment, and reclearing. In any event, the present forest area is close to 400 million acres; at least 50 million and probably not more than 100 million of these forest acres are on land that was once in agriculture. The only region without very much forest on former agricultural land is the Corn Belt. It should also be noted that at least three-quarters of the present eastern forest is on land that has not been cleared for other use.

If the history of forest vegetation of eastern North America is recounted centuries hence, the present epoch will perhaps be recognized as that in which "old-field" forest stands were common. Our posterity may indeed be somewhat puzzled about what these unplanned products of land-use history might have been. We are now entering a time when land is more likely to be recleared for agriculture than to revert to forest, so old-field stands will gradually become less common. However, the much more recent phenomenon of the pure stand planted after intensive site preparation will presumably continue as the future counterpart of the old-field stand.

The most important and common kind of old-field stand is the abnormally pure conifer stand that typically invades abandoned fields covered with grasses. Along the Atlantic Seaboard, where most of the land abandonment has been, there is a gradational series of coniferous species which participate in this phenomenon.

Starting from eastern Canada and, in order southward, the most important of these are white spruce (*Picea glauca* (Moench.) Vos.), red spruce (*Picea rubens* Sarg.), sometimes with balsam fir (*Abies balsamea* (L.) Mill.), eastern white pine (*Pinus strobus* L.), Virginia pine (*Pinus virginiana* Mill.), shortleaf pine (*Pinus echinata* Mill.) in inland areas but loblolly pine (*Pinus taeda* L.) over most of the South, and, near the Gulf Coast, slash pine (*Pinus elliottii* Engelm.).

One of the most remarkable characteristics of old-field conifer stands is they are generally more likely to be limited to a single species than the natural forests of the same localities. Sometimes this purity has been ascribed to the browsing of broad-leaved species by domestic animals during the periods of declining use. However, there are probably additional ecological factors, such as ordinary competition, chemical antagonisms, abnormal populations of soil organisms and microclimatic effects, associated with the exotic and native grasses of old fields which tend to hamper invasion by conifers less than that by woody angiosperms. The question of why conifers are so successful in the first stages of old-field forest succession is one which deserves more scientific investigation than it has received.

Not all of the first generation of trees on abandoned agricultural lands are conifers, although most of the exceptions appear to be in places where the conifer seed source was insufficient.

In addition to being typically composed of single species, old-field conifer stands are usually even-aged. Many seem to be the result of a single seed-year. However, it is also common to find two age-classes, the first being the scattered trees of an initial colonization and the second being the progeny of the first and usually two or three decades younger.

Because of prevalence of the pure, even-aged condition it is theoretically logical to anticipate that old-field stands should be unusually susceptible to attack by pests that are specialized to attack a given species or age-class thereof. In almost all instances, these pure, old-field stands of conifers occupy sites which would, under more natural conditions, have the same species growing in varying degrees of admixture with hardwoods. It is logical to suppose, but difficult to prove, that the availability of pure, old-field stands has increased the populations of and the damage caused by some pests.

One outstanding example is the white pine weevil which makes it very difficult to grow straight-stemmed white pines in the central and most important part of the range of the host. Boards in old buildings and the description by Peck (1817), who named the insect *Pissodes strobi*, indicate that this native insect could deform pine trees in the original forest. However, the insect must have burgeoned when land abandonment made hundreds of thousands of acres of open-grown white pine available starting in the 19th Century. In this particular case, it is important to note that land abandonment not only led to pure stands of the host species but also provided other highly favorable conditions for the pest insect.

The white pine weevil thrives on the thick-barked, vigorous shoots of white pines that are growing rapidly in the sunshine (Sullivan 1961). In much of the original forest, white pines simply had little opportunity to grow in the open when they were young. Even when there was abundant white pine regeneration after fires, stands that ultimately became nearly pure white pine were initially shaded by fast-growing, short-lived, pioneer hardwoods such as gray birch *Betula populifolia* Marsh or aspen, *Populus tremuloides* Michx. and *P. grandidentata* Michx. The more common and widely scattered white pines that grew in mixture with hardwoods were condemned, by their slow initial height growth, to development in small, accidental, chimney-like openings between the hardwoods. Such pines, shaded in youth, grew to become magnificent emergents mainly by continuing height growth long after their associates reached height culmination. It is only in the spruce-fir forest that white pine typically outgrows its associates in the early stages and even there there is much initial side-shading.

The crooks and forks of old-field white pine are not the only damage caused by the weevil. The dead terminals ultimately become infection courts for red rot caused by *Fomes pini* (Thore) Lloyd (Ostrander and Foster 1957).

The most extensive kind of old-field conifer is loblolly pine in the Southeast. Many of its damaging agencies, such as the Nantucket tip moth (*Rhyacionia frustrana* Comst.), fusiform rust caused by *Cronartium fusiforme* Hedgc. & Hunt ex Cumm., and the root rot, *Fomes annosus* (Fr.) Cke., are favored by stand purity and other attributes of old-field succession. In many parts of the Southeast, however, there are clear examples of the aggravation of forest pest problems by the soil damage that is a common legacy of agricultural use.

Soil Degradation from Agricultural Use

The degree to which temporary agricultural use altered soils now under forest cover varies tremendously. Clean cultivation on sloping terrain almost always induces some accelerated erosion, especially where the soils are fine-textured. The actual loss of topsoil can lead only to the degradation of site quality and, therefore, the reduction of health and vigor of tree growth. On the other hand, where agricultural use did not lead to significantly accelerated erosion, any degrading effects were much more subtle and are more often matters of presumption than proven fact. The continual removal of crops leads to removal of chemical nutrients if not compensated by fertilization. The rate of such loss would obviously vary widely depending upon the nature of the crops and the number of annual harvests.

By far the most important episode of soil degradation resulting from agriculture took place on at least 100 million acres of land in the Piedmont Plateau. Here the combination of clean cultivation and fine-textured residual

soils on rolling terrain led to such swift and spectacular erosion that only B- and C-horizon material of very low porosity remain over vast areas. Lands that originally supported rich and vigorous mixtures of hardwoods and pines are not often capable of supporting only very poor hardwood stands or pine stands with growth rates that vary from poor to moderately good. It has long been recognized that the poor internal drainage of these eroded sites favors the soil fungus, *Phytophthora cinnamoni* Rands, which causes the littleleaf disease of shortleaf and some other hard pines (Zak 1961). It now appears that reductions in tree vigor such as those caused by the littleleaf disease lead in turn to serious losses to the southern pine beetle, *Dendroctonus frontalis* Zimm. (Moore and Thatcher 1973). It may be presumed that after some centuries or even millenia of maintenance of forest cover the soils will rebuild and halt this dreary sequence of pest problems. However, in terms of the area affected and the enduring nature of soil damage, the problems started by clean cultivation have to rank as the most severe disruption of forest ecosystems on this continent.

The Piedmont is far from the only eroded forest area in the East. Even where the damage is less obvious it is probable that close examination would reveal erosive effects and pest problems not yet known to us, all a legacy of earlier population pressure and of the noble campaign to put every family on its own farm.

Another effect of erosion, although one presumed rather than directly evaluated, is the deposition of eroded material on downstream river flood plains. Unfortunately the patterns of deposition are more likely to be harmful than beneficial because most of the colloidal fraction is either carried to the sea or deposited in back-water swamps in such manner as to make poorly drained soils even more so.

MODIFICATIONS OF CONTINUOUSLY FORESTED LANDS

While land clearing and temporary agricultural use have had profound effects on the forests directly involved, most of the present forest is on land that has remained under forest cover since European settlement. Virtually all of this "permanent" forest has been cut over and it is plausible that most of it has been subjected to some sort of fire during the past 350 years. As previously indicated, the most important effect of these and other disturbances has been to reduce the average age of the forest stands. The next question of concern in forest pest problems is the way in which species composition has been modified.

Lists of species growing in each locality have changed scarcely at all. It is about as difficult to extirpate a plant species as it is one of an insect pest. In fact, most changes of species lists have been from addition of exotics. However, while the lists tend to remain the same, the frequency and abundance of species can be greatly changed.

To the extent that valid generalizations can be made, the most important alterations have come from effects which operate selectively for or against particular species. The greatest of such modifications tend to come from agencies, typified by fire and browsing by large animals, which destructively affect trees most in the seedling and sapling stages. The compositional development of forest stands is determined mostly when they are young; the alterations of composition that take place later depend mainly on the interaction of whatever species survived the initial stages.

Another moderately valid generalization is that timber cutting, fire, or any other destructively disturbing agency *operating alone* seldom produces long-lasting alterations in stand composition. This is probably because singly acting artificial disturbances usually just simulate the natural disturbances that were previously at work. Natural vegetation consists of species adapted to respond to such disturbance and is indeed the product of it. There have always been fires; cutting *per se* simulates the effects of windstorms and other agencies, including biotic ones, that kill sizeable trees.

Sequential *combinations* of destructive disturbances, which may be induced by man or purely natural events, cause the greatest amount of real change in forest vegetation. The most disruptive natural disturbances, short of landslides and similar geologic upheavals, occur when forest fires follow some other lethal event which left abnormally large amounts of readily combustible fuel in the forest. The initial events can be such destructive ones as insect outbreaks, windstorms, or commonly, earlier fires; the slash left in most logging operations has often acted as a similar augmentation of the fuel supply. The pioneer or early successional vegetation which appears after such combinations of events is usually natural. People have made it more common and it does have pest populations different from those of later successional stages.

Actions which destroy soil or involve mechanical disturbance of it, such as agriculture, mining, or road construction, are about the only things that disrupt forest ecosystems more than nature commonly has. Forest vegetation which is caused or allowed to grow on such sites is likely to be subject to all kinds of vicissitudes without much precedent in nature.

Major Alterations from Combinations of Destructive Events

The most noteworthy modifications of eastern forests have taken place in localities where large-scale conversion to agriculture or usage for grazing was planned, as matters of social policy, but did not take place as planned. The first instance resulted in the replacement, by aspen and jack pine (*Pinus banksiana* Lamb.), of much of the white and red pine (*Pinus resinosa* Ait.) forests of the Great Lakes Region; the second, the drastic reduction in the extent of longleaf pine (*Pinus palustris* Mill.) on the Southeastern Coastal Plain. The conscious management of North American forests probably owes much of its origin to public consternation, around the beginning of the present century, over these two events and the fear of a repetition in the West.

Heavy lumbering of white and red pine started in the region of the Great Lakes around 1860. Because of soils and climate conducive to fire and the presumption that the land was going to be farmed, the logging debris fueled some of the most catastrophic forest fires in history. The destruction of advance regeneration and seed sources of white and red pine, as well as of spruce and fir, has led to the existence of roughly 15 million acres of aspen and lesser areas of jack pine. The aspen grows well and remains acceptably healthy on the better soils. On large areas of poor soils, where natural succession is slow in leading back to species more adapted to the sites, the aspen is badly afflicted by hypoxylon canker (*Hypoxylon pruinatum* (Klotsche) Cke.) and other disorders (Graham et al. 1963). The abundance of aspen has also led to larger outbreaks of the forest tent-caterpillar (*Malacosoma disstria* Hbn.) than might otherwise occur. Neither forest fires alone or cutting alone would have produced this real and major change in forest vegetation and the pest situation.

Large-scale lumbering in the longleaf pines forests started somewhat before 1890 and was mostly finished by 1920. Open-range grazing and the annual woods burning associated with it had already gone on for many decades and continued during and after the logging. It was these practices which were almost totally destructive of advance-growth longleaf pine and set the stage for wholesale eradication of the forest (Wahlenberg 1946). Oddly enough, longleaf pine is almost fire-proof 9—10 months after germination; however, it could not survive the almost unfailing annual burning upon which the cattle-grazing economy of the region depended. Had the burning been somewhat less frequent, most longleaf pine seedlings would still have been lost to the razorback hog (*Sus scrofa* L.) which eats the root-bark of longleaf pine seedlings at rates up to 400 per day. It has been only during the last two decades that the end of open-range grazing has begun to make it possible to think about reestablishing the longleaf pine forest.

The initial product of the combination of annual burning, heavy cutting, and hogs was millions of acres of grass and stumps. When fire control efforts started to take effect around 1930, the former longleaf lands began to be invaded by other pines that were not palatable to hogs and also had more rapid juvenile height growth than longleaf. Loblolly pine has been most prominent in the northern part of the longleaf range and slash pine, in the southern part. This change has been partly from natural seeding but increasingly from a truly massive effort in artificial regeneration.

Substitution of these species for longleaf pine has become possible partly because of human alteration of the periodicity, of fires. The original stands of longleaf pine were favored by "natural" fires at intervals of several years, but not even this species could regenerate itself during the long period of widespread annual burning. The other pines can endure the intervals of a decade or more which now commonly elapse between fires. Longleaf pine is also unattractive from many management standpoints because it does not grow in height for at least several years after establishment and is also very difficult to plant successfully.

It is clear that the lengthening of intervals between fires does enable slash and loblolly pine to expand successfully beyond the moist sites to which they were often formerly restricted. Nevertheless uneasiness has long existed about the status of these two species on the driest sites to which longleaf pine is clearly better adapted. It is not yet clear how much root rot, fusiform rust, and bark beetle losses could be reduced by more serious efforts to grow longleaf pine on sites to which it is better adapted than the substitutes. Nevertheless, in this case as in that of aspen, the pest problems seem worst where the invaders are least adapted to site.

Species-selective Effects

Subtle and seemingly small changes in the composition of forests may ultimately be found fully as important in problems of pest management as the more major changes induced by efforts to replace forests with farms. The reduction or elimination of individual species formerly prominent in forests of mixed species has presumably altered the relationship between the forests and the pests dependent upon them. Unfortunately it is one thing to suspect such alterations and quite another to prove their nature and extent on any scientifically sound basis. Some of the changes can be enumerated even if one can only speculate about their consequences. In general, man has reduced certain tree species much more by the unintentional and indirect encouragement of certain pests and damaging agencies than by the selective harvest of given species. The fires and biotic pests set loose by man have been more persistent and effective in this kind of action than man himself has been in directly preying upon certain species for timber or fuel.

Introduced Pests. The most extreme example of this kind of selective reduction of a single species, both in eastern North America and the forests of the world, is that of American chestnut, *Castanea dentata* (Marsh.) Borkh. by the introduced Asiatic blight fungus, *Endothia parasitica* (Murr.) A.&A. Between 1908 and the 1930's this disease reduced one of the most important upper-canopy species of the Appalachian forest, from central New England to Georgia, to the status of understory shrub. Much of the replacement has been by oaks (Korstian and Stickel 1927, Woods and Shanks 1959), which previously occupied a subordinate position in the structure of mixed forests. The change has been so complete that it is virtually impossible to determine whether Hawley (1913) was correct in the view that the loss of chestnut would favor the gypsy moth (*Lymantria dispar* L.); he pointed out that oak foliage was the most favored food of the gypsy moth but that of chestnut was not. We are perhaps entitled to speculate that our chronic and alarming problems with the gypsy moth and other oak defoliators in the eastern or Appalachian portions of the mixed deciduous forest could be as evil a consequence of the chestnut blight as the loss of the chestnut itself.

The role of the gypsy moth itself in altering forest composition is not so pronounced as to be clearly apparent. A recently completed analysis (Campbell and Sloan 1975) of data gathered in eastern New England in 1911—31 indicated that uncontrolled defoliation led to substantial reduction in the oak component of the forest affected. However, these findings indicate that oak mortality was most heavily concentrated in the less vigorous trees of the lower crown classes. Furthermore, changes in species composition were partly offset by the tendency of some other species of the subordinate strata to be vulnerable to mortality from defoliation even though their susceptibility to defoliation is less than that of the oaks. The observed reductions in amount of oak are sufficient to lead to the conclusion that mortality from the gypsy moth can leave stands less susceptible to attack.

While the opinion is supported only by casual observation, I suspect that losses of oak to gypsy moth cause only temporary reductions in the amount of oak and of susceptibility to attack. The eastern New England forests that were presumably so severely affected several decades ago are again typically dominated by rather complete canopies of oaks. It is probable that most of the renewal of oak dominance comes from the ability of surviving oaks to develop the wide-spreading crowns characteristic of the genus. Recent findings of Oliver (1975) demonstrate that northern red oak (*Quercus rubra* L.) has a remarkable capacity to assert dominance at middle age over such associated species as red maple, *Acer rubrum* L., and black birch, *Betula lenta* L. A full canopy cover of red oak commonly develops from as few as 50 saplings per acre seemingly overwhelmed by other species during the first 2–3 decades of stand develop- ment. What he found to be true of red oak in central New England seems, from my observations, to be true of the red-black oak group in general in parts of the Appalachian forest as far away as southwestern Virginia.

The general effect of oak mortality from the gypsy moth seems to be that of random, chaotic thinning. Any tendency for the gypsy moth to be self-limiting through reduction of its favored food sources is probably temporary. The situation is, however, clouded by the fact that defoliation was greatly reduced by chemical control from about 1945 to 1960, and the consequences of the recent widespread mortality are yet to be learned.

Gypsy moth defoliation does have one effect which is the opposite of a self-limiting one. Eastern hemlock (*Tsuga canadensis* (L.) Carr.) is potentially a major constituent of the same forests now afflicted by the gypsy moth. An abundance of hemlock, upon which the early larval instars cannot feed, tends to forestall buildup of the gypsy moth. However, the later instars can feed upon it and a single complete defoliation leads to death. As a result, the gypsy moth has a tendency to thwart the increase of one species which could reduce the susceptibility of stands to attack.

American elm (*Ulmus americana* L.) and beech (*Fagus grandifolia* Ehrh.) are two other constituents of deciduous forests that are being reduced in abundance by introduced diseases. The fact that neither species is prized commercially does not mean that there will not be changes, desirable or undesirable, in the array of pests to which the forests are subjected.

Along the northern fringes of its range, eastern white pine has suffered such substantial reductions from the introduced blister rust, caused by *Cronartium ribicola* Fischer, that it seems destined to become an even less important component of spruce-fir forests.

Browsing Mammals. Insects and fungi are not the only organisms capable of altering forest composition by persistent selective attack on certain species. At various times and places, man has by different kinds of deliberate intent increased the population of certain wild and domestic browsing mammals, notably cattle and white-tailed deer, *Odocoileus virginianus virginianus* (Boddart). Since large animals browse on small plants, the effects are most pronounced on those tree species which regenerate mainly from pre-established, advance-growth seedlings beneath older stands. Any major resultant alterations of stand composition are delayed until the overstory is removed in cutting or by some other source of mortality. This increases the tendency for new stands to be dominated by pioneer species or ones unpalatable to the animals. Browsing can also have important selective effects during the early stages of development of new stands.

Such effects have proceeded over the longest time, with greatest severity and areal extent, from grazing of cattle and other domestic animals in farm woodlots, although the practice is less common than several decades ago. Blewett and Potzger (1951) and Elliott (1953) suggested that consumption of beech nuts may have caused major decreases in beech, and consequent increase of sugar maple (*Acer saccharum* Marsh.), since the settlement of parts of Indiana and lower Michigan. There has also often been substitution of grasses and similar plants for normal understory vegetation. An even more harmful consequence has been soil compaction, sometimes leading to serious erosion. The insects and fungi which participate in the degradation of stands subjected to this kind of treatment should be viewed as secondary rather than primary agencies of damage.

Cultural change has, in recent years and in the present context, caused enthusiasm for forest-browsing deer to increase as that for forest-grazing cattle has diminished. The effects of deer are generally more subtle, highly selective as to species, less localized, and much more difficult to detect than those of confined cattle. The most extreme effects are those that have been observed after heavy cutting on the Allegheny Plateau of northwestern Pennsylvania. Here, at least if well-established advance growth is absent at time of cutting, the large deer population can cause northern hardwood forests to be replaced by stands of ferns and other low vegetation (Jordan 1967, Marquis 1975).

Elsewhere in the Northeast there are forests in which certain species have been largely eliminated as effective future participants in stand development. Eastern hemlock is often one of these. Little et al. (1958) have reported severe reduction of the highly palatable Atlantic white-cedar, *Chamaecyparis thyoides* (L.) B.S.P., in southern New Jersey peat bogs. I have seen places of high deer population in the Adirondacks in which deer have browsed balsam fir so severely as to produce the uncommon result of a predominance of red spruce advance growth beneath spruce-fir stands. There is one heavily browsed forest in northwestern Connecticut in which various birches seem to be the only broadleaved species that can endure in the regeneration stage after harvest cutting. In one experimental area that I have under observation in southwestern New Hampshire, deer completely removed pin cherry (*Prunus pensylvanica* L.f.) from the important role that it normally plays after stand disturbance.

While the effects of browsing by deer are yet to be thoroughly studied, there is plenty of evidence to suggest that they may have more far-reaching effects on forest composition than most organisms that we now categorize as pests. The white-tailed deer is one wild animal that has definitely thrived and probably extended its range northward as a result of such attributes of civilization as agriculture, wolf eradication, logging, and misconceived hunting laws.

Fire. In considering the many and variable effects of fire for the purpose at hand, it is necessary to concentrate attention on human changes in the fire regime. Of all of the destructive influences to which forests are adapted, there is none more ubiquitous than fire. Long before man learned to make fire and became casual about burning forests, there was lightning to start forest fires. Even in the most humid of forested regions, such as that of the northern hardwood forest, there are periods during which fires can burn. Most of what man has done is to increase the frequency of ignition. Over most of the time since 1600, fires were simply more widespread geographically and perhaps more severe in their effects than when Indians burned the woods (Day 1953) in the somewhat restricted areas that they inhabited.

The major reduction in the extent of forest fires that took place during the period roughly between 1910 and 1960 is probably having effects as far-reaching as the accelerated burning of the centuries before then. It is probable that forest fires now affect less area each year than in any period during which the present vegetation evolved. In some localities, especially those where fire has always been common, there are already abnormally large accumulations of inflammable fuel that can make uncontrollable fires more severe. Furthermore, kinds and amounts of understory vegetation are appearing that did not exist in earlier centuries and perhaps not even in the pre-Indian time.

Fires vary tremendously in their effects depending mainly on the kind and amount of fuel available for combustion. The most extreme changes have taken place where fires have destroyed organic soils, usually after timber cutting. The two kinds of special or unusual sites where this has taken place are rock outcrops and swamps where any soil is almost entirely of organic origin. Fortunately the aggregate area involved is not large. On some mountain tops, once covered with spruce and fir, the forest has been almost permanently eliminated. On more area, the rooting stratum has been thinned enough to leave stunted forests that are probably prey to pests of feeble trees.

In peat or muck swamps, the situation is complicated by changes in water level. Fire or heavy cutting or both in combination can reduce transpirational water loss enough to cause significant rise of water tables. This may, in turn, cause some kinds of forests to be replaced by others or merely by kinds of shrubs adapted to the wetter conditions. During abnormally dry periods, fire can destroy a thick enough stratum of organic soil to hamper future tree growth.

Within the Lower Coastal Plain there are extensive peat-swamp areas where Atlantic white-cedar and what are normally thought of as upland pines have been displaced by such effects. One species that has greatly increased is pond pine (*Pinus serotina* Michx.) which is well adapted to both high water and fire. During recent years large tracts of such degraded vegetation have been drained and reforested with loblolly pine.

The most pervasive and widespread effect of unnaturally frequent burning was that of light surface fires that had their effect only in the stratum just above the soil surface. Fires of this kind have been remarkably effective in eliminating such species as eastern hemlock, white pine, and loblolly pine from forests in which these species once occurred in mixture with oaks and other hardwoods. The effect on overstory cover was slow in coming because it is many years before selective attrition in understory advance growth leads to changes on overstory composition. However, if seed sources are still present, the reduction in frequency of surface fires has, during recent decades, caused these same species to reappear, often with other vegetation that would have been less common when fires were frequent.

Frequent surface fires, especially in the more southerly kinds of hardwood forests, caused much basal wounding of living trees. This in turn led to high incidence of heart-rotting fungi and of various wood- and bark-boring insects (Hepting and Hedgcock 1937). Now that fires have been brought under control, we will see less of these organisms.

There are also places where fires severe enough to kill one kind of forest and replace it with different kinds have induced changes that we may suspect of aggravating pest problems. There are, for example, accounts of very large fires in the spruce-fir forests of the northeastern United States and eastern Canada during the 19th Century. One can only speculate whether these led to an abundance of paper birch, *Betula papyrifera* Marsh., ready for destruction by the mysterious birch dieback of the 1940's. The fire-induced oak forests of very dry soils in New England have been one of the chief havens for the gypsy moth.

Changes in the fire regime were not always of increasing frequency. In the prairie region along the western margin of the eastern forest, agricultural settlement led to a decrease in the fires that once perpetuated tall grass. In such places as southwestern Wisconsin, closed forest replaced the mosaic of interspersed patches of forest and grass and the invading members of the red oak group are more susceptible to disease than the bur oak (*Quercus macrocarpa* Michx.) which formerly prevailed (Cottam 1949). This change may indeed be part of the cause of problems with the oak wilt caused by *Ceratocystis fagacearum* (Bretz) Hunt. It is logical to anticipate that modern fire-control policies will induce alterations of forests and their pest populations. While the net effect will presumably reduce problems, there will doubtless be an increasing number of cases in which prescribed burning will be found desirable to combat certain pests that were once unimportant.

Timber Cutting. The harvesting of timber, *by itself* and when not followed by fire or similar additional disturbance, has usually not altered stand composition to any great extent. However, some species of high commercial value have been reduced in abundance by high-grading; frequently repeated cutting for fuelwood close to population centers has also increased the representation of certain sprouting hardwoods. The view that cutting alone has generally caused surprisingly little change of stand composition emerges from comparison of present forests with those represented by witness trees of early land surveys and other evidence about the original forests. The various studies are exemplified by those of Lutz (1930), Kenoyer (1934), Fassett (1944), Stearns (1949), Winer (1955), Steyermark (1959), Spurr and Barnes (1973), and Brender (1974). Such comparisons often reveal major changes in stand composition but such alterations are usually attributed to subsequent fire, agricultural use, animal browsing, or introduced pests, rather than to cutting alone.

Uncontrolled timber harvesting tends to be incomplete and haphazard. Often it simulated the natural disturbances to which forests are adapted so that appropriate ecological niches were created for new regeneration of almost all of the original species.

While many past timber harvests have been haphazard in the pattern of effects created they have commonly been very selective of species. The representation of the most valuable commercial species, especially certain softwoods, has almost surely been reduced where they occur in mixture with species deemed less useful. Usually such changes do not become large unless there is persistent and long-continued repetition of this kind of high-grading. In general, the early successional species are the ones most likely to be reduced by this kind of light and highly selective cutting.

Some important changes have also resulted from very heavy cuttings for fuelwood or charcoal. When such changes have taken place it has usually been because the regeneration environments created were especially favorable to a given category of species. The capacity of heavy-seeded hardwoods to sprout left the populous and chronically fuel-hungry Northeastern Seaboard full of chestnut for the chestnut blight and oaks for various defoliating insects. However, sprouting is a natural adaptation to fire and there is evidence to suggest that the cutting only accentuated a phenomenon which could have existed even before the appearance of woods-burning Indians.

The Allegheny Plateau of northwestern Pennsylvania and adjacent New York is one locality where important changes in stand composition have resulted from a sequence of cutting ending, often around 1920, with clearing off the residual trees for chemical-distillation wood (Marquis 1975). This reduced the representation of white pine and hemlock quite substantially. The initial partial cutting, in the absence of large deer populations, induced enough advance growth of black cherry, *Prunus serotina* Ehrh., that the post-clearcutting stands have a much higher proportion of this species than was the case in the original mixtures of northern hardwoods and conifers. The main pest problem generated by this series of events is an over-population of deer which now makes it difficult to emulate the fine results of what doubtless seemed like wholesale forest devastation around 1920.

This Pennsylvania case involves greater change than most but does serve to exemplify two important points. First, what people do to forests set off complex chain-reactions of events that are usually difficult to describe or analyze. Secondly, the history of past use of forests has often been one in which the same sort of treatment or disturbance took place over large areas all within short periods of time. The result has tended to be the imposition of an unnaturally high degree of uniformity of stand age and composition within localities that usually consist of several counties combined. Theoretical considerations suggest that this would set the stage for the aggravation of problems with pests peculiar to any given stage of forest development.

It is even more clear that, because the forests all grow older uniformly, the problems and solutions in the forest management of a locality change from decade to decade. In most places, the forests of 1975 have changed since those of 1955 and, by the time we learn to accommodate to the change, it will be 1995 and more changes will have taken place. It will be many generations before any sort of balanced distribution of stand ages is achieved in American forest management. While we may then perceive the whole span of stand development, we will also have all the pest problems simultaneously, perhaps in small doses, rather than a few at a time in large doses.

Urban Influences and Pollution

During the past quarter century, urban sprawl and massive increases in the use of fossil fuel have come to be a kind of modern counterpart of earlier shifts in use of land for agriculture. Most of the effects seem to be concentrated close to habitations and routes of travel. They are often of kinds that increase the multiplicity and severity of pest problems. The total effect on the vegetation may actually be less than that of the uncontrolled forest fires that so commonly used to spread from the same centers of habitation and transportation routes. The emissions from automobiles on an interstate highway are just a new variant on the sulfur dioxide, soot, and forest fires that spread from a railroad that might have traversed the same route.

There are some species-selective effects which might begin to modify stand composition, probably in places very close to pollution sources. White pine is, for example, vulnerable to damage from ozone and sulfur dioxide and maples to road salt. Some of the damage is so subtle that it is difficult to assess its extent. We must, as usual, be ready to anticipate a wide variety of strange effects. For example, the high population of feral dogs and cats can alter those of mice and deer which may be pests themselves or influence others.

Good Species in the Wrong Places

Many of the pest problems that have here been ascribed to human alteration of forests and forest soils have involved effects which induced tree species to grow on sites to which they were ill-adapted or in kinds of forest stands unduly favorable to certain pests. The known or suspected effects so far discussed have been the result of deliberate change of land use or accidental events. However, as the extent of deliberate forest management increases, it is inevitable that problems with pests are induced by errors of commission. A high proportion of these are caused by planting or otherwise encouraging the establishment of species in places to which they are inadequately adapted.

Essentially theoretical reasoning backed by empirical observation suggests that a species growing in a climate or on a site to which it is poorly adapted is likely to develop physiological disorders which predispose it to abnormal pest problems. Viewed in another way, it can be said that all plant species would grow naturally on all sites but for damaging agencies, including pests, that restrict them to certain ranges and sites.

It should be borne in mind that the natural occurrence or even the abundance of a given species on a certain kind of site does not mean that the species necessarily represents optimum adaptation to that site. As is the case with all organisms, trees have tremendous biological potential and are well equipped with dispersal mechanisms that enable them to colonize sites to which other species might be better adapted. Forest fires have not, for example, always been frequent enough to keep certain hardwoods off dry sites where various pines are well adapted and less subject to pest damage.

Tree planting is both the surest way of getting the right species in the right place and also the most common one of blundering into mismatches.

The most serious problems have arisen from what seem to be small extensions beyond the natural ranges of species or from moving species to unsuitable sites within their natural ranges. The attempt of 1910–1950 to extend the range of red pine southward has been made a fiasco by *Fomes annosus* root rot and the coincidental attacks of certain introduced insects. The ultimate success of northward extensions of loblolly and slash pine remains in doubt; so far damage from frozen precipitation has been more obviously limiting than biotic enemies. On the other hand, even more distant southward movements of white spruce have not yet caused any major problems.

North America is well enough supplied with tree species that there has been much more exporting than importing of exotics. In general, the movement of species across oceans or similarly effective geographical barriers to climates and sites to which the species are adapted has been more successful than extensions of range. The most successful introduction into North American forests have been of Norway spruce (*Picea abies* (L.) Karst.) and Eurasian larches (*Larix decidua* Mill. and *Larix leptolepis* (Sieb. & Succ.) Gord.), but the total area involved is very small.

It is simply too early to determine the extent to which the selection and development of seemingly superior strains of trees for planting will alter the forest pest situation. It would be unrealistic to fail to anticipate and allow for some discouraging surprises. It is very possible that some present pest problems in plantations established some years ago may have arisen from such practices as planting stock from Wisconsin seed in Connecticut.

The ultimate success of any exotic, extension of range, or genetic selection involving forest trees on a given kind of site cannot be judged adequately in any period of time shorter than several decades. Among other things there is always the risk of the rare event of weather to which natural populations may be adapted but the modified species are not. With trees one can lose the production of many years rather than just of one as is the case with crops of annuals.

These kinds of innovations by planting of trees have commonly and for many decades been viewed with apprehension by various prophets of doom. It is worth noting the sequence of events that often proceeds. Those enamoured by the benefits anticipated from planting species X are likely to request that the doomsayers be specific about the kinds of disasters that lie ahead. It is seldom possible to be specific at that stage so the responses have to be a sort of vague mumbling too easily put off as expression of ecological mystique. If the venture proves to be folly, those who perpetrate it often become so committed that they are not inclined to listen to reports of trouble or to look for it until it becomes too obvious to be ignored. At that point, which sometimes comes after a new human generation has taken over, the forest manager who is stuck with the problem is inclined to expect that protection specialists will hasten to the rescue of expensive plantations that the same kind of specialists warned against in the first place.

In the strategy of forest pest management the first kind of tactics to employ are neither direct nor indirect controls. They are instead simply the avoidance or evasion of pest problems by refraining from encouraging species in places where they are subject to unacceptable damage.

Most intensive plantation culture involves pure, even-aged stands of conifers native to the locality and very similar to old-field stands. Ordinarily the major pest problems of such stands are already well known. This knowledge can be used in such ways that the intensive culture can be more the procedure for solving old problems than the source of new ones. As the technology of wood utilization becomes more verstile, there is less reason than before to force economically popular species into the wrong places.

CONCLUSIONS

This account has necessarily been concerned more with the portions and attributes of eastern forests that have changed than with important ones that have changed little. We should not be so arrogant as to presume, in fits of self-recrimination, that forests were not afflicted with destructive organisms before we came; neither can we make forests pest-free.

However, human influences have changed forests and with them the interaction with pests. During the first three centuries after 1600, most of what man did to forests had the dismal effect of increasing difficulties with pests. During the present century this general trend has been completely reversed by the combination of real knowledge, constructive action, and unplanned events.

Since forests have been made younger, the pests of old age are less important, although those of youth and middle age will remain. The uncontrolled fires of the past probably set off more chain-reactions of pest problems than any other imaginable event short of nuclear warfare. These are now behind us; any problems that may now arise from not burning enough are correctable and insigifnicant by comparison. Most of the problems associated with upheavals in use of land for agriculture are probably matters of the past. However, intensively managed forest plantations will probably perpetuate most of the pests of old-field stands. Urbanization and environmental pollution will probably continue to bring new problems but society now has good intentions about such matters. Good transportation has brought many introduced, destructive pests during the past century and will bring more.

Above all, knowledge of the forest and its interaction with its pests has been increasing rapidly along with the will to make sophisticated application of such knowledge.

Chapter 2

The Connecticut Forest

George R. Stephens

Department of Ecology and Climatology
The Connecticut Agricultural Experiment Station
New Haven, Connecticut 06504

INTRODUCTION

Connecticut, the "land of steady habits", is an urban state renowed for insurance, inventions and industry. Despite being nearly centered in the populous eastern Megalopolis, it remains largely a forested state. Because Connecticut's 3 million inhabitants occupy far fewer than its 3 million acres, none of Connecticut's eight counties has less than 40 nor more than 70% forest land (Kingsley 1974). Over the entire state, farms comprise nearly 10%, and urban and industrial areas, about 30% of the land; nearly all of the remainder, 58%, is forested (Kingsley 1974). This intermingling of towns and trees was termed the "suburban forest" nearly two decades ago (Hicock 1957).

What is this suburban forest and how did it come to be? How have men, insects and diseases determined its present form and conditions? Much of D. M. Smith's commentary (Chapter 1) on events and changes in the deciduous forest of eastern United States is true for Connecticut. Landclearing, heavy cutting, indiscriminate burning and land abandonment began early in the history of the state. Let us briefly note the geography, geology and climate of the state as part of our examination of the suburban forest.

GEOGRAPHY, GEOLOGY AND CLIMATE

Connecticut is a rectangle, roughly 90 miles from east to west and 55 miles from north to south. It lies between 41 and 42°N latitude with Long Island Sound as its southern boundary. Elevation ranges from sea level to over 2000 ft in the hilly northwest and to 1100 ft on the hills and ridges of the northeast. Geologically, the state may be divided into eastern and western highlands of crystalline rock separated by a wedge-shaped central lowland characterized by sedimentary shales, sandstones and conglomerates (Flint 1930). Numerous trap intrusions and lava flows dot the central lowland and form a series of steep, rocky ridges. In the extreme northwest, the Taconic region contains a broad limestone valley flanked by crystalline rocks. The entire state was blanketed with a glacial ice sheet which ground and scoured the land. Its disappearance, 10,000–13,000 years ago, dumped a shallow mantle of rocky till on the uplands while glacial streams sorted and laid outwash deposits, ranging from coarse to fine, in level terraces along the valleys (Flint 1930).

Connecticut's position on the coast subjects it to the alternating influences of continental polar and maritime tropical air masses (Brumbach 1965). Mean annual temperature is about 10.5° C in the coastal and central lowlands and ranges from 7 to 9° C in the northwestern and northeastern highlands. Annual precipitation, evenly distributed throughout the year, ranges from 44 to 48 in. over most of the state. Tropical storms occasionally strike during summer and fall and historical records indicate that part or all of Connecticut has been battered by at least one major hurricane in each of the last three centuries (Brumbach 1965). In general, Connecticut enjoys a variable but temperate climate favorable to tree growth.

SUBURBAN FOREST

More than 50 tree species, some abundant, others rare, occur naturally in southern New England forests (Kingsley 1974); most occur in Connecticut. Deciduous broadleaf trees greatly exceed conifers both in numbers and volume of timber. According to a recent forest survey, oaks predominate, principally northern red (*Quercus rubra* L.), black (*Q. velutina* Lam.), scarlet (*Q. coccinea* Muenchh.), white (*Q. alba* L.) and chestnut oak (*Q. prinus* L.). Together they total 32% in number and 39% by volume. Maples, sugar (*Acer saccharum* Marsh.) and red, (*A. rubrum* L.) and birches, sweet (black) (*Betula lenta* L.), yellow (*B. alleghaniensis* Britton), and paper (*B. papyrifera* Marsh.) together comprise 39% in number and 30% by volume. Conifers contribute only 13% in number and 15% by volume, with pine (*Pinus strobus* L.) and hemlock (*Tsuga canadensis* (L.) Carr.) comprising nearly equal shares of the volume.

The variety of niches provided by the many combinations of soil, drainage, and local climate aids in maintaining great diversity within the suburban forest. However, Braun (1950) simply described the many combinations of vegetation as the glaciated section of the Oak-Chestnut Region. Bromley (1935) called the southern half of the state the Oak Region, the northern half the White Pine Region, and recognized a small intrusion of the Northern Forest Region in the northwest corner. Westveld et al. (1956) similarly partitioned the state. They placed the southern portion into the Central Hardwoods-Hemlock Zone and the northern portion into the Central Hardwoods-Hemlock-White Pine Zone. They designated the northwestern corner as Transition Hardwoods-White Pine-Hemlock Zone with a small inclusion of Spruce-Fir-Northern Hardwood Zone.

Recently, 24 local forest types were recognized in southern New England based on a plurality of basal area by species or species groups (Kingsley 1974). These 24 were further classified into 8 major types, all occurring in Connecticut. The predominant forest type throughout the state is oak-hickory, 40%, mainly on the drier uplands. A smaller amount of oak-pine, nearly 6%, features oak and pitch pine (*Pinus rigida* Mill.) on sandy outwash soils or oak and eastern redcedar (*Juniperus virginiana* L.) as an old-field successional stage or on open, rocky ridge tops. The elm-ash-red maple type, 23%, occurs mainly in the moist valleys particularly in central and eastern Connecticut. American elm (*Ulmus americana* L.), white ash (*Fraxinus americana* L.) and red maple appear singly or in combination on abandoned wet pastures and bottomlands. The northern hardwood or maple-beech-birch type, typically containing sugar maple, American beech (*Fagus grandifolia* Ehrh.) and yellow birch, constitutes 17% of the forest cover, mostly on the cool, moist slopes of the hilly northwest. Conifers, aggregated as white pine-red pine-hemlock, account for about 10% of the forest, mostly in northwestern Connecticut, but also in small areas scattered throughout the state. Red pine (*Pinus resinosa* Ait.) occurs almost exclusively in plantations, an estimated 37,500 acres (Unpublished Forest Survey data. 1972. Northeastern Forest Experiment Station, Upper Darby, Pa.).

The remaining three major types, spruce-fir, pitch pine-eastern redcedar, and aspen-birch comprise only 4% of the forest cover. The spruce-fir type includes native red spruce (*Picea rubens* Sargent) on the hills of northwestern Connecticut or plantations of white (*P. glauca* (Moench) Voss) and Norway spruce (*P. abies* (L.) Karst) scattered throughout the state. Balsam fir (*Abies balsamea* (L.) Mill.) occurs infrequently. The pitch pine-eastern redcedar type consists of nearly pure stands of pitch pine on outwash sand, particularly where fire was formerly prevalent, or as nearly pure stands of eastern redcedar, a successional stage on abandoned pastures in eastern and southern Connecticut. The aspen-birch type found throughout the state, but particularly in southwestern Connecticut, is an old-field successional stage occurring on burned-over or disturbed land and on recently abandoned cropland. Gray birch (*Betula populifolia* Marsh.), quaking (*Populus tremuloides* Michx.) and bigtooth aspen (*P. grandidentata* Michx.) are the principal species.

How does the current suburban forest compare with the forest of three or more centuries ago? Certainly, native species present today were also present then, but we can only conjecture on their relative abundance.

PRECOLONIAL FOREST

It seems likely that the original forest which developed since glaciation had already been modified by the activities of Indians. Day (1953) reviewed a large body of early literature describing coastal forests, clearing by Indians and their use of fire. From these descriptions we can infer that the park-like woodlands free of underbrush were maintained in that condition by regular use of fire. Whatever the reason for burning, improved visibility around villages, control of vermin, driving of game, or improvement of game forage, we can assume that fire-sensitive species would be restricted to moist lowlands or extremely rocky areas where fire could not burn well. Thus, the end result of prolonged periodic burning would be to favor vegetation which sprouts readily or is resistant to light ground fire, such as oak and pitch pine. The abundance of such species may be inferred from the mention in historical records of oak as early building material and exports such as oak pipe (barrel) staves and naval stores (Clark 1914).

Settlement by colonists in Connecticut was first along the coast and major river valleys, the same areas inhabited by the semi-agricultural Indians. In the more remote interior, uninhabited even by Indians, the occurrrence of fire was likely rare and a denser, more varied forest would be expected to develop. Northwestern Connecticut was likely such an area. Indeed, this area was called "Greenwoods" as late as the American Revolution because of the abundance of white pine and hemlock. It is in this region that we presently encounter most of the northern hardwood and white pine-hemlock types (Kingsley 1974). Nichols (1913) described the last large tract of undisturbed forest in Colebrook (Fig. 1). Beech and hemlock together comprised 55%; sugar maple, 12%; yellow birch, 10%; red oak, 6%; chestnut (*Castanea dentata* (Marsh) Borkh.), 6%; white ash and basswood (*Tilia americana* L.), 7%; black cherry (*Prunus serotina* Ehrh.),

FIGURE 1. *The last large remnant of virgin forest prior to cutting in 1912 at Colebrook, CT.*

sweet birch, red maple and white pine, 4%. Nichols estimated that this tract had not been burned for 300 years, the approximate age of some of the larger trees. In contrast to the coastal forests, oak was present but not predominant. However, this tract lies in the region described as northern forest (Bromley 1935) or northern hardwoods (Westveld et al. 1956).

DIMINISHING FOREST

Colonial settlement, begun in 1635, relentlessly pushed back the forest margin for nearly two centuries. Trees were cut for fuel and timber, burned to clear pasture and cropland and to produce potash for export (Jenkins 1925). It is estimated that the forest had shrunk from 95% of the land in 1635 to only 25% by 1820 (Harper 1918). However, the forest soon began to encroach again as new lands in the West and manufacturing in the cities lured men from the farms. Indeed, cropland was abandoned on the sterile outwash sand plain of the lower Quinnipiac Valley prior to 1820 (Olmsted 1937). By the outbreak of the Civil War only half the population remained on the farm (Clark 1914); a third of the land was estimated to be forested (Harper 1918).

EXPLOITATION AND FIRE

It was during the 19th century that the remaining forest was exploited. Growing cities required fuel; furnaces, forges and brass foundries required both fuel and charcoal, resulting in the frequent clearcutting of forests for both fuelwood and charcoal production (Figs. 2 and 3).

In 1838 introduction of the railroad created additional demands for ties and fuel. An old hazard, fire, reappeared and as the railroads extended, railroad fires burned hundreds, perhaps thousands, of acres annually (Fig. 4a). Accumulation of fuels and logging slash increased the danger and intensity of fire. Statistics on forest fires were not systematically compiled until 1905, but as late as 1910 railroad fires topped the list of known causes, contributing in that year 30% of the fires and 22% (10,000 acres) of the area burned (Spring 1911). No organized, effective forest fire-fighting force existed until 1921 when local fire wardens were appointed by the State Forester (Anon. 1968a) (Fig. 4b).

Introduction of the steam-powered portable sawmill made hitherto lightly cut or inaccessible woodlands available, leading to clearcutting, followed frequently by fire. Thus, although abandoned farms were gradually increasing woodland acreage from 1820 to 1900, the existing forest was being exploited and fire remained a serious threat even longer, until about 1930.

FORESTRY EMERGES

By 1900, forest land was estimated to cover 40% of the state (Mulford 1902, Harper 1918). Demands for native lumber, fuel and charcoal diminished

FIGURE 2 *Clearcut hillsides with stacked fuelwood and windrowed tops were common into the 1920's.*

with increasing use of coal, gas and western lumber. Much of the forest was young as a result of land abandonment or recent cutting. Interest increased for reforesting of abandoned farmland to protect watersheds and to produce a timber crop. In 1901 Walter Mulford was appointed forester of the Connecticut Agricultural Experiment Station (Jenkins 1902), and the General Assembly authorized a State Forester with authority to purchase and reforest barren land. The Station and State Forester were one, and in 1905 the additional duty of State Forest Fire Warden was conferred.

Uncontrolled fire was recognized as a serious deterrent to both reforestation and forest management. Mulford and his successors, Hawes, Spring, and Filley, continually urged landowners to prevent forest fires and to replant idle acres. In 1921 the duties of the State Forester and Forest Fire Warden were set apart as a separate function under the State Park and Forest Commission. The early campaign for fire prevention and later, for prompt detection and suppression, succeeded. During six decades, 1910 to 1970, the average acreage burned annually decreased from nearly 42,000 acres during the first decade to less than 2200 in the last (Anon. 1971). Indeed, as a result of continued farm

FIGURE 3 *Earthen or sod charcoal kiln under construction at Burlingtion, CT. 1913.*

abandonment and improved fire protection, forest occupied 63% of the land in 1952 (Griswold and Ferguson 1957), probably the zenith in return of the forest.

ROLE OF INSECTS AND DISEASES

One must suppose that insects and diseases were periodically troublesome in Connecticut's forest even prior to colonial settlement, but records are scarce. Josselyn (1672) chronicled for 1649, "This year a strange multitude of Caterpillers in New-England". Clark (1914) reported that "in 1666 the caterpillar and cankerworm appeared; trees were tarred to arrest this pest". One might suppose that fruit, not forest trees, were the concern in this instance. Britton (1908) reviewed information indicating that the fall cankerworm, *Alsophila pometaria* (Harr.), had been periodically abundant in the New Haven area since 1750. In more recent times, outbreaks of the elm spanworm, *Ennomos subsignarius* (Hübn.), in 1938 (Plumb and Friend 1939) and 1970 (Anderson and Gould 1974), the orangestriped oakworm, *Anisota senatoria* (J. E. Smith), in 1958 (Hitchcock 1958) and *Symmerista canicosta* Franclemont in 1973 suggest that similar local outbreaks of native defoliators occurred in the past.

FIGURE 4. *Forest fire presented a serious threat to rebuilding the forest after 1900.*
   a. Railroads long remained the single most important source of forest fire.
   b. Early forest fire wardens with their primitive equipment at Simsbury,
   CT. 1911.

Little is known of disease also, although their effects were likely insidious then as now. A blight of the imported Chinese mulberry (*Morus multicaulis* Perr.) doomed an already ailing silk industry before 1850 (Jenkins 1925). However, shortly after 1900, insects and diseases, mostly imported, assumed a more prominent role in forest change.

At the turn of the century when forestry was actively promoted, conifers were considered essential for a thriving forest industry. White pine was the principal native conifer and a portion of the initial forestry research of The Connecticut Agricultural Experiment Station involved direct seeding of white pine on open land (Mulford 1902). However, discovery in 1909 of the white pine blister rust (*Cronartium ribicola* Fischer) on nursery stock imported from Germany (Clinton and McCormick 1919), efforts to locate and control the disease beginning in 1916 (Filley 1917), and depredations by the white pine weevil, *Pissodes strobi* Peck, combined to augur a gloomy future for white pine. Hemlock was considered undesirable for planting. Consequently, red pine, scarcely native to Connecticut, but promising in early planting trials (Spring 1913), was widely planted. Subsequent events showed red pine to be a poor choice. Young plantations, particularly in the warm coastal counties, were attacked by the European pine shoot moth, *Rhyacionia buoliana* (Schiff.), during the 1930's (Friend and Hicock 1933). Later, many old-field plantations became susceptible to a root rot (*Fomes annosus* (Fr.) Cke.) when thinned. Presently, the red pine scale, *Matsucoccus resinosae* Bean and Godwin, of unknown origin, is slowly destroying and requiring premature liquidation of this softwood. Thus, the once-promising red pine appears doomed. However, blister rust is not a serious threat so that white pine and the formerly disdained hemlock now appear likely to remain the principal conifers.

During this same time even more dramatic changes were occurring in the deciduous forest as a result of other imported pests. About 1907 the "Chestnut bark disease" (*Endothia parasitica* (Murr.) A. and A.) was noted in southwestern Connecticut but was not considered serious (Clinton 1908a). By 1912 the infestation had spread throughout the state (Clinton 1913) and by 1918 ". . . there was scarcely a sizeable chestnut tree alive . . ." (Hawes 1968). Chestnut was estimated to comprise about 40% of Connecticut's forest (Clinton 1913) and this sudden loss created in many areas a large void which was quickly filled, largely by oaks. Thus, forests already abundantly supplied with oak became more so.

In 1905 the gypsy moth, *Lymantria dispar* L., was discovered in southeastern Connecticut (Britton 1906). An earlier decade of forest defoliation by this pest in Massachusetts made Connecticut wary and watchful. However, 33 years passed before the first large scale defoliation, about 1000 acres, occurred in 1938 in north-central Connecticut (Britton 1939). Defoliation by the gypsy moth became an increasing threat during the 1950's and 1960's (Turner 1963). Massive defoliation culminated in 1971 when the gypsy moth and elm spanworm together defoliated over 650,000 acres (Anderson and Gould 1974).

In areas once abundant with chestnut, and subsequently with oak, and undisturbed by fire and cutting for a half century or more, oak has been slowly disappearing for 40 years (Stephens and Waggoner 1970). Defoliation seems only to have accelerated the loss. Prior to the defoliation of the 1970's tree mortality was low, averaging 1 to 2% annually over a decade with not more than one defoliation and increasing to 3 to 4% with two or three defoliations (Stephens 1971). Losses were slightly greater on dry compared to moist sites and higher among oaks than maples and birches. By 1972, however, great oak mortality following defoliation was evident and ranged from about 20 to nearly 80% over a 5-year period in selected areas (Dunbar and Stephens 1975). Attack by the twolined chestnut borer, *Agrilus bilineatus* (Weber), was soon related to the observed mortality (Chapter 6). Consequently, oak, abundant in much of Connecticut's forest and repeatedly defoliated in many locations during the last two decades, is being replaced largely by maple and birch.

Another cause of widespread mortality in the suburban forest is Dutch elm disease (*Ceratocystis ulmi* (Buis.) C. Moreau). Discovered in southwestern Connecticut in 1933 (Clinton and McCormick 1936), it had spread to all but 22 of Connecticut's 169 towns by 1948 (Dimond et al. 1949). It is presently found throughout the state, spread by its principal vector, the smaller European elm bark beetle, *Scolytus multistriatus* (Marsh.). Although not as suddenly devastating as the chestnut blight, nevertheless, Dutch elm disease is relentlessly eliminating elm from forest and city alike. Although never an important timber tree, the loss of American elm has left a tragic void in many a village green and city street.

FUTURE FOREST

The suburban forest, like the colonial forest, is slowly receding. However, houses, highways and industry, but not farms, presently push back the forest margin. Whether the forest will shrink to its former size of the early 19th century, only time will tell. Yet despite past mistreatment and calamities little has been eliminated from the forest. Indeed, there is hope that the once versatile and valuable chestnut may return again (Chapter 5) to displace some of the oak.

Oak, host of many defoliators, renders our present forest susceptible to defoliation. We can anticipate a future forest, protected from fire and lightly cut, which will contain less oak than now and more maple, birch and hemlock. We cannot help but wonder if this change will make our forest more "defoliation-proof". On the other hand, as more of our generally young forest matures and as the demand for forest products increases, harvest will certainly help perpetuate oak and possibly our insect problems.

Chapter 3

Phenology and Leaf Growth of Defoliated Hardwood Trees

G. H. Heichel and Neil C. Turner[1]

Department of Ecology and Climatology
The Connecticut Agricultural Experiment Station
New Haven, Connecticut 06504

INTRODUCTION

Defoliation of deciduous hardwoods by insects might signal a catastrophic decline in vigor and productivity in the forest ecosystem. Although defoliation has long been known to reduce the radial growth of trees (Minott and Guild 1925), and repeated defoliation to increase mortality, a surprisingly small proportion of Connecticut's hardwood forests have perished from recent defoliations (Stephens 1971).

Unlike evergreen conifers, deciduous hardwoods seem particularly adept at surviving severe and repeated defoliations (Graham and Knight 1965). Stimulated by this knowledge and by the idea that the promptness and extent of canopy renewal following defoliation are important in maintaining forest productivity, we investigated the phenology of budbreak and the leaf growth of defoliated and undefoliated red oak, *Quercus rubra* L., and red maple, *Acer rubrum* L., to learn how these trees survive severe and repeated defoliations.

METHODS

We explored the physiological mechanisms mediating tree survival by applying successive controlled defoliations in the field. To simulate insect

[1] Present address: CSIRO, Division of Plant Industry, P. O. Box 1600, Canberra City A.C.T. 2601, Australia.

defoliation, we manually defoliated 9 to 11 yr old trees of red oak and 13 to 15 yr old trees of red maple that were about 8 m tall, had stem diameters of 5 to 9 cm, and were growing in open stands in 0.001 ha plots at Lockwood Farm, Mt. Carmel, Connecticut. The trees had been growing in closed stands with marked mutual shading, but in 1972 the stand was thinned from 36 to 12 trees per plot to facilitate experimentation. Three trees of each species were subjected to either 50%, 75% or 100% defoliation in the third week of June in 1972, 1973, and 1974 by removing every other leaf, 3 of every 4 leaves, or all leaves on every branch of each tree. In both species, defoliation was applied after spring extension growth and expansion of the primary leaves were complete, the time of year when insect defoliation reaches a peak in Connecticut forests. Defoliation was effected by removal of leaf blades, but without removal of the petiole or damage to dormant buds. Three undefoliated trees of each species served as controls.

Spring budbreak, measured as the number of days required for flushing of 50% of the buds on a tree, was observed before the 1972 defoliation, and in spring of each of the following 3 yr. Following defoliation each year, we measured budbreak of the terminal and lateral buds that initiated regrowth, and enumerated and measured regrowth foliage and that of control trees. Areas of leaves were measured with a Hayashi Denko AAM-5 automatic area meter. Analyses of reducing sugars, sucrose, starch and nitrogen in primary foliage produced after 2 and 3 yr successive defoliation were by standard procedures (Association of Official Analytical Chemists 1970).

RESULTS AND DISCUSSION

Leaf Regrowth After Defoliation

Onset of Refoliation. Deciduous trees are frequently stimulated to regenerate their leaf canopy in the interval following defoliation. This was the case with the oak and maple in our study (Fig. 1). Refoliation ensued from terminal buds, from lateral buds in the axis of leaf petioles, from dormant lateral buds on previous year's growth, and from epicormic sprouts.

Over the course of the experiments, refoliation of red oak commenced 8 to 22 days after 100% defoliation, and 22 to 34 days after 75% defoliation. Refoliation of oaks subjected to 50% defoliation occurred only in some trees, and then only after more than 30 days had ensued. Similarly, refoliation of red maple commenced 11 to 22 days after 100% defoliation, and 22 to 27 days after 75% defoliation. Like oaks, refoliation of maple subjected to 50% defoliation only occurred in a few cases, and then only after more than 30 days had elapsed.

In conformity with our results, complete defoliation has previously been observed to elicit foliage regrowth in elm, *Ulmus americana* L. (Wallace 1945), quaking aspen, *Populus tremuloides* Michx (Rose 1958), sugar maple, *Acer*

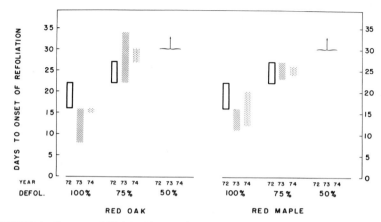

FIGURE 1. *Pattern of 50% bud break of red oak and red maple preceding the regrowth stimulated by removal of primary foliage in the third week of June. Vertical bars indicate the range of days to bud break and leaf exposure required for the 3 trees in each treatment.*

saccharum L., yellow birch, *Betula alleghaniensis* Britton, basswood, *Tilia americana* L., and ironwood, *Carpinus caroliniana* Walt. (Giese et al. 1964b). We have additionally shown that refoliation is exhibited by trees suffering partial defoliation, and that trees suffering severe defoliation regenerate their leaves more rapidly than those experiencing lesser damage. Although there were year-to-year variations in the onset of refoliation following a late June defoliation, 2 or 3 successive years of defoliation were without effect on the subsequent patterns of refoliation in either species.

The timing of the onset of refoliation is of additional interest when it occurs during weather that is favorable to the growth of pathogens. In 1972, for example, refoliation occurred during warm and rainy weather favorable to the fungus, Anthracnose, with the result that considerable regrowth on oak and maple succumbed to the disease (Heichel et al. 1972).

Growth of Individual Leaves. After refoliation, the average areas of individual regrowth leaves were reduced with increasing defoliation sustained by the tree (Fig. 2, A & D). Area of regrowth oak leaves averaged 39% and that of maple 33% of controls on completely defoliated trees. On 75% defoliated trees, area of regrowth oak averaged 73% and that of maple 47% of the control trees. Area of regrowth leaves on 50% defoliated trees averaged 60% of controls in oak and 66% of controls in maple. Interestingly, individual primary leaves of oak averaged 100% more area than maple, but regrowth oak leaves averaged 130% those of maple. The greatest relative increase in leaf size, 150 to 180%, was shown by 75% and 100% defoliated trees. Relative to undefoliated controls, therefore, regrowth foliage of maple was apparently smaller than that of oak.

The number of leaves produced after refoliation varied with the severity of defoliation (Fig. 2, B and E). At the onset of senescence, the completely defoliated oaks had regenerated leaves equivalent to 74% of their original complement of primary leaves; completely defoliated maples had regenerated 89% of their original complement of primary leaves. Oaks subjected to 75%

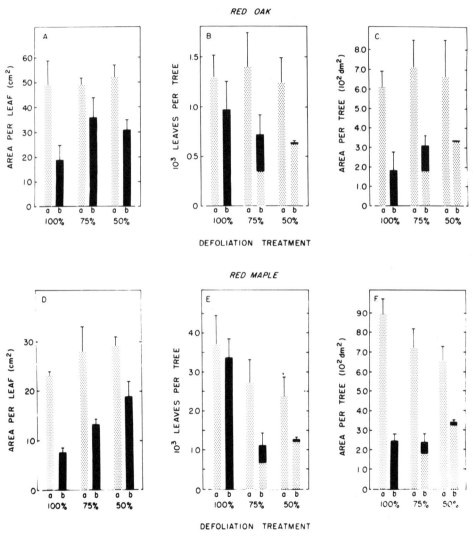

FIGURE 2. *Area of individual leaves, number of leaves per tree, and area of leaves per tree before (a) and after (b) defoliation in 1972,* ▦ *signifies primary foliage and* ■ *indicates regrowth foliage. Vertical bars are mean ± one SD.*

defoliation regenerated 35% of the leaves removed, and comparably defoliated maples replaced 21%. An average of 2% of the removed leaves were replaced in the three 50% defoliated oaks, and 6% in similarly treated maples.

Compared with the number of primary leaves prior to defoliation, therefore, oak and maple subjected to 75% defoliation approached senescence with primary and regrowth leaves equivalent to 51% and 41%, respectively, of their complement of primary leaves. Oak and maple suffering 50% defoliation neared senescence with primary and regrowth leaves equivalent to 51% and 53%, respectively, of their original primary leaves.

Regrowth of the Total Foliage Canopy. Knowing the area of individual leaves and the number of leaves each tree produced, we may ask how successfully defoliated trees replaced their decimated leaf canopies (Fig. 2, C and F). Following 100% defoliation, oaks replaced about 29% (0.39 x 0.74) and maples 28% of the total area of their original primary leaves. Subsequent to 75% defoliation, oaks regenerated 25% (0.73 x 0.35) of the removed leaf area, and approached senescence with 44% of the original area of their total leaf canopy. Maples subjected to 75% defoliation regenerated 11% of the removed leaf area, and terminated the season with 33% of the original leaf area. The three oaks suffering 50% defoliation replaced only 1% of the area removed, and neared senescence with 51% of the original area of leaves. Similarly treated maples regenerated 5% of the area removed, and possessed 53% of their original leaf area with onset of senescence.

Clearly, the extent of canopy regeneration decreased with severity of defoliation, with the result that oak and maple suffering 100% defoliation terminated the season with less canopy area than trees suffering only 75% or 50% defoliation. Comparing Figs. 1 and 2 also reveals that the product of canopy leaf area (dm^2) and leaf area duration (days) would be least for 100% defoliated trees, intermediate for 75% defoliated trees, and greatest for 50% defoliated trees. Thus, the potential for photosynthesis and growth subsequent to defoliation would appear greater for trees suffering the least defoliation than for those incurring complete defoliation.

Leaf Growth After Successive Years of Defoliation

Spring Budbreak. Prior to imposition of the defoliation treatments in 1972, onset of budbreak varied slightly among plots. After defoliation treatments, the onset of spring budbreak in each succeeding year varied with severity and duration of defoliation, and with species (Fig. 3). Compared with budbreak prior to the first defoliation in 1972, and with budbreak of control trees prior to defoliation in succeeding years, the onset of growth of primary foliage of oak was advanced from 1 to 4 days by successive defoliations. Interestingly, oak trees differing greatly in severity of defoliation varied similarly in their response of budbreak to successive years of defoliation.

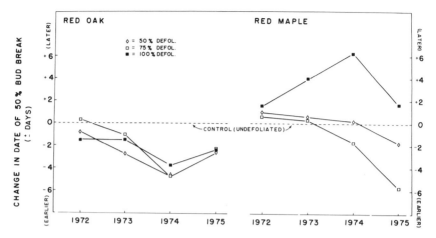

FIGURE 3. *Change in the time of 50% spring budbreak following successive years of 50%, 75% and 100% defoliation. The values for 1972 are the relative dates of budbreak for each set of trees prior to imposition of defoliation treatments. In each year, mean date of budbreak is normalized to that of the undefoliated control for each species.*

Fifty and 75% defoliation advanced the onset of spring budbreak in maple in each successive year of treatment (Fig. 3). After 3 yr of successive 50% defoliation, budbreak was advanced by 3 days. Budbreak of trees experiencing repeated 75% defoliation for 3 yr was advanced by 7 days. In contrast, budbreak of maple subjected to 100% defoliation was retarded 4 days by 2 yrs of defoliation and advanced 4 days, compared with 1974, in the third year of treatment.

Since our trees were changed from a closed, shaded stand to an open, sunlit stand in 1972, we sought to remove the anticipated advance of budbreak often shown by shaded compared with sunlit trees (Mc Gee 1975) by normalizing budbreak of defoliated trees relative to that of controls in each year. This normalization also minimizes the influence of yearly weather variations on the pattern of spring budbreak. Even after accounting for the environmental factors that modulate budbreak, it is clear that defoliation plays a heretofore unrecognized role in regulating the dormancy of buds (Fig. 3). Although we are without an explanation for the contrasting responses of the maple treatments and for the general advance of budbreak elicited by defoliation, it is tempting to speculate that growth promoting substances like gibberellins are more abundant in defoliated trees, and that they mediate the release of buds from dormancy in the spring (Kozlowski 1971).

Growth of Individual Leaves. The growth of individual primary leaves in the years following one to three successive defoliations directly reflected the severity of defoliation (Fig. 4). Primary foliage produced in the years following 100% defoliation averaged 56% of the area of the undefoliated controls in oak, and

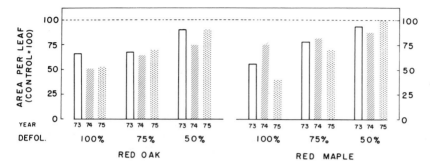

FIGURE 4. *Change of the average area of individual primary leaves after 1, 2, or 3 successive years of 50%, 75%, and 100% defoliation. Area is plotted as a percent of the red oak control in 1973 (67 ± 2 cm²), 1974 (81 ± 5 cm²), and 1975 (90 ± 3 cm²), and the red maple control in 1973 (59 ± 1 cm²), 1974 (39 ± 2 cm²), and 1975 (50 ± 3 cm²). Standard deviations were always less than ± 5 cm² for a random sample of 100 leaves.*

57% of controls in maple. Primary foliage in years following 75% defoliation averaged 67% of the area of controls in oak and 76% of controls in maple. Following 50% defoliation, the average area of primary foliage was 85% of controls in oak and 93% of controls in maple.

The results clearly illustrate the profound influence of defoliation on the growth of leaves in the subsequent year. Repeated defoliation is apparently without effect on the areas of individual primary leaves because the reduction in area relative to the control failed to increase with successive defoliations. This suggests that the initial defoliation in a series of defoliations exerted the greatest impact on leaf growth in subsequent years. Interestingly, maple averaged less reduction in leaf area by 3 yr of 50% and 75% defoliation than did oak. Both species responded similarly to 3 yr of 100% defoliation.

Annual Regeneration of the Foliage Canopy. Springtime growth of primary foliage revealed the persistent effects of repeated defoliation in previous years (Fig. 5). Following the first year of 100, 75, and 50% defoliation, a reduction in total area of 1973 primary foliage was imperceptible when compared with the 1972 leaf area. After 2 and 3 successive yr of 100% defoliation, however, the total area of primary foliage of oak averaged 55% and that of maple 50% of the area prior to defoliation in 1972. This reduction in area of canopy was attributable to a 38% decline in number of leaves per tree in completely defoliated oak, a 54% reduction of leaves per tree in completely defoliated maple, and to the nearly 45% decrease in the area of individual primary leaves in both species (Fig. 4). Decrease of leaf area in completely defoliated trees accompanied twig dieback and the depredations of pathogens (Heichel et al. 1972). Similar patterns were observed in *A. saccharum* subjected to complete defoliation for 2 successive yr (Giese et al. 1964b).

The second year of 75% defoliation reduced canopy leaf area in both oak

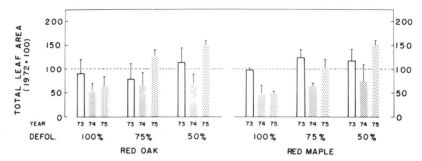

FIGURE 5. *Change in the average area of foliage per tree after 1, 2, or 3 successive years of 50%, 75%, or 100% defoliation. Area is plotted as a percent of the area of the trees in each treatment prior to defoliation in 1972. For each treatment, these original areas are plotted in column (a) of Figure 2, C and F.*

and maple, but the third year of 75% defoliation was followed by an apparent increase in canopy area in both species (Fig. 5). A similar pattern of leaf growth reduction following the second year and a growth increment following the third year of 50% defoliation was observed in oak and maple. This pattern of canopy growth mirrored the concurrent changes in area per leaf (Fig. 4), and in total leaves per tree. In contrast with completely defoliated trees, those suffering repeated 50 and 75% leaf loss failed to show twig dieback, and the yearly changes in leaves per tree reflected changes in number of active buds and the leaf production per bud (Heichel and Turner, unpublished data).

Although repeated 50 and 75% defoliation significantly diminished the total area of the leaf canopy in 1974, these partly defoliated trees substantially augmented their foliage in 1975 (Fig. 5). Significantly, oak and maple suffering 3 successive yr of 50% defoliation averaged 50% more leaf area in 1975 than before the initial defoliation in 1972. Loss of half the leaf area for 3 yr was insufficient to preclude growth of the trees.

Although 2 or 3 successive yrs of complete defoliation greatly diminished tree vigor and the total leaf area per tree (Fig. 5), it failed to elicit death of any of the trees. This contrasts with the observations of elevated mortality frequently associated with one or more years of drastic canopy decimation (Minott and Guild 1925, Houston and Kuntz 1964, Giese et al. 1964b, Staley 1965, Kegg 1971), but is compatible with the absence of mortality following insect defoliation and defoliation by freezing of *P. tremuloides* (Rose 1958).

There is ample circumstantial evidence that complete defoliation predisposes trees to depredations of secondary pathogens (Schoeneweiss 1967, Wargo 1972) and insects (Dunbar and Stephens 1975). The observations that defoliated trees must be deliberately wounded for successful invasion of certain pathogens (Crist and Schoeneweiss 1975), that weather favorable to growth of pathogens modulates the damage to defoliated trees (Heichel et al. 1972), and that

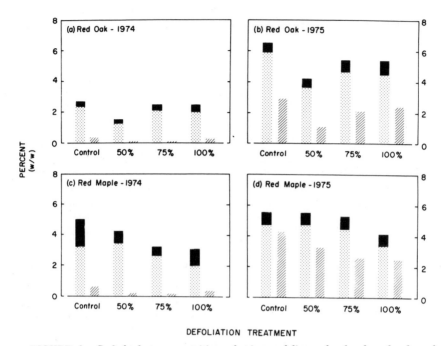

FIGURE 6. *Carbohydrate composition of primary foliage of red oak and red maple following 2 (a and c) and 3 (b and d) successive years of 50%, 75%, or 100% defoliation. Values for reducing sugars* ▨, *sucrose* ■ *and starch* ▧ *are percent dry weight of duplicate samples taken in the third week of June in 1974 and 1975.*

refoliation suppresses the expansion of stem cankers (Crist and Schoeneweiss 1975) illustrate some constraints that allow severely defoliated and weakened trees to survive. However, survival of trees after prolonged defoliation without damage by secondary invaders seems the exception; a better understanding of how defoliation predisposes trees to their attack is sorely needed.

Carbohydrate Content of Leaves. The carbohydrate content of primary foliage produced after 2 and 3 yr of successive leaf removal was modified by the severity of defoliation (Fig. 6). Foliage of oak and maple trees subjected to 2 and 3 yr of leaf removal consistently contained less total sugars (sucrose plus reducing sugars) and less starch than control trees. Nitrogen content of leaves was unaffected. Compared with controls, the greatest reduction in leaf carbohydrates of oak was exhibited by foliage of 50% defoliated trees, with lesser reduction of carbohydrate being shown by trees suffering 75 and 100% defoliation (Fig. 6, a and b). Oak suffering 50% defoliation had 63% of the sugars and 25% of the starch of controls after 2 yr of defoliation in 1974. After 3 yr defoliation in 1975, oak suffering 50% defoliation had 80% of the sugars and 38% of the starch of controls. Interestingly, the pattern of treatment responses observed in 1974 was similar to the 1975 pattern, and reinforced the contrast between trees suffering 50% defoliation and the remainder of the treatments.

In contrast with the pattern shown by oak, the carbohydrate content of maple foliage produced after 2 yr and 3 yr of leaf removal declined with severity of defoliation (Fig. 6, c and d). Foliage of maple subjected to 100% defoliation had 62% of the sugar and 67% of the starch of controls after 2 yr defoliation in 1974. After 3 yr defoliation in 1975, maple suffering 100% defoliation had 75% of the sugars and 58% of the starch of controls. Defoliation clearly modified the patterns of carbohydrate metabolism in leaves a year or more after the treatment was imposed. Similar responses have been shown by roots of sugar maple (Wargo et al. 1972). This continuing modification is clearly of longer duration than the changes in sugar and starch status of branches (Gross and Larsen 1971) and roots (Wargo 1972) induced by defoliation a few weeks prior to sampling, but the cause is presently obscure.

We conclude that defoliation modulates budbreak in the season of leaf removal and in the spring of years following leaf loss. Additionally, we conclude that the initial defoliation in a succession of yearly defoliations is the most significant to leaf growth in succeeding years, since we lacked evidence of additive effects of repeated defoliation on the areas of single leaves or on total leaf areas of tree canopies. Lastly, carbohydrate metabolism of primary leaves produced in the spring reflects the experience of defoliation applied in a preceding season.

ACKNOWLEDGMENTS

We thank Delores De Fonzo, Kathryn Woglom, Richard Mangen, David Ruth, Kenneth Faroni, Leonard Mukai, and Patrick Shanley for capable technical assistance, and Sherman Squires, Department of Analytical Chemistry, The Connecticut Agricultural Experiment Station, for the chemical analyses.

Chapter 4

Management of the Forest

Fred B. Knight

School of Forest Resources
University of Maine
Orono, Maine 04473

INTRODUCTION

A discussion of forest management, and more specifically pest management within that broader and inclusive objective, requires some description of the forest itself. We will confine the comments here to the forests of the United States and provide a few statistics to give a basis of magnitude. Sources of such information on the American forest are numerous. Two fairly complete and recent sources are "The Outlook for Timber in the United States" (Forest Service 1973) and "Report of the President's Advisory Panel on Timber and the Environment" (Seaton et al. 1973).

Forests of the United States total 753.5 million acres, or just under one-third of the land area of 2.27 billion acres. Estimates indicate that 70% of the land forested prior to the 17th century is forested today. Two-thirds of the forest lands have been classified as commercial timberland, which means that the forests growing there are both available and suitable for producing continuous crops of trees for harvest. Generally capability is defined as having a potential of growing at least 20 cu ft/acre/yr. Forest areas excluded from commercial status must either be of low productivity, or actually reserved and/or developed for non-timber uses (Table 1).

Ownership patterns for the commercial forests are variable from region to region and between states within regions. Federal lands are most common in the Rocky Mountains while farm and forest industry lands reach the greatest percentages in the South. The national data show land ownership in 1970; 27% public, 14% forest industry, 26% farm, and 33% in miscellaneous private holdings. These data begin to give us some feeling for the vast variety of

TABLE 1. Forests of the United States by classification and U.S. region, 1970 in thousands
of acres[1]

Land Classification	North	South	Region Inland West	West Coastal	United States
Commercial Forest	177.9	192.5	61.6	67.6	499.7
Productive-					
Reserved	4.3	1.7	7.9	3.3	17.2
Deferred	–	–	2.3	0.4	2.7[2]
Unproductive	4.2	17.6	66.5	145.6[3]	233.9
Total	186.4	211.9	138.2	216.9	753.5

[1] Adapted from Forest Service Report #20, 1973.

[2] Deferred lands are those acres of productive lands on National Forests under study for
for possible inclusion in the wilderness system.

[3] A large portion of this acreage is in the unproductive forests of interior Alaska.

programs that may be supported by our forested lands. Numerous recommendations were made by Seaton et al. (1973). Some of the points made regarding the
various ownership classes are important to this discussion.

(1) Too little money is provided to prepare the National Forests for the
present and future multiple use requirements that are expected from them.
National Forest timber output is declining at a time of increasing demand for
wood. A greatly expanded program of quality forest management on national
forests and elsewhere is recommended.

(2) Forest industry lands are of better than average quality for timber
production, are generally well managed, and are being brought under intensive
management more rapidly than other classes of forest lands.

(3) The immense area, low stocking, modest growth, and modest harvest of
the "other private" lands, both farm and miscellaneous, makes them the "listless
giant" of forestry. Part of the problem of getting more output from these lands
is technical, part is economic, and part is motivational.

The statements above are similar to those made in the panel report and seem
to be quite descriptive of some of the problems facing us in reaching a goal of
high production on all forest lands. This goal is now not merely one way that we
might be inclined to look to the future in preference to several alternatives.
Today more than we have ever imagined, we can see the future need for all that
we can produce from this vast renewable resource. One of the basics of forestry
training has always been that harvested trees should be used as fully as
economics will allow. We are getting to the point now where residues are
becoming less and less and we are using more of each tree. This usage is excellent
progress, but total use of each tree growing under today's management standards
is not enough to meet the needs of future generations.

Productivity of all forest lands must be and can be increased within biological restraints, but only if the public provides the incentives through fair taxation and a recognition of the real value of each acre of forest land to the future of the nation. The President's panel judged that growth of all forests in the Nation, considered as a whole, might be doubled by 2020 by a reasonable increase in management input. But, this will cost money that will only be made available through a change in thinking about the real value of the basic resource. The exploitation viewpoint is difficult to overcome but, though the effect is not apparent in all sections of our country, there are significant changes that will hopefully spread. Additional management investments that are needed will not be made on a significant portion of those lands where the return for raising timber will hardly pay for the taxes on the land. If this vast resource is essential to the future of this nation, then the resource should be worth far more.

So far we have considered forests from a commercial viewpoint and have stressed greater growth and the economic problems associated with attaining the additional increments. Forests have a major role in many other ways, all of which relate directly to multiple-use management. Our forests are the greatest converters known for changing solar energy to chemical energy and they do this more economically than any engines, converters or heaters that man has yet devised. Wood also has the potential of conversion to useful compounds such as sugars, alcohol, fodder yeasts, and many others which add to its utility.

There is also the role of our forests in the maintenance of a quality environment. Forests and trees protect our soils, filter our water, carry on photosynthesis, beautify our streets, and make life more pleasant for all by providing sound and wind barriers. Forests provide amenities for life in improving the scenic qualities that people seek for picnicking, hiking, camping, and nature study. They provide habitat for many animals and plants that otherwise would not be present. These many uses must be nurtured and provided for in our management. Since these uses compete directly or indirectly, all should be considered in the discussion of management. One of our prime responsibilities will be to provide the maximum benefits to our people from both the timber and non-timber outputs.

FOREST MANAGEMENT

The forest must be understood with more than an idle fancy for something virtually unknown. One quote will illustrate that point. Aldo Leopold (1949), in his beautiful little book, *A Sand County Almanac*, wrote[1] :

---

[1] From "A Sand County Almanac with other essays on Conservation from Round River" by Aldo Leopold. Copyright Oxford University Press. Used with permission of Oxford University Press.

There are two spiritual dangers in not owning a farm. One is the danger of supposing that breakfast comes from the grocery, and the other that heat comes from the furnace. To avoid the first danger, one should plant a garden, preferably where there is no grocer to confuse the issue. To avoid the second, he should lay a split of good oak on the andirons, preferably where there is no furnace, and let it warm his shins while a February blizzard tosses the trees outside. If one has cut, split, hauled, and piled his own good oak, and let his mind work the while, he will remember much about where the heat comes from and with a wealth of detail denied to those who spend the weekend in town astride a radiator.

Forestry is defined as "The scientific management of forests for the continuous production of goods and services" (Society of American Foresters 1958).

Note the use of *management* in this definition. It has been the central issue since the earliest development of the profession. The breadth of the effort as defined is not a modern concept, despite the efforts of some to claim that timber was once the only concern. Graves and Guise (1932) stated the idea this way:

Forestry is first of all concerned with the constructive management of forest land—timber is not the only resource with which the forester has to deal, the science is concerned with various other resources that are an integral part of the forest.

In summary, and in the simplest possible terms, forestry is the management of forest and included lands. It deals with all the goods and services provided by the forest and aims at their continuous production for such purposes and by such means as will best serve mankind, including owners, users, and the community at large. It is an art based on science and practiced with due regard to economic, social, and personal considerations. Forestry is thus an essential activity of broad scope, great complexity, and major importance, the successful practice of which requires professional ability of high order.

Next we read from Dana and Johnson (1963):

Of the many resources with which forestry is concerned, five may be regarded as outstanding from the managerial point of view; timber, water, forage, wildlife and recreation. Of these, timber alone is always a part of the forest . . . when the other four resources occur on non-forested lands, their management is no longer a part of forestry.

Now comes the definition of *forest management* from Forestry Terminology—"The application of business methods and technical forestry principles to the operation of a forest property."

Davis (1966) writes[2]:

_____

[2] From "Forest Management" by Kenneth P. Davis. Copyright 1966, McGraw Hill Book Co. Used with permission of McGraw Hill Book Company.

Forest management is consequently the core, the main line of forestry. The forest manager is concerned with anything that affects the operation of the area in his charge. He needs to have the earthy and intimate forest understanding of the silviculturist, the long-range viewpoint of the planner, the skills of the administrator, and the alertness, flexibility, and all-around resourcefulness of a successful businessman.

The French forester, Charles Broilliard, stated in 1860, (Davis 1966):

Every forest offers a real and living individuality. It differs from every other forest by its situation, its aspect and configuration, by its soil, by its component crops, and also by the character of the surrounding country. There are no two forests, any more than two towns, exactly alike, and it would be a great mistake to suppose that the management of forests adjoining each other or situated in the same region can be built upon the same framework or pattern. The forester laboring under so erroneous an impression would lack the very fundamental idea that should guide him, and instead of adapting himself to circumstances, would vainly endeavor to force circumstances to suit his silly imaginings.

The great dangers to be avoided in forest management are preconceived ideas and foregone conclusions. Every rigid system refusing to yield to the varying requirements of different forests and localities must be equally vicious, and more than this, it must infallibly result in its staves (prescriptions) over-looking some important facts and indispensable conditions. Indeed, it is this very danger of carrying into effect preconceived opinions that justifies us in warning the forester against seeking any perfect solution of the problem before him, the realization of any impossible ideal, and in advising him to confine himself to doing his best to obtain the results required.

Silviculture is defined as: "The art of producing and tending a forest. The application of the knowledge of silvics in the treatment of a forest" (Society of American Foresters 1958). Another definition of silviculture states: "The science and art of cultivating forest crops based on the knowledge of silvics, the study of the life history and general characteristics of forest trees and stands with particular reference to site factors as a basis for the practice of silviculture."

These definitions help us in focusing on some of the many issues we face in managing our forest resources, but at the same time they serve to emphasize the diversity of forest resources. As we begin to study this complex, we realize a responsibility to maintain that great diversity through our care and management. Any review of intensive forestry will reveal that attempts to apply precise prescriptions to large forested areas are likely to lead to disastrous consequences, both to the ecosystem and to the economy. Nevertheless, broad principles may be applied in an effective way that will protect the ecosystems, develop productivity, and improve the economy.

There are many ways in which we could manage and maintain the diversity of our forests. There is an interwoven complex of diversity that includes a biological and a societal mix. There are at least three complicated sets of constraints relating to how the land is managed.

(1) The forest is made up of a variety of species mixtures which change rapidly in space and time. No one would suggest that our large variety of forest types be managed with one silvicultural system even if for some strange reason we should decide that management has one objective. So we start with biological variety in the system.

(2) The forest is made up of a variety of ownership patterns. The management practices of a large ownership would be quite different from those of a small tree farm, and they should be, because of differing management objectives. Also, the objectives in a public park would likely vary considerably from those of a private timber producer, and they should.

(3) The forest produces a variety of products and services which may be obtained from a forest managed for multiple use, or in an area maintained for a single purpose. This variety of needs leads to more diversity in the management practices applied.

In the future we must keep the options open as we develop more and more intensive management of forest lands. Use will be more intense and demands will require more complex procedures rather than simplistic solutions. Pressure for use may lead to controversy, but it also permits intensive management and utilization. While these conflicts happen, the manager must assure that the forest remains healthy and productive.

BIOLOGICAL, ECONOMIC AND SOCIAL RELATIONSHIPS

Many pest problems of the forest must be managed as a part of the whole system. Waters (1971) stated, "To manage forest insect populations by sound ecological means—to prevent rather than suppress outbreaks—is the continuing dream of forest entomologists and, generally, forest resource managers." This clearly states a basic premise managers might have as a goal; but having such a fine goal does not mean that we can expect to reach an ecological solution to all pest problems. Such goals might be more feasible if we based management on the ecological aspect of the management equation without much emphasis on the social and economic aspects. Unfortunately, this cannot be done because management must be based on all three. We sometimes seem to lose our sense of reality when we begin to discuss ecological principles, and we fail to express clearly what we really mean by forest management. I'm afraid that some may get the impression that we will no longer have pest problems once we have ecologically sound management programs. Actually, we should expect the problems to continue, but through intensive management, we would hope their impacts would be minimized.

One objective of intensive management should be to contain pests at innocuous and manageable levels (Campbell, 1974), but this might be impossible if the procedures required were more expensive from a societal standpoint than combatting the pest. For example, we all know that we are likely to have more problems with the southern pine beetle, *Dendroctonus frontalis* Zimmerman, after planting large acreages of its host trees. We could virtually eliminate the problem by ceasing planting and allowing natural succession to hardwoods. But, does that provide the solution needed, or does society need the pines so badly that the southern pine beetle must be dealt with more directly? We have chosen the latter route; thus, our procedure should include management of the pines in a design which minimizes the southern pine beetle problem. This is not a purely ecological solution because we have chosen to interfere with the natural succession process.

Marty (1965) expresses the basis for expenditures clearly in the following statement: "Timber owners ought not to invest in insect control except in situations where it is reasonably profitable for them to do so—that is, where there is a reasonable relation between cost and value saved." There is always the recommendation that control should offer as good a return as investing in some other fashion.

But, failure to control may result in a large loss to other investments. When computing returns from other investments, the real losses resulting from failure to do control work should be added as a cost of following the alternative investment plan. These and other common sense notions have been addressed by many economists, but in practice are often neglected by managers.

The idea of an economic threshold is an interesting concept that many of us have talked about for years. Stern (1973) provides a fairly comprehensive review. The definition of the term is (with minor variations in wording by different authors) the density at which control measures should be started to prevent an increasing pest population from reaching the economic injury level. The economic injury level is a rather nebulous figure for forest pests because of the variety of values involved and the fluctuations in those values in both time and space. Some insects and diseases which cause injury to trees never can be classified as above the economic threshold even though their damage impact may be sizeable. This is because the economic threshold must take into account the various alternatives for preventing the "economic" damage. Perhaps the only viable alternative for a specific pest is to salvage any trees that may die. Waters (1971) brings in the idea of "ecological threshold", which may be a valid substitute for economic threshold because of the difficulty that many individuals develop in relating economics to values other than product values. In either case the definition would relate to the critical density of the pest which would call for a decision. These critical densities may vary greatly according to the objectives for which the particular forested acreage is being managed.

Much could be added about the evaluation of pest management systems, but we should avoid making decisions without a review of the whole of forest management rather than on fragments that might lead to poor decisions. Let's not waste money on elaborate studies of pest impacts in situations where nothing would be done anyway. However, methods should be developed to meet potential needs—some pest problems that are non-economic today may become serious at a later date as management becomes more intensive and/or resources become scarcer.

During the past 50 years methods for evaluation of pests have been improved greatly although much more will be required as forest management becomes more intensive. We need a system that provides information on important pests on a regional and national basis. Control is becoming more expensive, and the resource to be protected is becoming more valuable. We cannot afford to lose as much of the resource as we have tolerated in the past, nor can we afford to continue to apply control unless absolutely necessary. The key to all of this is in the understanding of pest impacts that are based upon accurate measurements of biological information, on thorough economic analyses, and on an understanding of the social needs and constraints of the public. The constraints mentioned are significant, as we all know. We are scrutinized on most of our management practices, whether they may be the application of insecticides, our methods of harvesting timber, the construction of campground facilities, or how we use our water, to name a few. In no area of forest management are these constraints more thorough and more widely applied than in pest management.

PEST CONTROL THROUGH MANAGEMENT

Graham and Knight (1965) described the basic strategies of direct and indirect control with a clearly expressed thought that one cannot be substituted for another on short notice. Direct control is a superior strategy for emergencies where applications of indirect control methods would have little effect. On the other hand, indirect control should be a preventive strategy that, when applied, will prevent the occurrence of an emergency. Such indirect procedures are not exciting because nothing seems to happen, and are therefore difficult to administer. The public likes to see something happen when its resources are expended. Thus, our indirect methods are difficult to sell; efforts which merely keep the forest healthy are rather passive and are easily forgotten.

Swingler (1959) stressed the importance of prevention through good management and constant vigilance. Every operation in a forest has an influence on the environment so that conditions are made either more or less favorable for the work of pests. Many of our actions have encouraged pest problems; some of these actions are unavoidable, but many are, and can be avoided in the future. Graham (1963) expressed some additional thoughts on silvicultural control and some of the problems that arise even in forest types which are typically less hazardous than others to pest problems. These are the highly mixed forest types where insect outbreaks seldom occur. Graham pointed out three very important steps in maintaining such resistant conditions in northern hardwood forests.

(1) Management practices should be aimed at creating maximum diversification.

(2) Partial cutting should be relatively heavy, removing 50% or more of the crown cover to permit reproduction of all species.

(3) Despite these efforts, when numerous deer are present, there is a greater tendency toward the development of the more hazardous pure maple forest. Steps should be taken to reduce the number of deer. These points seem relatively straight-forward and should be easy to apply, but often they are not. The third point is especially difficult because of social constraints.

We are more knowledgeable about methods for preventing outbreaks of pests than we often realize, but we often cannot apply them because of various biological, social or economic constraints. We have, however, sometimes developed problems by following apparently good practices from a public (social) point of view that have directly affected pest management. I discussed the problem on the Goodman Forest in Wisconsin with Professor Samuel Graham of Michigan, now deceased, who published a brief summary of the story that details the process which lead to a problem (Graham 1965). Graham contended that light, selective cutting and the removal of hemlock changed the character of the forest from a mixed to an almost pure maple forest in those parts of the tract where the blight was most severe. He agreed that the two defoliators and other associated factors, especially root rot, led to the mortality (Giese et al. 1964 a,b, Giese and Benjamin 1964, Houston and Kuntz 1964, Skilling 1964). But, he pointed out that unwise planning dating back to the earliest days of management led to the difficulty. His conclusions were supported by lack of blight in areas where light cutting had not been practiced, and severe mortality on relatively low-lying areas where hemlock had once been abundant.

A number of authors have touched on the various silvicultural procedures that have been suggested for forest pests (Bennett 1965, Graham 1956, 1959, Balch 1958, Prebble 1951, Sartwell and Stevens 1975). Any number of other authors have recited the various common ideas about silvicultural control. Most of them seem to agree on the following generalizations:

1. Steps should be taken to assure a maintenance of stand vigor.
2. Management practices should be designed to control the abundance of various species and the mixture of age classes.
3. Managers should not allow the development of plantations of species not suited to soil and climate.
4. Stands should never develop to a stage of overmaturity.
5. If possible, maintenance of stand mixtures found in the climax forests of the region and site should be an objective.

These principles or variants of them express the basic concepts of silvicultural control. However, we often cannot apply them because of the constraints already expressed. The five points are also generalizations which may not always apply to specific situations. Balch (1958) points out that "the problem is to determine those stand characteristics that favor outbreaks, and to what extent and by what methods they can be avoided."

Graham (1956) discussed the basic principles of what was referred to as the "law of natural compensations". Some of us might dispute the terminology a bit because the use of the word "law" might be a little extreme due to known variations in biological populations. He does point out the generally accepted point that the degree of stability in a community is directly proportional to the number of species. This ecological principle is well known. We are all aware of the various complex forest mixtures which are relatively more stable than simpler stands in the same areas, though we also know there is a confusing effect because of successional stages involved in the process. However, we have also seen examples where stable forests become unstable for both natural and man-caused reasons. Graham stated that we can maintain less susceptible conditions by encouraging multiple species stands or by limiting the size of areas occupied by the same age class of the same species.

Smith (1975) points out some of our problems in finding solutions. He warns us of our tendency toward over-simplification of situations which are much more complex. There is no single, best, and universal system for producing more wood, while providing more aesthetic values, nor are there simple ways of protecting the forest from pests without some effects on other values.

SILVICULTURAL METHODS—APPLICATION

Earlier comments on use of cultural procedures to maintain the vigor of trees and the diversity of forest stands are good ideas which will often work if widely applied. A major reason among many for the lack of application of such well-known principles relates to the development of management intensity in our forests. Generally the application of advanced practices is related directly to the intensity of management; some of these methods have been used when the returns from investments are reasonable. As we intensify management of our forests, we may see many variations in the effects on pest problems. In some cases, intensive management may cause further problems from pests that at present seem unimportant. In other situations we will create conditions where some insects and diseases that were formerly severe pests will no longer be a problem. We will learn to accommodate other problems through integrated practices utilizing silvicultural and natural controls, and chemicals for emergencies. A few selected examples will be useful in illustrating the development of management procedures.

Western Pine Beetle

The use of tree classifications for ponderosa pine, *Pinus ponderosa* Laws, was recommended by Keen (1943) for prevention of damage by the western pine beetle, *Dendroctonus brevicomis* Hopkins. Keen developed a classification of ponderosa pine on the basis of age and vigor, as indicated by bark and foliage characteristics. The accuracy of this classification is shown in Table 2. Descriptions for the table are not precise. Various classes are much more readily understood and applied when comparisons are made to specific photographs or drawings. Generally speaking, the oldest trees with the poorest crowns show the greatest risk. Keen's classification system has led to the risk-rating system that is directly applied in field operations (Salman and Bongberg 1942). The fundamental difference between risk-rating and the tree classification system is based on the probability of survival to the next cutting cycle. In application, sanitation-salvage operations are designed to remove all trees which have a high risk of bark-beetle attack. Keen and Miller (1960) reviewed the western pine beetle problem and presented a thorough summary of this method. The value of sanitation-salvage is a matter of record; the method works effectively to reduce losses due to the pine beetle through management procedures. The method does not apply to other bark beetles affecting ponderosa pine, nor to other parts of the ponderosa pine region.

TABLE 2.   Average mortality rate per year. Based on 206,037 ponderosa pines.

Keen's Age Class[1]	Keen's Vigor Class[2]				Weighted Average
	A	B	C	D	
1	0.1	0.3	0.8	1.1	0.3
2	0.2	0.6	1.0	1.5	0.8
3	0.3	1.0	1.9	1.9	1.0
4	0.4	1.4	2.7	3.8	2.1
Weighted Average	0.3	0.7	1.8	1.7	1.0

1. Age Class Descriptions

   1. Young
   2. Immature
   3. Mature
   4. Overmature

2. Vigor Class Descriptions

   A. Full, long, dominant crowns
   B. Full, shorter, co-dominant crowns
   C. Narrow, long, intermediate crowns
   D. Narrow, short, suppressed crowns

Mountain Pine Beetle

The mountain pine beetle, *Dendroctonus ponderosae* Hopkins, kills pines of several species in the western United States. No specific silvicultural method has been developed for control, though managers have recognized that stress is an important component in the development of outbreaks (Beal 1943). Typically this insect attacks and kills groups of trees (Fig. 1).

We have no long record of silvicultural control for the mountain pine beetle which could be compared to that reported for the western pine beetle. But we do have a long period of experience with bark beetles to support the belief that silvicultural control will work. Sartwell and Stevens (1975) have presented a very strong appeal for silvicultural control of the beetle in ponderosa pine. Their program should be applied as a control measure on as wide a scale as economically possible. They recommend thinning for the control of this insect and provide specific illustrations that show the procedure works. The process requires thinning over vast acreages to prevent the continued occurrence of outbreaks. Thinnings on the scale required are not likely at present, but thinning can be applied on high value sites and in localities where there are markets for the materials to be removed. The development of further needs for products during the next 10 to 20 years will eventually make thinnings an operational reality for all commercial stands. Hopefully, expensive control projects will become an historic relic except on non-commercial and/or reserved lands.

Safranyik et al. (1974) developed a similar analysis for the mountain pine beetle in lodgepole pine, *Pinus contorta* Dougl. Since this tree species is different in site and growth characteristics, the results of their research suggest different management. High beetle hazard in the Canadian lodgepole pine stands was correlated with age; those older than 80 years were more prone to beetle attack. The risk of beetle damage was lessened if stands in high hazard areas were harvested as soon as possible after 80 years of age. Investigators also suggested that stands should be developed in a mosaic of age classes by cutting in small blocks so that future losses would be lessened.

Spruce Budworm

The two bark beetles are typically secondary insects that are capable of doing severe damage under rather specific host and/or environmental conditions. Defoliators have differing habits and requirements, and often are not secondary. Thus, we find an entirely different set of requirements for their control. The spruce budworm, *Choristoneura fumiferana* (Clemens), is one of many species that reach outbreak numbers at intervals. The cycles of this particular pest are closely related to the ecological development of balsam fir, *Abies balsamea* (L.) Mill, though red (*Picea rubens* Sarg.) and white spruce (*Picea glauca* (Moench) Voss) are also severely damaged. Records of outbreaks stretch back to the earliest settlers of the spruce-fir regions. This insect has been the subject of

FIGURE 1 *Pines killed by the mountain pine beetle in Colorado. Note that these trees are not large, over-mature individuals.*

intensive research for several outbreak cycles, but the devastation continues (Fig. 2).

Outbreaks develop in response to two circumstances. First, there is the apparent need for an ample supply of forested stands with a high proportion of mature balsam fir. Second, a weather pattern consisting of 3 or 4 years of favorable conditions for budworm development precedes an outbreak (Wellington et al. 1950). These weather patterns generally include a minimum storminess and low precipitation. Once the outbreak is in progress, the weather patterns may not necessarily continue, though patterns of low precipitation coupled with heavy defoliation could lead to greater mortality of the stressed trees.

Suggestions for control of the spruce budworm through silvicultural procedures have been proposed since the early twenties (Craighead 1924). Westveld (1945, 1946) developed specific formulae for rating vulnerability and described the action that should be taken to prevent outbreaks and build resistance into the forests of the future. Westveld recommended that the most vulnerable stands of overmature balsam fir be removed as rapidly as possible and that short cutting cycles of approximately 20 years be adopted in the entire forest type. Prebble (1951) warns that the scope of silvicultural management will have to be greatly intensified before there can be any hope of preventing recurrent budworm damage over large areas. We plainly have not reached the stage of management intensity where such control can be expected. The prospects for the next generation of balsam fir trees could be much better.

It is doubtful that any method of control other than management will provide a reasonable answer to the spruce-budworm problem. Many managers have expressed doubt about the effectiveness of the procedures that have been suggested. These doubts are sincerely expressed and are based upon observations made by many experienced individuals. Budworm outbreaks develop and spread through the spruce-fir type, killing stands that have been carefully managed along with those that are mature and untended. The response, in all cases, has been to treat with chemical pesticides to keep trees alive, or to commence salvage of the dead material.

The future accommodation of this problem must still rely on the use of management as the only long-term solution. The key may be in the intensity of management. As long as the growth in the spruce-fir forests remained far in excess of the quantities of wood used, there was no real hope that outbreaks could be prevented because large quantities of mature balsam fir continued to develop. Since the demand for wood is increasing, we may have an opportunity to develop intensive management practices.

Plantation Problems

There are several serious pests of our young forests which have become problems because of silvicultural practices that lead to even-aged forests of single

FIGURE 2 *The spruce budworm is a tree killer. These dead balsam firs were photographed in northern Maine.*

species. Such practices have been logical systems for reforesting abandoned acreages and areas devastated by fire or other agent of destruction. Large-scale plantation forestry has also been selected for management of certain species which would be difficult to maintain in a productive status with other methods. It is sufficient to say that there are valid management reasons for the planting of trees in pure-species stands.

These plantations have been affected by native and introduced insects and diseases. Since ceasing plantation forestry is not generally an acceptable alternative, the next best procedure is to develop guidelines for management of such stands which minimize the effects of the pests. Several pine sawflies have become problems in plantations; some of these may require chemical pesticides to prevent serious damage. Evidence suggests that the particular species chosen for planting was not well suited for that particular location. Similar problems have developed from spittlebugs, scale insects, shoot moths, and bark beetles.

Many other serious problems have developed which are not site-related and may even seem more serious on the very best sites for the tree species. The white-pine weevil, *Pissodes strobi* (Peck), has been a vexing problem from the beginning of plantation work. Severe infestations in white pine plantations can completely destroy the value of the future production. We know many of the habits of this native insect, and we have knowledge of techniques that will effectively control the problem. Unfortunately, most are not economically justifiable on any large scale. Management practices may be modified during the next decade or two so that this insect can be held in check to allow the development of straight white pine trees.

This discussion of applied silvicultural management procedures for the control of forest insects has only been a brief glimpse at the present state of the art. As a whole, we have some examples of successes, but not a good record. Morris (1951) stated a problem that all entomologists are confronted with in terms of their ability to cope with these problems. I quote: "In conclusion, attention is drawn to the need for long-term thinking and planning. The entomologist is accustomed to starting experiments that can be completed in a year or, at most, in a few years. In management work, however, he must follow the practice of the research forester and resign himself to the initiation of certain studies and experiments for which many of the answers may not be obtained during his lifetime."

Research on silvicultural procedures for forest pest control lags far behind all other pest management research. Reasons are obvious, but we continue to provide only a minor portion of our research dollars for the study of silvicultural methods. Such experiments are expensive, and the results are long in coming. I believe we could get some good answers on a well planned and expensive white-pine weevil experiment in 12 to 15 years, and we could refine a good management program in an additional 10 years. If we start intensive work now, by applying the theories we have presented on a broad scale, we might have some answers on spruce budworm in 25 to 30 years.

Nevertheless, we will continue to use silviculture in control, and through our experience and somewhat educated guesses, we may continue to develop reasonable procedures. The increasing need for wood will require the application of intensive management on a wider scale. The associated pest problems will provide interesting silvicultural problems that will require our very best efforts to solve.

FOREST MANAGEMENT–THE FUTURE

Forests of the future will continue to provide a multiple of products and services as they have in the past. They will be more heavily used for recreation, by wildlife, for water production and for grazing, as well as for timber production. More forest lands must come under intensive multiple-use forestry if we are to meet the demands that are projected for the year 2000 and thereafter.

Zivnuska and Vaux (1975) discussed projections of timber needs. Their figures show a current consumption of wood amounting to 12.7 billion cu. ft. per year. The consumption predictions for 2000 vary from a low of 19.2 to a high of 22.8 billion cu. ft. They cite the most important element that will be required in achieving these goals as the development of intensive and efficient timber production of *all* prime timber-growing land.

Many of our public policy constraints serve to prevent the development of such an effective wood supply policy. We need only to look at the current controversy over clear-cutting to realize the breadth of this problem. We have the potential to double forest productivity during the next 50 years, but there are very few signs that efforts are developing on anywhere close to the scale that is required to meet that greater productivity. The only place where we see signs of progress is on the privately-owned industrial lands which include only 14% of our total commercial forest. The largest category of ownership is the farm and miscellaneous ownerships which include 59% of our total acreage and 44% of our prime Site I and II lands. Currently only 5% of these timber lands are intensively managed (Forest Service 1973) on a continuing basis. Schallau (1975) emphasized that the Forest Service figures were based on data that predated the oil embargo. Subsequent changes could upset the projections considerably; demand for conventional wood products could be reduced, but there could develop a greatly increased demand for wood production to meet other needs related to energy.

McKnight (1975) does not completely share the pessimism expressed by Zivnuska and Vaux. He expressed confidence that productivity, at least in the South, is improving on private lands. We need to encourage the advancement of management practices on more of our forest lands nationwide.

Manthy (1975) provides further reasons for optimism. The nation is currently growing 33% more wood than is removed. Also, even though we are utilizing more wood for some products, there are still situations where substitute materials may be used.

Perhaps most important of all is the area of more complete utilization of the tree and all its component parts. This has been developing from the earliest days of forest practice. Much that was once merely waste is now in demand; those parts of the tree that are now left in the woods as waste materials will probably be in demand within a few years. In some parts of the world the leaves and needles of trees are now being used (Keays and Barton 1975) for animal feed supplements; we may find that such uses are economically feasible.

Manthy (1975) makes the point that we will have a sizeable quantity of material as a reserve to help us meet the projected needs.

High Yield Forestry

We have all heard varying reports on the Weyerhaeuser High Yield Forest Program. The discussion of that program in American Forests (1974) provides considerable detail on what that progressive company is doing on its own lands to meet the high yield goals for the future. Their objectives are simple, and should be the objectives of all forest landowners. Most might cite similar objectives, but many landowners have no action program:

(1) The owner should maximize the present value of the resource.
(2) The land should provide a continuous flow of raw materials over time.
(3) The total forest land base must be brought to optimum productivity in as short a time span as possible.

It was stated that the most important aspect of the Weyerhaeuser program is its urgency. The policy is to take urgent and intensive action now to assure that corporate needs are met in the future. Their high yield forest plan is based upon sound economics in the same way as all other investments of the company. The time frame may be longer, and the exposure to risk may be greater, but the earning expectations are the same.

The Weyerhaeuser land managers state their reasons for investment in simple, common-sense terms. "Wood and wood fiber are no longer abundant, essentially valueless materials, put at man's disposal by nature for endless exploitation. We've come to the point in history when our wood resource will have to be cultivated if we are to have sufficient quantities of this basic building material of civilization." This is not an idle statement; in 1973 the company planted 97,640,000 seedlings and fertilized 200,134 acres of young timber. They plan to invest $100,000,000 a year in this High Yield Program. Along with this emphasis on high yields, there is a commitment to multiple use of the forests under management. As an example, in 1974 the company had a staff of 12 professionals and technicians devoting their full time to wildlife management.

Generally speaking, this high yield forest is beneficial to the wildlife populations.

I mention Weyerhaeuser's program to show what can be done for the future. Such policies will have to be applied to vast acreages of forest lands before we can have any confidence that we can meet future needs. We know that many other industrial concerns are following similar programs, but their land holdings are only a small portion of our forests. With increased demand and the associated higher prices for timber, we could easily slip into an exploitation era once more. This would be a disaster to the nation and must be avoided at all costs.

Nutrient Relationships

The stress on high yields and a more complete utilization of all the fiber produced by our trees has led to much speculation and some research on the nutrient relationships of forest stands (Jorgensen et al. 1975, Patric and Smith 1975). Stone (1973) has provided a thorough review of the material available on this vital topic. The fears relate to our historic knowledge of the nutrient losses in the Bavarian forests where everything, including leaf litter, was removed over centuries. The loss in tree growth was readily established. Our general harvest procedures remove an accumulation of nutrients that were gradually removed as the tree developed. Much more is recycled back into the soil in the form of leaves, twigs and other so-called wastes of the operation. Generally, there has been no upset of nutrient balances from logging trees in conventional operations and over fairly long rotations.

There is more concern now because of several new developments related to the demand for more wood fiber.

1. Complete tree logging removes more of the stem and much of the finer materials as well. Most soils would not be affected if this happened on long cutting rotations as nutrient replacements would still provide ample materials for future tree generations.

2. There have been suggestions that the natural mortality which occurs as the forest develops should be salvaged to avoid waste and to meet fiber needs. Such a harvest would be very expensive, but it would also begin to cut into some of the replacement materials.

3. The greatest concern should be voiced against the increased nutrient losses that would be associated with the development of extreme short rotation operations. As we reach this stage of operations we are getting close to cropping in much the same manner as in raising corn or potatoes. Nutrients would have to be replaced.

4. The fourth stage could be the extreme, though it may seem highly unlikely at this time. If the leaves of trees were developed as a food source for animals we could be harvesting them on an annual basis, thus removing the very last of the material returned to the soil from the tree. Such a development on a

large scale might be far in the future, but the effects of it are worth thinking about.

The literature is incomplete on this problem, but there is enough evidence to support our confidence in the present harvesting levels. Caution should be the watchword for the future; we should begin to utilize with greater intensity only if we are sure that sites will be maintained by either natural or artificial (fertilization) means. Before we plunge head-long into a total utilization philosophy, we must know that this will not result in environmental degradation. We have enough knowledge now to give us some fairly good guidelines, but we must have more research before we develop total utilization on a large scale.

SUMMARY

Our forests are varied in ownership patterns, in forest composition, and in multiplicity of uses. Management must be keyed to all three of these variables, and is further held within limits by economic, biological and social constraints.

In general, the theory of pest management through silviculture is far ahead of practice, possibly because such preventative measures are dependent upon markets for wood and the intensity of management. Most managers are developing pest management systems which will include the use of silvicultural procedures as one of the strategies.

The future indications are for a much greater demand for forest products and a closer utilization of the entire forest. Conflicts related to the many uses will be intense for a time, but the increasing needs should lead to a greater attention to multiple use forestry on most lands. Major problems must be solved in the management of the large acreage of private farm and miscellaneous ownerships.

Many of our serious outbreak pests will become less troublesome as we develop management procedures which accommodate their habits. At the same time other pest problems will increase as intensive management develops in more forest types, on more ownerships, and for more specific objectives.

Chapter 5

Chestnut Research and Biological Control of the Chestnut Blight Fungus

Richard A. Jaynes, Sandra L. Anagnostakis, and Neal K. Van Alfen[1]

Departments of Genetics and Plant Pathology
The Connecticut Agricultural Experiment Station
New Haven, Connecticut 06504

INTRODUCTION

The death of the American chestnut, *Castanea dentata* (Marsh.) Borkh., may well have been announced prematurely. To be sure, this once majestic forest tree of the eastern United States has been reduced to a mere shadow of its former self by the chestnut blight fungus, *Endothia parasitica* (Murr.) Anderson. However, persistent sprouts from the old stumps do survive and occasionally reach a trunk size of 25 cm diameter at 137 cm from the ground (10 in. dbh) and fruit before the wound parasite attacks again and the sprouting cycle is repeated. These sprouts could reestablish the chestnut in American woodlands as a forest tree, because for the first time in over 70 years there is evidence of a biological means to control the disease. Chestnut blight was discovered in North America in 1904. This paper reviews work since that time to develop resistant trees and other methods for protecting them.

"The story of the disease that destroyed the glorious American chestnut tree is a plant tragedy second to none and symbolizes the need for man's unceasing struggle against forest pests," (Hepting 1974). Hepting vividly described the former role of chestnut in everyday life:

[1] Present address: Department of Biology, Utah State University, Logan, Utah 84321.

While chestnut trees meant chestnuts to us city boys, they meant much more to the rural folks and the country in general. From southern New England to northern Georgia the average mountain cabin was made of chestnut logs and a chestnut shingle roof. Chestnut made fine fire wood. Fence posts, rails, and poles for rural telephone lines were made of this durable wood. The farmers' hogs were fattened on chestnuts, and, to no small degree, his children were also. Chestnuts made up a large part of the diet of wild turkeys, squirrels, and other wildlife.

The attractive grain of this fine wood made it ideal for interior uses such as paneling, trim, and furniture. Not only was baby's crib likely made of chestnut, but chances were, so was the old man's coffin. Chestnut has always been preferred for buryin' boxes. Heavy leathers were tanned almost exclusively with chestnut extract or blends and it took twenty huge plants to serve this one industry. Extract wood has been a major source of income to the Appalachian farmer. Among over 100 commercial hardwood species, chestnut made up over one-fourth of all hardwood timber cut for lumber in the southern Appalachians. In a nation that abounds in versatile trees, the grand, stately American chestnut was easily the most versatile.

The disease was first noticed on trees at the Bronx Zoological Park in New York City (Murrill 1906). Although somewhat erratic in its spread, it moved approximately 20 miles per year in ever increasing concentric circles (Anon. 1954). Chestnut blight was first noted in Connecticut in Fairfield County in 1907 (Clinton 1908b) and by 1917 most of the trees throughout the state were dead or dying.

Initial reaction to the epidemic was mixed. There quickly evolved three theories to explain the sudden outbreak and rapid spread of this disease. Clinton (1908b), Connecticut Station botanist, suggested that the disease was endemic, its increase a result of the chestnut trees being weakened by a succession of cold and dry winters. Murrill (1906) also believed the fungus was native, but that it had suddenly acquired unusual virulence. Metcalf (1908) suggested that the fungus was imported from Japan basing his conclusion on the observation that it was relatively harmless to Japanese chestnut trees planted on Long Island. Discovery of the fungus in China by F. N. Meyer in 1913 (Fairchild 1913) provided substantial support for Metcalf's theory. Numerous reports on the life history, spread, and control of the fungus appeared in these early years.

Several strategies were attempted to combat the disease and to restore chestnut as a forest tree. In 1911 the Pennsylvania Chestnut Blight Commission was formed to direct efforts to control the blight. The record of the conference called by the state governor on February 20, 1912, documents the range of opinions. Stewart (1912) of the New York Agricultural Experiment Station, expressing a minority view, claimed that it was too late to exert any control:

It is better to attempt nothing than to waste a large amount of public money on a method of control which there is every reason to believe cannot succeed. I believe in being honest with the public and admitting frankly that we know of no way to control this disease. I favor moderate-sized appropriations for investigation of the disease, but none at all to be used in attempts to control it by any method or methods at present known.

What will be the future course of the disease can only be conjectured, but it can be safely predicted that nothing which man can now do will materially alter its course.

Few agreed with Stewart, and those in favor of an affirmative action program carried the day.

QUARANTINE AND CLEAR-CUTTING

The Pennsylvania legislature appropriated over $500,000 for the use of the commission during 1911–1914. Studies of the life history of the fungus continued (Anderson 1913). Control measures were chiefly prevention of the movement of nursery stock and infected chestnut wood into noninfected areas and the clear-cutting of chestnut trees in advance of the spreading blight. Eradication by burning of newly-infected trees in previously disease-free areas was also attempted. By 1914 the early optimism of the Pennsylvania Blight Commission had vanished, and it was conceded that the program was essentially a failure (Schock 1914).

RESISTANT SPECIES

The Chinese and Japanese chestnut trees (*C. mollissima* Bl. and *C. crenata* Sieb. & Zucc.) were not seriously affected by the blight fungus and efforts were made from imported seed to replant with these Asiatic chestnut trees (Galloway 1926). Between 1927 and 1930 U. S. Forest Pathologist Kent Beattie sent more than 250 bushels of nuts from various regions of China; more than one quarter million trees were raised (Beattie and Diller, 1954). The Chinese chestnut proved well adapted to the soil and climate of the eastern United States but was not a forest tree. In habit it is more like an apple tree, and is better suited for nut production than timber. *Castanea henryi* Rehd. & Wils., another forest tree species of chestnut from China, was also introduced but proved to be ill-adapted to our eastern U. S. environment and had insufficient field resistance to the chestnut blight fungus.

HYBRIDS

The possibility of recombining the best traits of two or more chestnut species was clear to plant breeders, for great successes had been achieved with agronomic crops by such methods. In 1909 the U. S. Division of Forest Pathology began breeding chestnut trees under the leadership of Walter Van

Fleet (Clapper 1954). Arthur H. Graves, who worked with chestnut from 1911 to 1962, made a perceptive statement in 1914, 15 years before he began his own chestnut hybridizing in Connecticut: "Work of this kind [breeding] is extremely valuable and, although slow in yielding results, may eventually prove to be the only means of continuing the existence in our land of a greatly esteemed tree." Considerable progress has been made in developing hybrid chestnut trees that have the growth and form of the American chestnut plus the resistance of the Chinese or Japanese chestnut; however, much remains to be done to obtain a true-breeding, forest-type tree (Jaynes 1974). The best trees to date are clonal selections, which are difficult to reproduce from cuttings or by grafting, and they segregate widely from seed.

Recent breeding efforts have concentrated on single tree selections and mass culture of open-pollinated hybrid seedlings from such selections. A planting of 10,000 seedlings, largely from selected Connecticut hybrids was established in recent years at the Lesesne Forest, Virginia, under the care of the Virginia Division of Forestry. Other small plantings are scattered in several eastern states (Keys et al. 1975).

MUTATION AND RESISTANCE WITHIN THE AMERICAN CHESTNUT

To many it seemed inconceivable that a species represented by millions of heterozygous individuals with a broad geographic distribution could be uniformly susceptible to this disease. Occasional trees can be found today with trunks in excess of 25 cm diameter that have kindled hopes of natural resistance, but to date no evidence for substantial field resistance within the American chestnut has been demonstrated. Large trees are either escapes or derelicts of gnarled form and weakened condition. American chestnut trees do not respond to chestnut blight infection uniformly but such resistance as may be present is of little immediate practical value. Bingham et al. (1971) and others have suggested that a major breeding effort be undertaken to combine the resistance that may occur throughout the natural range to develop trees with field resistance. Other workers, notably Thor and Singleton, have pursued the objective of inducing mutations in the American chestnut by irradiating seed, so far without success (Jaynes 1974).

CHEMICALS

Effective therapeutic agents for controlling chestnut blight have long been sought. Caroline Rumbold (1920a, b) had begun curative treatments by topical application and injection of chemicals into trees at the time of the Pennsylvania Blight Commission Conference in 1912. Weak solutions of lithium salts injected in the spring months tended to enhance callus formation on existing cankers. However, no effective chemical controls were known until Jaynes and Van Alfen

(1974) reported significant reduction in growth of the blight fungus in American chestnut trees pressure-injected with MBC (methyl 2-benzimidazole carbamate) both before and after they were artificially inoculated. This material remains biologically active in the trees for at least 9 months and offers a means to protect valuable ornamentals and specimen trees. It is costly and impractical to use in large plantings.

HYPOVIRULENCE

Almost since the blight was first discovered there was speculation and optimism that the worst was over and the American chestnut would soon regain its stature and former place in the forest. Clinton (1908b) said this would come about when normal weather conditions returned. Zimmerman (1936) claimed that the trees were building up immunity, and many others were certain they had found one or more blight-resistant American trees. However, none of these claims was substantiated.

Hence, it is not surprising that the scientific community paid little attention to A. Biraghi's report in 1951 that a remission of the disease on European chestnut trees, *C. sativa* Mill., had occurred in certain districts of Italy. He suggested two possible explanations: 1) a gradual increase in the level of resistance of the European chestnut, and 2) a loss of virulence by the parasite. In 1966 he discounted the first explanation, which he had favored (1953), but he failed to substantiate or explain the situation in detail. Grente (1965) reported the isolation of a less virulent form of the fungus, which he called "hypoviru-lent", and subsequently with Berthelay-Sauret published several reports on its unique characteristics (Grente 1971, Grente and Sauret 1969a, 1969b, Berthe-lay-Sauret 1973). Their findings can be summarized as follows:

1) Spontaneous healing (callusing) of cankers caused by the chestnut blight fungus was observed on European chestnut trees in central and northern Italy, southeastern France, and in the Pyrenees between France and Spain.

2) Strains of *E. parasitica* isolated from callusing cankers were nearly white in pure culture in contrast to the rusty orange color of the normal virulent (V) strain, conidia were more sparsely produced, and the white strains were almost completely non-virulent, hence the name "hypovirulent" (H). Pigmented H cultures designated "JR" were also observed and they, upon plating of conidia, were capable of segregating V and H strains.

3) The ratio of V to H strains isolated from trees was directly proportional to the state of health of the chestnut grove. Virulent strains predominated in severely damaged groves; both types were recovered in groves where callused cankers predominated; and in a grove with entirely healed cankers, virulent strains were not found and hypovirulent strains were isolated with difficulty.

4) Simultaneous or co-inoculation of the V and H strains resulted in limited growth of V.

5) Consecutive inoculations, V followed by H, suggested that V was "excluded" by H.

6) Certain strains of H were more effective than others. "Exclusion" appeared more effective if both cultures were obtained from the same geographic region, suggesting the need for hyphal fusion for exclusion, and the presence of a fusion incompatibility between strains.

7) Active cankers could be cured by inoculation with H.

8) Three years after introducing H into a chestnut grove, the H strain was becoming dominant and the disease was regressing.

9) In the laboratory, cultures of H could segregate into V and H or revert to V, whereas V never gave rise to H.

10) The use of cultures with genetic markers was indicated by Berthelay-Sauret (1973) in an abstract. Details of the research apparently have not been published.

Grente and Sauret offered several hypotheses for the mechanism of "exclusive hypovirulence" including:

1) The secretion of a substance by H which affects the vitality of V. They felt this was rather unlikely.

2) Competition for the occupation of host tissues or for nutritive substances present. They also deemed this to be unlikely.

3) Activation of the defense mechanism of the plant by H, resulting in exclusion of the pathogen.

4) "Infection" of V with something after hyphal anastomosis with H. They favored this hypothesis based in part on the evidence from the use of marked cultures mentioned above.

Grente and Sauret (1969a) concluded that the phenomenon of hypovirulence opens a vast domain of important consequences for the plant pathologist.

Bonifacio and Turchetti (1973) also studied the morphology and physiology of *E. parasitica* strains isolated in Italy. Their strains were phenotypically like those of Grente and Sauret except that their colored "H" or JR strain was stable and did not segregate. Bonifacio and Turchetti concluded that they were dealing with a cytoplasmic factor, perhaps mitochondrial, and that the unstable form existed with mixed cytoplasm.

Hypovirulence in the United States

Cultures from Grente were first received at The Connecticut Agricultural Experiment Station in 1966, and again in 1972 when research with them was begun in earnest. Anagnostakis and Jaynes (1973) demonstrated that the H strain (2025) of Grente and Sauret was effective in controlling a French V strain

(2024) on inoculated American chestnut trees. Effects of the French H strain on an American V strain were inconclusive.

Van Alfen et al. (1975) were able to transfer hypovirulence into American strains of the blight fungus by repeated co-inoculations of the host. The hypovirulent American strains recovered in these experiments were much more effective in limiting growth of American V strains in host tissue than was the original French H strain. Auxotrophic mutants were used to demonstrate that hypovirulence is caused by a cytoplasmic determinant which is transferred by hyphal anastomosis, thus confirming Grente's hypothesis. This work clearly demonstrated that the H strain might serve as the basis for biological control of the disease in the United States.

Attempts to detect double-stranded RNA in H strains of *E. parasitica* by serological methods were positive, but virus-like particles have not been demonstrated (Moffitt and Lister 1975, Day unpublished data).

Current Research

Much remains to be done to elucidate the nature and mechanism of action of hypovirulence. We have a unique opportunity in the eastern United States to study its establishment and spread in the field from known starting points in time and space.

Field Plots

In the late fall of 1974 and early spring of 1975, 12 field plots were established in natural woodlands in Connecticut. Each plot, approximately 1 hectare in size, contained 25 American chestnut clones (sprout clumps) consisting of one or more stems at least 2.5 cm in diameter at 137 cm height from the ground. Stems up to 14 cm diameter were present.

The size and location of blight cankers within each plot was recorded, plots were arbitrarily paired, and the plot of each pair having the highest incidence of disease was treated with the derived American H strain.

Treatment consisted of removing 9 mm diameter plugs of bark from the lateral (horizontal) extremities of cankers and placing similar sized plugs of potato dextrose agar (Difco) containing the H strain into the holes. The inoculation sites were then covered with masking tape to prevent drying. With few exceptions, each naturally-occurring canker received two inoculations. First inoculations were made in the fall of 1974. As new infections were noted in treated plots during the 1975 growing season, they were also inoculated with H. The diameters of cankers were measured at monthly intervals from April to October.

The results at this time are preliminary but most encouraging. Cankers inoculated with H stopped growing after an initial lag of 1-2 months. Thus the following data for treated cankers are based on those that had been exposed to

FIGURE 1. *Naturally occurring cankers on native American chestnut inoculated with H (A and B) and uninoculated control (C). Photos taken one year after inoculations; arrows indicate points of inoculation with H.*

Treatment	Stem diam, cm	Canker limits, cm	
		April '75	Oct. '75
A) Inoc. with H Oct. '74	13	25	8
B) Inoc. with H Oct. '74	8	18	7
C) none	10	14	28 girdled

Note the callus growing in from the edges of the wound on A and B and the concave area of wound in C where the tissue is dead and dry.

H for two or more months. Of 42 cankers in the non-treated plots, 40 (95%) continued to increase in size whereas 2 appeared to be arrested. Of the 90 cankers inoculated with H in the treated plots, 77 (86%) were arrested and the trees were beginning to callus the wound (Fig.1). Of the 13 cankers not arrested with H inoculations, six were on weak and suppressed stems and three of the other cankers were three-fifths or more of the way around the stem at the time of inoculation. The two arrested cankers in the control plots are probably a temporary phenomenon.

It remains to be determined whether the H strain will effectively establish and spread by itself in our native woodland and, if it does, how. Its establishment may depend on its ability to survive as a saprophyte. We do know that it will overwinter in American chestnut tree sprouts in Connecticut.

TABLE 1 Families and species of native and exotic woody plants inoculated with American virulent and hypovirulent strains of *Endothia parasitica*.

Family	Species	Common Name
Aceraceae	*Acer pensylvanicum* L.	Moosewood
	A. rubrum L.	Red maple
	A. saccharum Marsh.	Sugar maple
Anacardiaceae	*Rhus copallina* L.	Shinning sumac
Annonaceae	*Asimina triloba* (L.) Dun.	Common pawpaw
Aquifoliaceae	*Ilex verticillata* (L.) Gray	Winterberry
Betulaceae	*Betula populifolia* Marsh.	Gray birch
	Carpinus caroliniana Walt.	Ironwood
	Corylus colurna L.	Turkey tree hazel
	C. hybrid	Filbert
	Hamamelis virginiana L.	Witch hazel
Calycanthaceae	*Lindera benzoin* (L.) Blume	Spice bush
Cornaceae	*Cornus florida* L.	Dogwood
Ebenaceae	*Diospyros virginiana* L.	Persimmon
Ericaceae	*Rhododendron viscosum* (L.) Torr.	Swamp azalea
Fagaceae	*Castanea dentata* (Marsh.) Borkh.	American chestnut
	C. hybrid	HHR4T7 JAXC
	C. mollissima Bl.	'Crane' Chinese chestnut
	C. mollissima hybrid	'Eaton' chestnut
	Quercus alba L.	White oak
	Q. cerris L.	Turkey oak
	Q. prinus L.	Chestnut oak
	Q. velutina Lam.	Black oak
Hippocastanaceae	*Aesculus hippocastanum* L.	Horsechestnut
Juglandaceae	*Carya illinoensis* (Wang.) K. Koch	Pecan
	C. ovata (Mill.) K. Koch	Shagbark hickory
	Juglans cinerea L.	Butternut
	J. nigra L.	Black walnut
	J. regia L.	Persian walnut
Leguminosae	*Albizia julibrissin* Durazz.	Hardy silk tree
	Gleditsia triacanthos L.	Honey locust
	Sophora japonica L.	Chinese scholar tree
Magnoliaceae	*Magnolia acuminata* L.	Cucumber tree
Nyssaceae	*Nyssa sylvatica* Marsh.	Sourgum
Pinaceae	*Metasequoia glyptostroboides* Hu & Cheng	Dawn redwood
	Tsuga canadensis (L.) Carr.	Hemlock
Rosaceae	*Amelanchier canadensis* (L.) Medic	Shadbush
	Aronia arbutifolia (L.) Elliott	Red chokeberry
	Malus pumila Mill.	Apple
	Prunus persica (L.) Batsch	Peach
	Sorbus aucuparia L.	European mountain ash

Experiments are in progress to determine whether hypovirulence can be transmitted to V cankers on native sprouts by spraying them with H conidia grown in the laboratory.

Concern has been expressed over the possible virulence of H strains on other hosts. No problem of this kind has been noted in Europe. V strains of *E. parasitica* are occasionally pathogenic on post oak, *Quercus stellata* Wang., and live oak, *Q. virginiana* Mill., and can be saprophytic on other woody plants (Clapper et al. 1946, May and Davidson 1960). We inoculated stems of red oak, *Q. rubra* L., in 1973 with the European H and V strains and observed no notable growth of the fungus. Three months results of inoculations of American V and H strains on 40 different woody species, exotic and native, belonging to 17 families were also negative except for the chestnut trees (Table 1).

If the hypovirulent strain of *Endothia* can survive and spread in the woodlands of eastern United States as effectively as it apparently has in the chestnut groves of Europe, there is the prospect of reestablishing the American chestnut as a significant forest tree. Our research is directed at determining the best ways of promoting and assisting the spread of hypovirulent strains.

SUMMARY

The chestnut blight fungus reduced a major forest tree of eastern United States to essentially an understory shrub within 40 years. Early attempts to confine or control the disease were unsuccessful. Blight-resistant species were introduced, but they were not good timber trees. Development of blight-resistant hybrids has progressed but they are not yet an adequate substitute for the American chestnut. A systemic fungicide was recently demonstrated to be capable of protecting specimen trees. The discovery of a hypovirulent strain of the chestnut blight fungus that converts virulent strains to hypovirulent promises a natural control of the blight like that recently observed in Europe.

II

INSECT BIONOMICS

Chapter 6

The Bionomics of
the Twolined Chestnut Borer

Dennis M. Dunbar[1] and George R. Stephens

Department of Entomology and Department of Ecology and Climatology
The Connecticut Agricultural Experiment Station
New Haven, Connecticut 06504

INTRODUCTION

The twolined chestnut borer, *Agrilus bilineatus* (Weber), has been known to kill chestnut, *Castanea dentata* (Marshall) Borkhausen, and oak, *Quercus* spp., for almost a century. As a result, it is the most widely recognized of the more than 120 described species of *Agrilus* in North America. Even so, its biology and role as a forest insect pest, particularly in New England, remain obscure.

This beetle, named for the two prominent stripes on its elytra (Fig. 1), was recognized by Hopkins (1894) as being responsible for the death of oak in Ohio, Wisconsin, Indiana, and West Virginia. Its life history and control were first described by Chittenden (1897, 1909). Later, Chapman (1915) conducted further observations on its life history in Minnesota. Until recently, this work was the main source of information on its biology.

During the last decade, *A. bilineatus* emerged as a principal cause of oak mortality in the eastern United States, and interest in its role as a forest insect pest was renewed (Staley 1965, Nichols 1968, Kegg 1971, 1973, Dunbar and Stephens 1974a, 1975). Since the summer of 1972, when oak mortality was most noticeable in Connecticut, we have studied various aspects of its biology and control as well as its association with declining oak. We present here a review

---

[1] Current address: FMC Corporation, Agricultural Chemical Division, Box 1589, Richmond, CA. 94804.

FIGURE 1. *Adult (top) and larva in feeding galleries (bottom) of* Agrilus bilineatus.

of the pertinent published and unpublished works on this beetle, which should facilitate future study of its role as a forest pest.

TAXONOMY AND DISTRIBUTION

A. bilineatus, native to North America, was described in 1801 as *Buprestis bilineata* and was later transferred to the genus *Agrilus*. Its description may be found in the book by Fisher (1928). It is widely distributed in eastern Canada and in the United States from Maine westward to the Rocky Mountains and southward to Texas (Horn 1891, Chittenden 1897).

HOSTS

Chestnut and the following species of oaks are listed as hosts: white, *Q. alba* L.: scarlet, *Q. coccinea* Muenchh; bur, *Q. macrocarpa,* Michx: red, *Q. rubra* L.; black, *Q. velutina* Lam. (Hopkins 1893, Chittenden 1900, Chapman 1915) and chestnut, *Q. prinus* L. (Britton 1914).

A. bilineatus var. *carpini* Knull attacks beech, *Fagus* sp., bluebeech, *Carpinus caroliniana* Walt., and ironwood or hophornbeam, *Ostrya virginiana* (Miller) Koch (Fisher 1928, Doane et al. 1936). Reports of *A. bilineatus* attacking beech by Harrington (1897), Felt (1933), Faull, (1936) and Pirone (1970) should probably be reserved for the variety *carpini.* Moffat (1900) attributed extensive injury to birch in Ontario, Canada to *A. bilineatus*; however, it is likely that this damage was caused by the bronze birch borer, *A. anxius* Gory.

LIFE HISTORY AND RELATIONSHIP TO HOST

A general life history of *A. bilineatus* may be found in most books that include a section on insect pests of oak. Briefly, adults emerge from infested trees by boring D-shaped holes through the bark in June and July and fly to foliage of host trees where they feed. Later, females oviposit in clusters of up to 10 eggs in cracks and crevices in the bark of host trees. Eggs hatch in 10–14 days and larvae (Fig. 1) burrow through the bark to feed in the cambium. They feed throughout the summer, constructing zigzag or meandering galleries in the inner bark and on the wood surface of the main trunk and larger branches. In the fall, near the end of larval development, larvae move into the bark and construct hibernation cells. Pupation occurs the following spring. Generally,

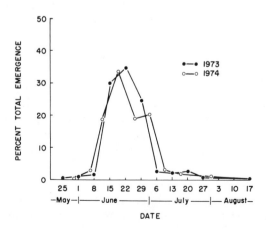

FIGURE 2. *Emergence of* Agrilus bilineatus *adults from infested oak trees in Connecticut during 1973 and 1974.*

there is one generation per year; however, Baker (1972) suggests that two years are required for one generation near the northern boundaries of its range.

Adult Emergence

Adults emerge from the last week of May to the first week of July in Virginia (Chittenden 1909) and from mid-June to the latter part of July in Minnesota (Chapman 1915). To obtain additional information in Connecticut, we caged infested oaks during two seasons, 1973 and 1974, and captured emerging adults. During each year, cages 90 cm long and made of plastic screening and wooden lath were placed around a section of the lower bole of each of 36 trees. Beginning in early May and continuing through August, adults were removed from the cages at weekly intervals. A total of 900 and 573 adults were collected in 1973 and 1974, respectively.

The first adults were collected on May 25, 1973 and June 5, 1974 (Fig. 2). Peak emergence occurred on or about June 22, 1973 and June 19, 1974 and appears to coincide with the period when oak trees are often under stress from spring defoliation. Adult emergence declined markedly during the first week in July in both years. By July 6, 1973 and by July 3, 1974, 94% of the total adult population had emerged. Small numbers of adults continued to emerge throughout July and August of both years. This may explain why larvae in all stages of development are found in infested trees in late fall. Emergence may be associated with temperature as is the case of emergence in *A. anxius* and other species of *Agrilus* (Carlson and Knight 1969).

The sex ratio (male to female) of emergent adults was 1:1.1 in 1973 and 1:1.2 in 1974. At $24 \pm 1°C$, unfed adults lived 3.9 ± 0.5 days while adults fed red oak foliage lived 20.1 ± 10.4 days (females) and 16.2 ± 7.6 days (males).

During both seasons, large numbers of the emergent adults were covered with brown mites identified as the hypopial stage of *Histiogaster* sp. (det. by E. W. Baker, U. S. Dept. Agric.). These mites live on fungus-infested bark and in the tunnels of beetle larvae. They use adult beetles as a means for distribution (Hughes 1959).

Adult Feeding Behavior

Previous studies have not established whether *A. bilineatus* adults feed indiscriminately on foliage of many species of trees. Chapman (1915) observed them feeding on the leaves of red oak and Felt and Bromley (1931) reported that they fed readily on the leaves of red and black oak. Laboratory experiments were therefore initiated to test the food preferences of newly emerged adults. In each of three experiments conducted at $24 \pm 1°C$, fresh foliage discs which averaged 2.71 cm^2 in area/disc, from six hardwood species (Table 1), were placed on moist filter paper in a random pattern in a petri dish (100 x 20 cm). One unfed adult was introduced into each dish. The amount and type of foliage consumed were visually estimated after 48 hrs. The accuracy of this visual method was compared to actual measurements made with a leaf-area meter and was found to be comparable.

Results showed that when offered only white oak foliage females on the average consumed more foliage in 48 hrs (2.26 cm^2) than males (1.90 cm^2). When offered a choice there was no difference between the sexes regarding species preferences. Consequently, the data for both sexes are combined in Table 1. Adults are not indiscriminate feeders and they prefer oaks over non-oak species. Among the oaks, scarlet oak foliage is preferred. We note that while chestnut is suitable for larval development, adults do very little feeding on its foliage.

TABLE 1. *Food preference of* A. bilineatus *adults when offered a choice between foliage of different hardwoods*

Tree Species	Mean consumption/beetle (cm^2) over a 48 hr period		
	Test 1 (n=19)	Test 2 (n=18)	Test 3 (n=54)
American beech[1]	0.70 a[2]		0.03 d
Red oak	.46 a	0.20 c	.27 c
Hybrid chestnut	.13 b		
Sugar maple	0 b		
Trembling aspen	0 b		
Black cherry	0 b		
White oak		1.24 a	.41 bc
Chestnut oak		.63 b	.47 b
American chestnut		.02 c	
Red maple		0 c	
Shagbark hickory		0 c	
Scarlet oak			.63 a
Black oak			.27 c

[1] Species names not previously given include: American beech, *Fagus grandifolia* Ehrh.; hybrid chestnut, *Castanea* sp.; sugar maple, *Acer saccharum* Marsh.; trembling aspen, *Populus tremuloides* Michx.; black cherry, *Prunus serotina* Ehrh.; red maple, *A. rubrum L.*; and shagbark hickory, *Carya ovata* (Mill.) K. Koch.

[2] Means within a column followed by the same letter are not significantly different at the P=0.05 level of probability (Duncan's multiple range test).

Dispersal and Host Selection

Little is known about adult dispersal and host selection. We observed as did Chapman (1915) that newly emerged adults immediately fly in a zigzag pattern toward the tree tops, possibly in response to light. How far they fly is unknown. Carlson and Knight (1969) stated that while *Agrilus* beetles may have the capacity to fly considerable distances, they rarely do so because they usually only have to fly short distances to find suitable hosts. Our field observations tend to substantiate this hypothesis. Trees killed or infested with *A. bilineatus* are often clustered, and evidence of an infestation in the cluster may go back several years.

A. bilineatus may select hosts that are well exposed to sunlight as is common for other species of *Agrilus* (Carlson and Knight 1969). Certainly Chapman (1915) found that the daily behavior of adults was at least regulated in large part by temperature and sunlight. Adults were most active during the heat of the day and on those parts of trees most open and exposed to sunlight. Felt and Bromley (1932) found that *A. bilineatus* was attracted to sunlit trees at the forest margin.

Olfactory responses may play a role in host selection. Anderson (1944) found that *A. granulatus liragus* Barter and Brown detected trees which were in poor condition and, as Carlson and Knight (1969) suggested, the stimulus is undoubtedly olfactory arising from decomposition of substances in the bark or phloem.

Although *A. bilineatus* attacks all species of oaks, Chapman (1915) stated that it appeared to favor black oaks while Decker (1933) stated that it appeared to show a definite preference for red oak. In contrast, Kegg (1973) supposed that *A. bilineatus* was associated with much of the dead or dying white oak in New Jersey, and Dunbar and Stephens (1975) found that significantly more dead and dying trees in the white oak group than in the red oak group were attacked by *A. bilineatus*. It is not known what caused these differences in attack by this insect. It may be associated with which species of oak is dominant or the condition of the oak in the area studied.

Host Condition in Relation to Successful Attack

Although the literature contains numerous reports which document the destruction of chestnut and oak by *A. bilineatus*, the debate continues on whether it prefers to attack healthy trees or only those that are first weakened by drought, windstorms, defoliation, or other predisposing agents. *A. anxius* (Barter 1957) and A. *liragus* (Anderson 1944, Barter 1965) prefer to attack weakened trees, but under some conditions such as a high population density they will attack healthy trees. Likewise, when *A. bilineatus* populations are high as they often are following extensive heavy defoliation of oaks, healthy trees often become infested (Hopkins 1895, Chittenden 1909, Chapman 1915, Decker 1933, Felt 1935, Craighead 1950, Dunbar and Stephens 1975).

No experimental evidence is available to document the reports that *A. bilineatus* prefers to attack weakened trees. Two field experiments were therefore conducted during 1973 and 1974. In the first experiment, 28 ten-yr-old red oak trees which were vigorous and uninfested were selected and injured. The treatments included total defoliation, root-pruning, total defoliation plus root-pruning and no treatment. Up to two pairs of field collected female and male adults were placed in cages constructed at breast height around the boles of the trees at various intervals throughout the emergence period. Red oak foliage was placed in each cage for food. Cages were constructed of clear plastic and nylon screening.

Removal of the bark within the caged area of each tree in the fall of 1974 revealed that 57% of the defoliated and defoliated plus root-pruned trees had either larvae or galleries present and thus, had been attacked. No trees that were only root-pruned or uninjured had been attacked. None of the trees had died.

The other field experiment was conducted in two stands of oak in Warren, Connecticut, where the *A. bilineatus* infestation was low. At one site, red oak was dominant and no dead or dying infested trees could be found. At the other site, about 1 mile away, white oak was dominant and several infested dying trees were present. To assure that some *A. bilineatus* adults would occur at the red oak site, logs heavily infested with pupae were transported to the site from another region of the state.

During June 1974 in the red oak stand, 20 oaks varying in size from 12.7 to 30.1 cm dbh were selected and treated as follows: 5 trees were axe girdled at breast height; 5 trees were root-pruned; 5 trees were axe girdled and root-pruned and 5 trees were left uninjured. Root pruning was accomplished by washing the soil and litter away from the roots with a stream of water produced by a fire pump and then cutting with an axe all visible lateral roots to a depth of 30.2 to 35.6 cm. In the white oak stand, 15 trees which varied in size from 16.3 to 30.6 cm dbh were axe girdled at breast height and 5 trees were left uninjured. No trees were root-pruned.

In September 1975, all 40 trees in the two stands were felled and examined from ground level to the top of the crown for evidence of *A. bilineatus* attack. Approximately 14% of the bole surface was debarked and examined by the method described by Dunbar and Stephens (1975).

Three of 5 (60%) girdled red oaks and 3 of 5 (60%) girdled and root-pruned red oaks had been attacked. None of the root-pruned or uninjured trees had been attacked. However, a small overtopped red oak near 3 treated trees and not part of the experiment also succumbed to *A. bilineatus* attack. Two of the girdled trees infested with *A. bilineatus* died during late summer 1974, and 2 others died during late summer 1975.

Results in the white oak stand were similar. However, 8 of 15 girdled trees partially healed the wound area and survived in good condition as if they had not been injured. None of these trees had been attacked. Of the 7 trees that did not heal the wound, 6 (86%) had been attacked. Four of these trees died in fall 1974. One of 5 control trees also had been attacked in the branches of the upper crown. This tree was overtopped by the main canopy and exhibited some previous dieback of the upper crown.

The results of our cage and field experiments show that *A. bilineatus*, when at low populations, successfully attacks injured but not healthy trees. While other field observations suggested that it was attacking and killing healthy trees, we were not able to demonstrate this experimentally when low populations of the insect were present.

Effect on Host

A. bilineatus causes death of the host through attacks on the branches and stem. Larval feeding destroys the phloem and cambium which effectively girdles trees by interrupting translocation. The time required for oaks infested with *A. bilineatus* to die, 1 to 3 yrs, is consistent with the results of mechanical girdling (MacKinney and Korstian 1932, Bull 1939, Greth 1957). The more numerous the galleries, the greater the girdling effect. Dunbar and Stephens (1975) reported that the estimated number of larvae per tree varied considerably, but generally increased with increasing bole diameter. The population density of larvae in dying trees (73 ± 20 (SE) larvae/m^2) was essentially the same as in recently dead trees (74 ± 15), but the location of the maximum density shifted downward on the bole from 9 m in dying trees to 1 m in recently dead trees. These data agree with Craighead's (1950) observations that A. *bilineatus* attack usually begins in the crown of the tree and proceeds downward along the bole in each succeeding year of infestation.

Larval Behavior

An excellent discussion of larval behavior of *Agrilus* other than *A. bilineatus* is given by Carlson and Knight (1969). Based on our general observations and those of Chapman (1915) much of what is recorded about behavior of larvae of other *Agrilus* is applicable to *A. bilineatus*. We noted, as did Chapman (1915), that shape and length of galleries depend greatly on host condition. In trees where wood is dry, feeding is restricted and galleries are shorter.

We also noted that not all larvae overwinter in cells in the bark. During April 1973 and 1974, 37 infested oak trees were felled and sampled to determine the extent of overwintering larval mortality. A total of 2,142 specimens of *A. bilineatus* were observed during this study. Of those observed, 72.8% were located in the bark. Mortality among these individuals which were prepupae was only 9.8% and indicates that low temperature probably had little effect once they were in the cells. On the other hand, 84.6% of the larvae still in the feeding position in the cambium were dead. Some of this mortality may have been attributed to winter temperature; however, much of it may have been caused by a change in the quality of food before winter. In other sampling (Dunbar and Stephens 1975), we observed that the phloem and cambium dried out rapidly in trees killed during late summer and that many larvae died of starvation and/or desiccation. A few larvae (15.4%) did survive on the wood. These survivors may complete their feeding the following summer and overwinter a second time. If so, then occasionally there may be a 2-yr life cycle for *A. bilineatus* in Connecticut as Baker (1972) suggested for this species in areas near the northern boundaries of its range.

ASSOCIATION WITH FUNGI

Certain plant diseases like the shoestring fungus, *Armillaria mellea* (Vahl.) Quel, are frequently found attacking trees in conjunction with *A. bilineatus* (Chapman 1915, Decker 1933, Baker 1941, Staley 1965, Nichols 1968, Kegg 1973). Dunbar and Stephens (1975) examined 84 dead trees at 13 different locations which had a previous history of defoliation and found that 47 were infested with both *A. mellea* and *A. bilineatus*, 33 were infested with only *A. bilineatus*, 2 were infested with *A. mellea* only, and 2 had neither organism. They concluded that *A. mellea* had a minor role and *A. bilineatus* a major role in causing the death of the observed defoliated oaks.

Smith (1911) and Metcalf and Collins (1911) stated that spores of the chestnut bark disease fungus, *Endothia parasitica* (Murr.) Anders, sporulated in galleries of *A. bilineatus*. Metcalf and Collins (1911) further reported that *A. bilineatus* was associated with 90% of all cases of the disease. This association, according to Ruggles (1913) and Anderson and Rankin (1914), is an overestimation because most of the galleries observed by Metcalf and Collins were made not by *A. bilineatus* but by the larvae of a small moth called the bast miner. The identity of this moth is not known to us.

A. bilineatus has also been associated with the oak-wilt fungus, *Ceratocystis fagacearum* (Bretz). Spores of this fungus are generally spread from infested to healthy oaks by sap-feeding beetles belonging to the family Nitidulidae. However, other beetles, including *A. bilineatus*, have been shown to be associated with diseased trees (Dorsey and Leach 1956, Fowler 1958, Stambaugh et al. 1955). Stambaugh et al. (1955) found that in Pennsylvania up to 17% of the *A. bilineatus* adults examined carried viable spores of *C. fagacearum*. They concluded that due to the abundance of *A. bilineatus* in the range of the susceptible white and red oaks that it was a good potential agent in oak wilt transmission.

Parmeter et al. (1956) found that feeding galleries made by *A. bilineatus* in the wood of infected branches were commonly associated with recurrence of oak wilt symptoms. They suggested that beetle injury may be instrumental in perpetuating the infection in some trees.

While adults of *Agrilus* generally feed on foliage, some species feed on spores of fungi. Burke (1917) stated that *A. bilineatus* is of benefit in destroying chestnut blight fungus, but obviously it had little effect considering how important the fungus became in destroying our native chestnut.

NATURAL ENEMIES

Parasitoids

Few parasitoids have been reported form *A. bilineatus*. Hopkins (1892) found a number of cocoons of a braconid, *Spathius simillimus* Ashm., in galleries of *A. bilineatus*. Chittenden (1909) credited *S. simillimus* for reducing beetle numbers in infested chestnut in the vicinity of the District of Columbia. Chapman (1915) identified a braconid, *Atanycolus* sp., from a larva and a *Trichogramma* from an egg.

Predators

Larvae of a predaceous Elateridae, *Adelocera oculatus* LeC., were observed feeding on larvae in Pennsylvania (Kirk 1922). *Tenebrioides bimaculatus* (Melsh.), a predaceous Ostomid beetle, was collected from mines and pupal cells in New York and Pennsylvania (Champlain and Knull 1923).

Birds prey upon prepupae, pupae and adults. Beal (1915) recovered adults from the stomach of a wood thrush, *Hylocichla mustelina* (Gmelin). We have observed on several occasions where woodpeckers extracted *A. bilineatus* from cells in the outer bark. Although we have no estimate of the impact woodpeckers have on lowering the populations, we have noted that in certain trees the impact appears to be substantial. Barter (1957) and MacAloney (1968) reported that woodpecker predation reduced bronze birch borer numbers by 50%.

CONTROL

Two important points have to be considered in a discussion of *A. bilineatus* control. First, this insect generally attacks trees that are weak and in declining health. Therefore, anything that stimulates growth and promotes tree vigor should help prevent attack. Second, damage in infested trees is nearly always completed before there are any outward symptoms. Therefore, practically nothing can be done to save trees that are already infested because the larvae live and feed in the cambium where they are well protected from chemicals and natural enemies.

Under forested conditions, control is usually impractical except where strict management practices are employed. Spraying to reduce defoliation will limit the number of trees susceptible to attack (Felt and Bromley 1931). Sanitation, through cutting and burning of infested or otherwise weak trees, is another common management practice recommended for reducing beetle populations (Hopkins 1903, Chittenden 1909, Chapman 1915, Clement 1917, Felt 1924, Pirone 1970). This method was used in a community on Long Island where cutting and burning 911 infested oaks within an area of 1,200 acres effectively reduced the borer population (Craighead 1915, Anon. 1916).

Today, however, burning infested trees to kill borers is not possible due to environmental restrictions placed on open burning. In lieu of burning, Dunbar and Stephens (1974b) found that sprays of lindane, chlorpyrifos and dimethoate when applied in May to the bark of infested trees killed borers and reduced adult emergence by 95%. They also found that adult emergence from slabs of processed logs was high, but that when slabs were converted to woodchips, emergence was reduced to nothing and a saleable product was gained.

In a small woodland or on valuable shade trees where expense is not often a limiting factor, watering, fertilization and spraying to prevent defoliation are useful in maintaining tree growth and vigor (Felt 1935, Pirone 1970). Control has also been aimed against leaf-feeding adults. Early attempts to control the beetle included sprays of lead arsenate and DDT applied to trees in June (Felt and Bromley 1930, Decker 1933, Craighead 1950). We found that red oak foliage sprayed with either acephate, carbaryl, methoxychlor or Imidan at a rate of 1 lb AI/100 gal water was highly toxic up to 7 days after treatment when fed to caged *A. bilineatus* adults.

Repellent sprays such as lime sulphur, white wash, iron sulphate, Bordeaux mixture and poisoned kerosene emulsion have been successful in preventing adult females from ovipositing on treated trees (Chittenden 1909, Chapman 1915, Kotinsky 1921, Decker 1933). It would seem, however, that the difficulties encountered in getting suitable bark coverage as well as the possibilities that rain would wash the materials off soon after application would make the use of repellent sprays questionable.

CONCLUSION

Despite its name, the twolined chestnut borer is principally a pest of oak. Although little is known about the population dynamics of this borer, it is likely always present at low levels in the forest where it breeds in weakened trees. However, following severe oak defoliation such as that recently experienced in Connecticut, it has the capabilities of increasing in numbers rapidly and bringing about large-scale oak mortality.

III

INSECT BEHAVIOR

Chapter 7

Applying Behavioral Studies in Entomological Problems

W. G. Wellington

Institute of Animal Resource Ecology
and
Department of Plant Science
University of British Columbia
Vancouver, B.C., Canada

OLD PROBLEMS AND CONFLICTING OPINIONS

Nearly 30 years ago, an attempt to control a spruce-budworm (*Choristoneura fumiferana* (Clem.)) outbreak by aerial spraying failed in an unusual way. As the aircraft roared over the tree tops, so many late-stage larvae tumbled from the branches that observers began to predict final eradication. Within hours, however, most of those presumably moribund insects had already returned to the trees, where they remained to complete their development.

Elsewhere that summer, comparable mass drops of spruce-budworm larvae seriously hindered attempts to record the insects' exact distribution on the trees; information which was urgently required for developing reliable methods of estimating abundance. In order to determine larval distribution on a tree, survey crews had to record each insect *in situ*, so the whole tree had to be carefully lowered within reach. Sometimes, trees could be cut and lowered without disturbing many larvae. Often, the slightest vibration would produce a shower of squirming insects.

Given some knowledge of the responses of *Choristoneura* larvae to dry air, the explanation of this annoying behavior and the solution of the problems it was creating were both very simple. Late-stage larvae of the spruce budworm become hypersensitive, responding violently to the slightest touch whenever ambient temperatures and rates of evaporation rise (Wellington and Henson 1947). On a hot, dry afternoon, therefore, the propeller-wash of a low-flying aircraft, or even the vibration from a single axe-blow, will bring down most of the late-stage larvae on a tree. In contrast, during cool wet weather, or early in the morning when the rate of evaporation is low, the larvae are so torpid that a bulldozer could knock down the tree without dislodging them. Only very minor changes in the timing and day-to-day operations of each project were required, therefore, to allow the work to resume.

Those incidents are still good examples of the way in which a knowledge of insect behavior may be applied in field work. But they also reveal a tendency (which still exists) to ignore insect behavior until it gets in the way of field work. Whatever its earlier roots, that tendency presently seems to spring from the opinion that there is already enough basic information about insects to support any new applied program that may be devised; i.e., there is a more urgent need for better technology and better managerial techniques.

That opinion occasionally surfaces even in relatively neutral documents; e.g., the ESA-sponsored report on integrated pest management (Glass 1975). And there is strong supporting evidence for that view in such specialized fields as insect vision, where the caliber of recent research has been exceptionally high (Horridge 1975, Mazokhin-Porshnyakov 1969, Wehner 1972). After such dramatic advances, it seems unreasonable to demand still more biological data before making the needed improvements in technological areas of pest management.

But is our knowledge of requisite biological facts so far ahead of our technological and managerial information? In the years since those early encounters with spruce-budworm behavior, the published information on the booms and nozzles, the carriers, the droplet sizes and the ambient conditions required to minimize drift and maximize the delivery of pesticides and other sprays would fill many library shelves. How many pages describe methods the living targets may use to evade the spray, and thus nullify that expertise?

Since those early attempts to apply statistical methods in spruce-budworm research, both the theory and practice of sampling have been greatly refined. In fact, with the aid of computers, population biologists have moved beyond mere statistics to construct mathematical models to penetrate the tangled webs we now perceive within even the simplest ecosystem.

Current models of spruce-budworm population dynamics are highly sophisticated, extremely complex, and firmly based on voluminous life-table data accumulated during the Green River Project (R.F. Morris 1963). Despite that wealth of actuarial and ecological information, the major submodel required a small but essential fragment of behavioral data on larval dispersal through different types of stands to generate acceptably realistic output (C. S. Holling, pers. comm.). In less explicit circumstances, a computer can obscure the need for behavioral data, thus encouraging the modeler to make the same mistakes at electronic speeds that his predecessors in population sampling made more slowly and more laboriously by hand.

Those remarks should not be construed as a wistful Luddite plea to smash the computers and scanning microscopes so that we can return to a simpler world comprised solely of life-history studies. We must maintain a systems approach to solve the complicated problems confronting us. That method of analysis has already given good service in the physiological and ecological fields. But somewhere in the gap between those rapidly diverging areas of study lies a forgotten part of the systems hierarchy—the individual—the entity that originally sparked the other enterprises.

It is individuals, not physiologies or communities, that become pests. It is the actions of survivors, not the percentage of the population killed, which change the dimensions of a pest problem. By asking behavioral questions, we can quickly estimate the extent of our knowledge or the depth of our ignorance about those survivors, and so judge whether we need additional basic information to solve a problem in pest management.

I believe that our knowledge of entomology exceeds our understanding of insects. Therefore I cannot yet share the view that we already have most of the basic information we need to move confidently into more complicated enterprises. In the remainder of this paper I should like to show some of the reasons for my skepticism.

As there are already published examples, I need not dwell on complicated studies incorporating behavior or its consequences into mathematical models which deal with patterns of occurrence (Campbell et al. 1975) or inter-related changes in abundance and viability (Wellington et al. 1975). For present purposes it will be more instructive to ask a few simple questions that involve behavior, to see whether the answers shed a different light on an established practice. I should like to examine a minor area—the effects of polarized light on insects in natural situations—and its implications for some of the standard methods of monitoring flight during field studies.

NEW OBSERVATIONS AND IMPLICATIONS

Information on diurnal or seasonal changes in flight activity is often required for planning large-scale field programs. There are several kinds of automated collecting devices which can be used to obtain that information. No one seems to worry much about where they should be placed or whether they sometimes give misleading information concerning peaks or troughs of activity.

The data in Fig. 1 were obtained by counting passing insects which would have been caught in a suction trap or comparably automated collector. The numbers of insects passing within 1 m during one 10-min period each hour were counted in two places only 15 m apart. One site was near the middle of a 24 x 24 m lawn. The other was 1 m from the shrubbery on the lawn's northern edge. The records were taken on a clear midsummer day in Vancouver, B.C., just above 49°N. Lat.

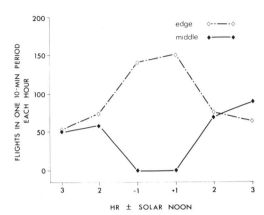

FIGURE 1. *The numbers of insects flying within 1 m of an observer during one 10-min period each hour near the middle and the edge of a lawn. Observers were 15 m apart. Observations were made during a clear midsummer day, with noon air temperature near 21°C. Hourly intervals were related to local solar noon, when the sun reached its maximum altitude for the day and eliminated zenith polarization.*

Near 49°N., the patch of unpolarized glare around the sun begins to intrude into the zenith as the sun climbs to an altitude of 60° above the horizon (Wellington 1974a). During late spring and early summer in Vancouver, the sun is above that altitude for varying periods daily. During periods when there is no polarized light in the zenith, insects that cannot steer by landmarks no longer fly for long distances, though they may continue to flit from branch to branch along hedgerows.

Figure 1 shows one result of that change in habit. The solid line shows that long flights across the lawn by all the non-landmarking insects—the Diptera, some beetles, wasps, and butterflies—ceased before midday and only resumed when the sun's glare receded from the zenith. In contrast, the broken line shows that there were more flights along the edge of the lawn while there was no polarized light overhead.

Figure 1 (and its companion, Fig. 2) do not include changes in the number or the duration of other kinds of behavior which did not involve flight. As those activities also increase near midday, or whenever clouds pass overhead, the curves for *flight* activity in the different places do not strictly represent the changes in *total* activity, and therefore should not be added together to suggest a final total in Fig. 1 (or in Fig. 2). In addition, neither landmarking bees nor drifting aphids were included in Fig. 1. The former are unaffected by changes in zenith polarization (Wellington 1974b). The latter are affected by so many factors (Johnson 1969) that they require special study.

The vast collections made by Lewis and Taylor (1964) and other investigators using automated equipment have already revealed several kinds of

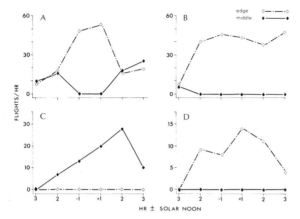

FIGURE 2. *Changes in the flight activity of the drone fly,* Eristalis tenax *(L.), near the middle and edge of the lawn. (A) on a clear midsummer day; (B) on the following day, when cloud covered the zenith about 2h before solar noon, but the air temperature remained near 20°C; (D) on the third day following, when air temperature under the overcast never reached 10°C; (C) on a clear day in autumn. Figs. 2A, B and D refer to one individual which could be followed from its territory to its feeding sites during the same period on each of three consecutive days. Fig. 2C shows that the feeding flights of a member of the non-territorial autumn generation were affected only by low morning and afternoon temperatures, because the low autumn sun did not affect zenith polarization.*

single and multiple peaks in the daily flight patterns of different insects. The shapes of the curves in Fig. 1 are therefore neither unexpected nor unusual. It is their derivation which demands attention, because they were produced only a few meters apart, mainly by the same species, and on the same day. The only physical variable that differed appreciably during the period was the amount of overhead polarization, an atmospheric phenomenon that the human eye can scarcely detect. In the absence of any information on where the data were collected, however, one could draw some unwarranted conclusions about either of the changing trends in activity that developed during the midday period. The problems of interpretation that may arise because of such misunderstandings can be illustrated in more detail by examining the actions of a single species.

The curves in Fig. 2 show some changes in the flight activity of the drone fly, *Eristalis tenax* (L.), on different days. Figs. 2A, B, and D were obtained on three consecutive midsummer days. Fig. 2C was obtained during the autumn.

The same patch of lawn and bordering shrubbery used for Fig. 1 were employed again to gather the data for Fig. 2, but the observational methods were adapted to the drone fly's habits. Drone-fly males of the midsummer generation are highly territorial, dividing their time between short rests and brief flights within their 1 x 2 m territories, and longer flights during which they travel to neutral feeding or grooming stations several meters beyond the territory. In Fig. 2, therefore, all of the flights along the edge of the lawn were territorial, and many included attacks on honey- or bumblebee foragers. In contrast, flights near the middle were directed toward the more distant feeding or preening stations. As individuals tended to reappear daily in particular places, they could be marked and then re-located at their various stations. Figures 2A, B, and D in fact show all of the flights by one individual which was followed continuously from its territory to its other stations during the periods indicated on the three consecutive days. Each hourly total is centered on its respective time mark in the figure.

Figure 2A resembles Fig. 1, as its data were also collected during a clear midsummer day. When the solar altitude was <60°, the fly moved frequently between its territory on the northern edge of the lawn and the feeding sites on other edges. Those long flights ceased, however, as the sun climbed to 60°. Over midday, all flights were confined to the territory, where landmarking bees were continually harassed. Between territorial inspection flights, the fly rested on particular twigs overlooking the site.

Figure 2B shows the change in behavior that occurred on the second day when clouds began to cover the zenith some 2 hours before solar noon. Activity was restricted to the territory as soon as the cloud drifted overhead. Despite the cloud, the number of flights within the territory was not much reduced over midday, because the air temperature remained near 20°C. On the following cloudy day, however, the air temperature remained below 10°C. As before, the fly never left its territory, but its flights there were drastically reduced compared with the previous days' (Fig. 2D), because it basked for long periods on leaves warmed by incoming radiation.

The autumn generation of *E. tenax* is not territorial in Vancouver, nor is its midday activity there hindered by the sun. Near 49° N. Lat., the autumn sun never rises to an altitude of 60°. Figure 2C shows that activity during a clear autumn day was confined to long flights between various feeding and grooming areas, which in this instance did not include the northern edge of the lawn. Morning travel was delayed until the air temperature reached 10°C. Thereafter, the amount of travel increased as the day warmed, and decreased quickly as afternoon heat waned.

Figure 2 shows that comparatively small differences in the location of automated traps could produce very different results. No flies would be caught near the middle of the lawn during sunny middays, nor at any time during cloudy days. Even on the edge, differences in territorial activity on clear and cloudy days would produce different results and consequently different opinions concerning the duration and amount of activity.

Ordinarily, data from single specimens should not be given much weight. I have included them, however, to show that even such a well-known insect as the drone fly may still have a few habits which are not common knowledge. I think it is fair to suggest that lack of information on those habits and their possible

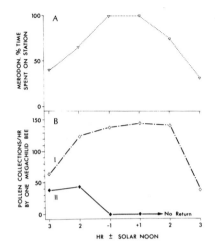

FIGURE 3. *The effect of territorial behavior of the narcissus bulb fly,* Merodon equestris *(Fab.), on pollen-collecting by a megachilid bee. (A) the percentage of each hour during which the fly normally occupied its territory on a clear day; B(I) the number of pollen collections per hour that could be made on the territory by one megachilid bee when the fly was caged; B(II) the reduced number of pollen collections when the fly was free to harass the bee. Note the final effect of the concentrated attacks over midday when the bulb fly, like the drone fly in Fig. 2, was constantly present on its territory.*

side effects could create some methodological problems or, even worse, some procedural errors, if it were suddenly necessary to develop a program to monitor the activity of this insect.

That such well-known insects may need a little more attention is shown in Fig. 3, which depicts the interaction of another common syrphid with a megachilid bee. Like the drone fly, the narcissus bulb fly, *Merodon equestris* (Fab.), is a favored subject for experimental biologists and geneticists. It is also sufficiently damaging to attract economic notice, so its life history is as well known as its biology.

The male bulb flies are also highly territorial when they emerge in midsummer, harassing any bee or other insect that enters their domain. Figure 3A shows the percentage of each hour a male fly spent flitting and resting on its territory during a clear midsummer day. Curve I of Fig. 3B shows the maximum number of successful pollen collections per hour that could be completed by one leaf-cutter bee foraging in that space (1 x 1 x 2 m) when the resident bulb fly was caged. (Megachilid bees landmark as well as honeybees, so they also continue to forage during the midday period.) In contrast to curve I, curve II in Fig. 3B shows how an unfettered resident bulb fly affected the pollen-collecting. After being continually harassed throughout the midday period, the leaf-cutter bee abandoned its attempts to collect pollen from that area and did not return.

During the late spring and early summer in the vicinity of Vancouver, bulb flies on occasion may bar megachilids and honeybees from blossoms growing within 1 m of the soil surface. Above that height, drone flies often drive honeybees away from berry- or fruit-tree blossoms. Possible effects on pollination, and thus on the yields of some fruits or berries, have yet to be determined. Those effects may prove to be unimportant. The point, however, is that the existence of such interactions between such common and ostensibly well-known insects has never been seriously considered. Nor has any possible association of those interactions with the state of the sky ever been suspected.

Recently I described how some predators—hornets, dragonflies, ladybird beetles and mosquitoes—expand and contract their searching areas as zenith polarization waxes and wanes (Wellington 1974a, 1974c). In the absence of overhead polarization, bald-faced hornets, *Vespula maculata* (L.), and dragon-flies may even resort to pouncing from ambush, but this drastic change from their more usual tactics is only an extreme version of the general phenomenon already illustrated here; i.e., the diminished radius of action associated with reduced polarization.

We have seen that such constraints on longer flights can be imposed on residents as well as on individuals merely passing through the locality. Figure 1 was based on a mixture of transients and residents. In Figs. 2 and 3, the two flies and the bee were residents.

The phenomenon of residency at present is virtually ignored by entomol-ogists. With the exception of some nest builders, adult insects generally are viewed as vagrant automata, mindlessly and almost randomly flitting through and between appropriate habitats until they perish.

Southwood (1962), Kennedy (1961), and Johnson (1969) each shed some light on the problem of dispersal. The mass of literature which Johnson discussed (op. cit.) apparently has convinced many entomologists that there is a genuine dispersive phase within the adult stage of many different kinds of insects. The impression remains, however, that nothing very important in the way of flight transpires after that phase ends. (Applying the term, "trivial", to post-dispersive movements to emphasize differences between them and dis-persive travel unfortunately has reinforced that impression.)

What happens to insects which live on for days or weeks after their dispersal ends? Do they flit so haphazardly, or do they, like many vertebrates, occupy home ranges? Those are not trifling questions, as the existence of home ranges could seriously affect sampling or monitoring schemes, or even some types of control measures, which did not take them into account.

We can easily accept the territories of dragonflies, the "trap-lines" of some tropical nectar feeders, and the nests and foraging areas of social insects as examples of "home range" or "residency", because they are so familiar to us. It is not so easy to visualize "home ranges" of Diptera. Nevertheless, I have already mentioned two species which display all the characteristics of established residents living out their lives in one locality. And there are others. The problem is to develop techniques that will lead to their discovery, instead of preventing it, as destructive methods of recapturing marked individuals inevitably do. (In fact, merely following and re-locating marked insects may disturb them too frequently and thus drive them away.)

Large, conspicuous insects, such as nymphalid, pierid, or papilionid butterflies are easy to find and usually easy to follow without disturbing them. Thus they are good subjects on which to practice "shadowing" techniques, especially since much of the information gained during those sessions can be applied later in studies of less conspicuous species. For example, some large butterflies make daily rounds along well-defined routes covering hundreds of meters. It is only necessary to locate one of the places where they regularly stop to feed, rest, or wait for mates to be able to follow them from that station to the next. Sequential observations then show that individuals frequent particular stations during the same period each day, often timing their arrival and departure by the onset of a particular change in the polarization pattern of the sky (Wellington 1974c). Long-lived specimens will cover the same route daily for nearly 4 weeks.

That type of information can be helpful when one is searching for the feeding, basking, or hovering stations of smaller, less obvious insects, such as syrphids. As those stations also differ markedly in exposure and appearance, depending on whether they are used for basking or for shelter, and as they may be separated by comparatively long stretches of ecologically dead ground, locating them can be a formidable task even when the fly is present. When it is not, there is no way of knowing that the apparently empty station in fact has an absentee tenant. Consequently, it is helpful to extrapolate from butterflies' habits to discover whether flies may follow comparably rigid timetables. Apparently, some do. They appear punctually at the same time daily at a particular station, from which they can then be tracked. For example, one syrphid, which ranged through the same 480 m^2 during each of the 7 days on which it could be followed, could be found hovering and feeding in one particular cubic meter of hedgerow between, and only between, the fourth and fifth hours after solar noon each day. From there it moved to a resting station some 10 m away, where it spent each night.

As with butterflies, accidental encounters at one such station ultimately lead to a map of a fly's home range. An alternative approach, which may be helpful during studies of the effects of ambient conditions on establishment of home ranges, is to rear and release marked adults in much the same fashion as one releases marked insects to study their dispersal. But adults in a dispersing phase cannot be used to study establishment. Even when they are freed during the midday minimum in zenith polarization, they merely delay their departure for an hour or two. Flight exercise before release will decrease the dispersive tendencies of young adults.

Adults that are ready to settle can be released within 20-30 m of appropriate habitats with good expectations that some can be re-located within 3 days. Recent trials with various common syrphids have shown that as few as 50 marked adults released in such circumstances will give a 3-day re-discovery rate as high as 10%.

There is not time to dwell further on these preliminary studies of home ranges. They began as an outgrowth of polarization studies, but they have already shown that the rules for determining where and when one should monitor flight activity are not so easy to establish as one might expect. Consequently, in a game plan which includes territories and home ranges, conventional random sampling may not be so random after all. In fact, a conventional approach to sampling may impose undesirable biases by ensuring better coverage of places where there are no home ranges, or by ensuring that such ranges are covered when the majority of the residents are uncatchable because they are concealed, resting, or absent. Sampling schemes for disease-bearing flies may be as affected as those intended for parasitic or predaceous species.

CONCLUDING REMARKS

Most of the preceding examples involved some aspect of insect vision, through responses to overhead patterns, to other insects, or to features within the habitat. But the most dramatic aspects of recent research on insect vision are not much involved in the phenomena described here. In contrast, those phenomena—or more properly, their ramifications—may directly affect some of the sampling or monitoring procedures originally intended to assist pest-management programs.

Even recent advocates of better methods of pest management show a curious reluctance to learn more about the enemy. In more conventional wars, that attitude has ultimately led to vanquished armies and cashiered generals. Applied entomology has had its share of both. Some of those defeats can be traced to our reluctance to ask how the species with which we have been so concerned have managed to survive in very hostile environments far longer than we have been trying to eliminate them. Perhaps it is time to realize that we should be less interested in the lethal agents that reduce numbers within a generation, and more concerned with how the survivors evade extinction.

To be able to ask such questions about any animal, we must temporarily abandon our own viewpoint and try to see the world from its point of view. We have been told many times that we and the insects dwell in very different worlds. But they seem to have been more successful than we in penetrating whatever barriers may separate those worlds. At the very least, they have discovered some of our ports of entry, while we remain largely ignorant of theirs. We reap the consequences of that ignorance each time one of our pest-management programs fails.

In the future, therefore, one more item could be profitably added to the agenda on strategies for pest management; i.e., how can we identify and interpret the *pests'* strategies? Behavioral studies can provide a direct method of determining how closely our interpretations match the insects' view of reality.

ACKNOWLEDGMENTS

I am indebted to C. S. Holling for fruitful discussions of some of the ideas put forward in this paper, and to members of my family for assistance with some of the observations. The work was supported in part by an operating grant from the National Research Council of Canada.

Chapter 8

Behavior of Forest Insect Parasitoids

Ronald M. Weseloh

Department of Entomology
The Connecticut Agricultural Experiment Station
New Haven, Connecticut 06504

INTRODUCTION

The use of insect parasitoids for biological control has typically involved very little behavioral research. This is so because the primary objective in most such projects is the importation and establishment of exotic parasitoids. Little time is left for more exacting studies on their nature. In this review I will survey what is known of the behavior of forest insect parasitoids, emphasizing behavioral mechanisms (why and how behavior occurs). Hopefully, the diversity of parasitoid responses to environmental conditions—responses which influence their effectiveness as biological control agents—will be convincing evidence that more intensive studies on parasitoid behavior are justified.

The behavior of forest insect parasitoids is basically not different from that of other organisms. Accordingly, much of what will be discussed is not unique to them. The forest environment does cause some shifts in emphasis, however, and these will be especially noted where they occur. Subjects reviewed are diel periodicity, mating behavior, host finding and acceptance, parasitoid interactions, adult food relationships, and host habitat finding. Most work on forest parasitoid behavior has been on host selection processes. This subject has been subdivided by Doutt (1959) into host suitability, host acceptance, host finding, and host habitat finding. All of these but host suitability will be reviewed here.

DIEL PERIODICITY

Most forest insect parasitoids are active only during daylight hours. Juillet (1960) analyzed catches in rotary traps in a red pine plantation and found that ichneumonids were most active in early morning and evening hours, braconids became more active as the day went on, and chalcids were consistently active throughout the day. Heatwole and Davis (1965) state that three species of *Megarhyssa* (Ichneumonidae) actively attack hosts during daylight hours and spend other hours resting on the undersurfaces of tree leaves. Also diurnal are the tachinids, *Parasetigena silvestris* (=*segregata*) (Robineau-Desvoidy) (Prell 1915) and *Blepharipa scutellata* (=*pretensis*) (Robineau-Desvoidy) (Weseloh 1972b); the chalcids, *Brachymeria intermedia* (Nees) (Minot and Leonard, ms. submitted) and *B. compsilurae* (Crawford); the braconid, *Apanteles laeviceps* Ashmead (Weseloh 1972b); and the encyrtid, *Ooencyrtus ennomophagus* Yoshimoto (Kaya and Anderson 1974b). Apparently, the only known forest parasitoid that is not strictly diurnal is *Ooencyrtus kuwanai* (Howard), the females of which continue to oviposit on gypsy moth egg masses past midnight (Weseloh 1972b).

MATING BEHAVIOR

Few studies have investigated mating behavior by forest insect parasitoids. Mating behavior has been described for *Brachymeria intermedia* (Hosley 1975) and *Chrysocharis laricinellae* (Ratzeburg) (Quednau 1967). A braconid parasitoid, *Agathis pumila* (Ratzeburg), does not mate readily in small cages, thus suggesting the presence of a sex pheromone which saturated the air (Quednau 1970). Stronger evidence for a sex pheromone in the ichneumonid, *Phaeogenes invisor* Thunberg, a parasitoid of *Tortrix viridana* L., is given by Cole (1970). He relates that host pupal cases from which female parasitoids have emerged are attractive to males for at least a week.

Males of the braconid, *Coeloides brunneri* Viereck, a parasitoid of bark beetles, apparently locate females emerging through the bark of trees by the chewing sounds they make (Ryan and Rudinsky 1962). Males of *Megarhyssa* spp., which are parasitoids of siricid wood-wasps, also detect females by their chewing noises in wood, and sometimes exhibit precopulatory behavior if the other side of the board they are on is scratched (Heatwole 1964).

HOST FINDING AND ACCEPTANCE

The processes of host finding and acceptance enable a parasitoid to restrict the number of hosts it attacks. Unlike "true" parasites which often do not actively seek out hosts, adult parasitoids are extremely mobile. They have developed sophisticated mechanisms for finding and recognizing hosts most suitable for their progeny, and the behavior of the adult largely defines the host range of the species.

Physical Factors

A variety of physical factors have been shown to lead forest parasitoids to hosts. One that has long been thought to be important for parasitoids attacking wood- and bark-feeding insects is substrate sound. DeLeon (1935) states that the braconid, *Coeloides dendroctoni* Cushman, detected its bark beetle host (*Dendroctonus*) by the latter's feeding sounds. Ryan and Rudinsky (1962) came to the same conclusion for *C. brunneri* because females only attacked the mobile larvae and adults of *Dendroctonus pseudotsugae* Hopkins and also laid eggs through a piece of bark which was scratched on the undersurface with a pin. However, the importance of substrate sound has been challenged by Richerson and Borden (1971), who found that *C. brunneri* oviposited in dead (frozen) larvae as well as living ones. They state that host sound, magnetism, and odor were unimportant (Richerson and Borden 1972a), although their experimental technique did not definitely rule out olfaction. They did find that host activities caused a localized temperature increase on the bark surface, and that artificially heating local parts of bark with resistors caused the parasitoid to exhibit ovipositional activities at the heated sites. From this, Richerson and Borden (1972b) concluded that *C. brunneri* found its host by local heat differences rather than by substrate sound. Possibly, this parasitoid uses a variety of cues to find hosts.

Movement has been implicated in host finding by the tachinid, *Drino bohemica* Mesn. Monteith (1956) showed that small fluttering feathers placed in an arm of a "Y" olfactometer biased adult females toward the arm with the feathers, provided both arms carried odor streams from the sawfly host, *Neodiprion lecontei* (Fitch). Monteith (1963) also found that caged *D. bohemica* females learned to associate movement of a tray with presence of hosts.

Associative learning was used extensively by Arthur (1962b, 1966) to show that females of the ichneumonid, *Itoplectis conquisitor* (Say), distinguished between crepe paper tubes of different colors (red, green, blue, yellow) when they were preconditioned by exposing them to colored tubes containing host pupae (*Galleria mellonella* L.). *I. conquisitor* could also distinguish between long and short tubes and tubes mounted on different bases, but not between vertically- and horizontally-oriented tubes (Arthur 1967).

Host size was important for the eulophid, *Hyssopus thymus* Girault, a parasitoid of *Metzneria lappella* Zeller (Purrington and Uleman 1972). By probing with its ovipositor it could distinguish the size of hosts concealed within glass tubes and would lay an appropriate number of eggs in them. Using gelatin capsules and other artificial models, Ullyett (1936) showed that host size influenced the chalcid, *Microplectron fuscipennis* Zett., a parasitoid of *Diprion* sawflies. This parasitoid responded to large host models over small ones. It also responded to hollow models over solid ones, and to opaque models over transparent ones.

In some cases host surface-characteristics are important. Weseloh (1974a) found that gypsy moth larva hairs were important host recognition stimuli for the braconid, *Apanteles melanoscelus* (Ratzeburg). The encyrtid parasitoid, *Ooencyrtus kuwanai*, laid the most eggs in normal, intact gypsy moth egg masses which were covered by hair from the adult female. Least acceptable were eggs that had been separated and cleaned of hair (Schiëferdecker 1969).

Thus, forest parasitoids find hosts from a distance by responding to sound, temperature differences, movement, and colors associated with hosts. Suitable hosts are recognized by their characteristic sizes, shapes, or surface textures. Often, however, physical characteristics are not solely involved. Detection and recognition of hosts by the chemicals they produce (kairomones) are also important and will be considered next.

Chemical Factors

Sometimes the response of a parasitoid to host chemicals is over a distance and rather dramatic. Ullyett (1953) indicated that when a cocoon of *Euproctis terminalia* Wlkr. was broken open in a forest, a swarm of female *Pimpla bicolor* Bouché (Ichneumonidae) covered the hands of the observer within minutes. Monteith (1955) used an olfactometer to show that *Drino bohemica* responded positively to the odor of its hosts (various species of sawflies).

Chemicals perceived by contact or over short distances are also active. Ullyett (1936) found that *Microplectron fuscipennis*, in addition to responding to physical host characteristics mentioned above, also intensively examined and probed moist smears of host haemolymph. Similarly, Weseloh (1974a) found by indirect evidence that a chemical(s) in the integument of gypsy moth larvae led to increased examinations and probing of hosts by *Apanteles melanoscelus*. Leonard et al. (1975) have obtained direct evidence that integumentary chemicals from the gypsy moth are important stimuli for *A. melanoscelus* and *Brachymeria intermedia.*

Recently, good evidence has emerged which shows that the large ichneumonid parasitoids of siricid wood wasps find their hosts through olfaction. Madden (1968), working with *Ibalia leucopsoidea* (Hochenu.), *Rhyssa persuasoria* (L.), and *Megarhyssa nortoni* (Cresson), found that a symbiotic fungus, *Amylostereum* sp., associated with *Sirex noctilis* F. produced an odor which caused the parasitoids to exhibit ovipositional-related activities. Extracts of the fungus were active as well. Spradbery (1970) confirmed these observations for *R. persuasoria*, showing that host frass containing the fungus was also active. Evidently these parasitoids detected a fungal odor even when the host was several inches inside a tree.

Responses of parasitoids to host pheromones is a theoretical possibility, but has only been reported in forest situations for the pteromalid, *Tomicobia tibialis*

Ashmead. Bedard (1965) caught this parasitoid in the same field traps which caught its host, the bark beetle, *Ips confusus* (LeConte). Subsequently, Rice (1968, 1969) showed that the parasitoid was only attracted to *Ips* males in the field and that it responded to the aggregation pheromone produced by male hosts.

Chemical factors mediating the last stages of the host-acceptance process (i.e. oviposition) have been studied intensively only for *Itoplectis conquisitor*. Arthur et al. (1969) showed that *I. conquisitor* could be induced to oviposit into a parafilm tube filled with haemolymph of the greater wax moth. A polypeptide-like chemical in wax-moth haemolymph was the active substance. Further research by Hegdekar and Arthur (1973) showed that amino acids and sugars in haemolymph were most active in inducing oviposition. In fact, Arthur et al. (1972) found that a chemically defined, synthetic medium consisting of amino acids, magnesium chloride, and trehalose was more effective than wax moth haemolymph in inducing oviposition.

INTERACTIONS BETWEEN PARASITOIDS

Parasitoid interactions may involve mutual avoidance by adults as was found by Price (1970, 1972b) for various ichneumonids attacking cocooned pupae of the Swaine jack pine sawfly, *Neodiprion swainei* Middleton. Female parasitoids avoided areas walked on by other parasitoids because of the deposition of avoidance pheromones.

Avoidance of hosts previously parasitized by the same or different species of parasitoid is common for insect parasitoids in general. Forest parasitoids which exhibit such discrimination are listed in Table 1. Such avoidance mechanisms are generally thought to enable parasitoids to deposit progeny uniformly among the available hosts and to avoid wasting progeny.

In two recorded cases, female parasitoids preferentially parasitize hosts already parasitized by other species. Their progeny then destroy the older parasitoid and feed directly on the original host. These insects are called cleptoparasitoids and differ from hyperparasitoids in that the latter feed on the first parasitoid and not the original host. Schröder (1974) presents evidence that the ichneumonid, *Temelucha interruptor* Grav., preferentially attacks pine shoot moth larvae already parasitized by the braconid, *Orgilus obscurator* Nees, and so is a cleptoparasitoid. *T. interruptor* larvae always destroy *Orgilus* larvae, and adults detect parasitized hosts by chemicals deposited by *Orgilus* females on hosts and over surfaces walked on (Arthur et al. 1964).

Pseudorhyssa sternata Merrill (Ichneumonidae) is a cleptoparasitoid associated with the wood-wasp parasitoid, *Rhyssa persuasoria* (Spradbery 1968). This cleptoparasitoid often remains near a *R. persuasoria* female while the latter drills into a log. When *R. persuasoria* completes oviposition, *P. sternata* inserts its

TABLE 1 *Forest parasitoids known to discriminate between parasitized and non-parasitized hosts.*

Parasitoid	Host	References
Exenterus amictorius Panzer[1]	*Neodiprion swainei*	McLeod 1972
E. diprionis Rohwer[1]	*N. swainei*	McLeod 1972
Pleolophus basizonus (Gravenhorst)[1]	*N. swainei*	Price 1972b
Orgilus obscurator Nees[2]	*Rhyacionia buoliana*	Schröder 1974
Hyssopus thymus Girault[3]	*R. buoliana*	Syme 1970
Ooencyrtus kuwanai[4]	*Lymantria dispar*	Lloyd 1935, 1938
Apanteles melanoscelus[2]	*L. dispar*	Weseloh 1976
Microplectron fuscipennis[5]	*Diprion* sp.	Ullyett 1936
Agathis pumila (Ratzeburg)[2]	*Coleophora laricella (Hbn.)*	Quednau 1970
Apechthis (=Ephialtes) ontario[1]	Forest defoliators (Lepidoptera)	Ryan 1971
Itoplectis quadricingulatus[1]	Forest defoliators (Lepidoptera)	Ryan 1971
Apanteles fumiferanae[2]	*Choristoneura fumiferana*	C.A. Miller 1959

[1] Ichneumonidae
[2] Braconidae
[3] Eulophidae
[4] Encyrtidae
[5] Chalcididae

ovipositor down the drill hole and lays an egg on the host. The cleptoparasitoid larva, when it hatches, almost always kills the *R. persuasoria* larva. Female *P. sternata* respond to water extracts of the vaginal gland of female *R. persuasoria*, and so find and recognize parasitized hosts by chemical means.

ADULT FOOD RELATIONSHIPS

Most adult parasitoids require nutrients and moisture for survival. This is certainly true for forest parasitoids (Györfi 1951, Hassan 1967, Townes 1958). For one tachinid, *Cyzenis albicans* (Fall.), this requirement is host-related. The fly lays microtype eggs on tree leaves which are then eaten by its host, the winter moth, *Operophtera brumata* (L.). Embree and Sisojevic (1965) found a close correlation between leaves damaged by chewing and leaves with eggs on them. Varley and Gradwell (1958) observed that these parasitoids feed on nectar of flowers and sweet sap fluxes of leaves damaged by hosts, and hypothesized that they lay eggs close to feeding locations. Hassel (1968) confirmed these observations and showed by caged experiments that parasitoids always laid many eggs on damaged foliage (natural or artificial) and foliage sprayed with sugar solutions. Non-damaged, non-sprayed, and washed leaves always contained much fewer eggs. By laying eggs on damaged leaves near sweet sap fluxes, the fly exhibits an effective mechanism for depositing eggs where hosts will most likely encounter them.

Parasitoids attacked the pine shoot moth in the Soviet Union most abundantly in areas where nectar-bearing plants were located (Gulü 1963). In Canada, *Orgilus obscurator* was most effective on the pine shoot moth in an area where wild carrot (*Daucus carota* L.) was abundant (Syme 1971). The scale insect, *Quadraspidiotus* (*Diaspidiotus*) *perniciosus* (Comst.), was parasitized 10 times higher by the aphelinid, *Aphytis proclia* (Walk.), on trees associated with a *Phacelia* flower (Chumakova 1960). Also, Leius (1967a) showed that percent parasitism of eggs and pupae of tent caterpillars, *Malacosoma americanum* (F.), was positively correlated with the quantity of nectar-producing flowers in the undergrowth.

Leius (1961, 1963) also demonstrated that increased fecundity could be obtained from *Itoplectis conquisitor* and another ichneumonid, *Scambus buolianae* (Htg.), when they were fed pollen-sugar mixtures along with host-fluids. Longevity and fecundity were both increased when *Aphytis proclia* was provided with flowers of red clover (Chumakova 1960). Longevity was increased for two parasitoids (*Exeristes comstockii* (Cresson) and *Hyssopus thymus*) of the pine shoot moth when they were caged with different flowering plants (Syme 1975).

Adult parasitoids often show preferences for certain nectar-producing plants over others when given a choice. *E. comstockii* fed preferentially on those flowers most favorable for increasing its longevity (Syme 1975). In cage studies, *Brachymeria intermedia* responded to flowers of the Asteraceae preferentially (Hosley 1975). Working with *I. conquisitor, S. buolianae,* and *O. obscurator*, Leius (1960, 1967b) found that umbelliferous plants, especially wild parsnip, *Pastinica sativa* L., were preferred over other plants for adult feeding. Leius (1967b), states, "Flowers of Umbelliferae are, in general, better sources of nectar for adult parasitic Hymenoptera than are those of most other plants, because the structure of the individual blossoms is such that the parasites can readily reach the nectar with their biting mouth-parts." Much the same is stated by Györfi (1945).

Alternate food sources for adults of forest parasitoids are probably more important than is generally recognized. The usually heterogeneous forest environment is more conducive for supporting long-lived adult parasitoids than are the more homogeneous, ephemeral habitats of agro-ecosystems. The probability that sources of pollen and nectar are necessary for adequate longevity and fecundity of many forest parasitoids should be recognized in any attempt to evaluate or establish them.

HOST HABITAT FINDING

It is with this topic that the behavior of forest insect parasitoids takes on special significance. Owing both to the large vertical extent of forests and heterogeneity of plant forms, many microhabitats are available to host insects. Effective parasitoids must find these hosts, and often do so by restricting their activities to small parts of the available habitat. In some cases, habitat selection is so strong that a parasitoid's host range in the field is restricted more than would be expected from knowledge of its polyphagous habits (Zwölfer and Kraus 1957).

In forests as in other environments, parasitoids may respond directly to the biotic component of the habitat or to physical factors. These subjects will be taken in turn.

Biotic Components

The main biotic components besides the host which influence parasitoids in a forest are plants. These may modify the behavior of parasitoids considerably. In at least one case the presence of non-host food plants or their odor (both trees and ground cover) reduced the response of the tachinid, *Bessa harveyi* Tns., for its sawfly hosts both in the field and in olfactometer studies in the laboratory (Monteith 1960).

Parasitoids may attack hosts more readily on some host plants than on others. Allen (1972) showed that *Telenomus coelodasidis* Ashmead, an egg parasitoid of the saddled prominent, *Heterocampa guttivitta* (Wlkr.), parasitized this host to a greater extent on beech (*Fagus*) than on sugar maple (*Acer saccharum* Marsh). Graham and Baumhofer (1927) found greater numbers of parasitoids attacking pine tip moths (*Rhyacionia frustrana*(Comst.))in red pine (*Pinus resinosa* Ait.) than jack (*P. banksiana* Lamb.) or yellow pine (*P. ponderosa* Laws). Parasitoids of *Ips* bark beetles were reared more often from hosts taken from some tree species than from others (Berisford et al. 1971). Also, Arthur (1962a) found that *I. conquisitor* emerged more often from pine shoot moths collected from Scots pine (*P. sylvestris* L.) than red pine. Adult parasitoids were also observed more often near Scots pine than red pine, and females in olfactometer tests were attracted more by the odor of Scots pine than red pine. Arthur also found that *I. conquisitor* oviposited more often in hosts feeding on Scots pine than red pine. The pteromalid, *Heydenia unica* Cook & Davis, responded to a tree substance, α-pinene, more readily in a field olfactometer test than to pheromones of its bark beetle host, *Dendroctonus frontalis* Zimmerman (Camors and Payne 1972). C. A. Miller (1959) showed that female parasitoids of *Apanteles fumiferanae* Vier., a parasitoid of the spruce budworm, prefers odor of white spruce (*Picea glauca* (Moench) over balsam fir (*Abies balsamea* (L.) Mill.) in olfactometer experiments. Much the same was shown by Monteith (1955) for the tachinid, *Drino bohemica*, which responded both to the odor of its sawfly host and to odor of its host's food plants; the preferences from most attractive to least attractive being red pine, white spruce, Scots pine, jack pine and Australian pine (*Pinus nigra* Arnold). Another tachinid, *Bessa harveyi*, laid eggs more readily on hosts reared from jack pine than on those reared on red pine (Monteith 1958). Syme (1970) found that the presence of red pine needles stimulated *Hyssopus thymus* to oviposit in the pine shoot moth.

The preferences of parasitoids for certain plants may change with age. Here, of course, one must mention the classic work by Thorpe and Caudle (1938), who found that females of the ichneumonid, *Pimpla ruficollis* Grav., were repelled by the odor of pine early in adult life, but following ovary maturation were attracted to pine odor. This was interpreted to mean that the parasitoids initially disperse to feed on flowers, probably Umbelliferae, and then return to pines to attack the pine shoot moth. Herrebout (1967, 1969) showed a similar pattern for the tachinid, *Eucarcelia rutilla* Vil1., which attacks pine-dwelling Geometridae. The parasitoids initially were attracted to oaks infested with honeydew-producing insects and then returned to pines to attack their hosts.

In addition to these gross interactions, many forest parasitoids respond to (or are limited by) microhabitats associated with their host's food plant. The tachinid, *Parasetigena silvestris* (*=agilis*) (Robineau-Desvoidy) attacks hosts exposed on trunks of trees and not on leaves (Weseloh 1974b). *Drino bohemica* responds more to old foliage of host food plants than to new foliage (Monteith 1966). Large ichneumonids of the genus *Megarhyssa* only attack siricid hosts when these are at a depth of wood equivalent to the length of the parasitoid's ovipositor. Different species of *Megarhyssa* have ovipositors of different lengths, and so attack hosts at different depths in logs (Heatwole and Davis 1965). Herrebout (1960) found that *Eucarcelia rutilla* attacks larvae of the pine looper moth, *Bupalus piniarius* L., which are located near the top of pine needles more often than those located deeper among the needles. Finally, Arthur (1962a) found that the bud diameter of red pine tended to be larger than for Scots pine and this may influence the "ease" with which *Itoplectis conquisitor* reaches pine shoot moth larvae within the buds, as Scots pine is the plant from which parasitized hosts are most commonly collected.

Physical Factors

Many physical factors influence the behavior of forest parasitoids. Two related ones are humidity and temperature. Juillet (1960) trapped insects in rotary traps in a red pine plantation and determined that ichneumonids were most active at average temperatures and high humidities, and braconids and chalcids at high temperatures and low humidities. In laboratory tests, Ryan (1974) found that 100% RH suppressed oviposition in *Ephialtes ontario* (Cresson) and *Itoplectis quadricingulatus* (Provancher). Price (1971) could differentiate between distributions of various forest parasitoids which attacked the pupae of the Swaine jack pine sawfly on the basis of moisture gradients in field plots. In laboratory tests *Ooencyrtus kuwanai* oriented to dry environments at 24°C if they were water-satiated (Weseloh 1971). Minot and Leonard (ms. submitted) recently showed that *Brachymeria intermedia* has a strong preference for dry environments and prefers warm temperatures in gradients (see Hosley 1975).

Parasitoids of different species respond differently to different lighting conditions and colors. Ryan and Medley (1972) found that *I. quadricingulatus* was more active at higher light intensities in cages than was *Apechthis* (=*Ephialtes*) *ontario*. *B. intermedia* actively orients to lighted ends of laboratory cages (Hosley 1975, Minot and Leonard ms. submitted). Ryan and Rudinsky (1962) working with *Coeloides brunneri*, and Bedard (1965) working with *Tomicobia tibialis*, state that these bark-beetle parasitoids avoid hot, sunny areas in favor of cooler, shaded ones for ovipositional activity. Also, Weseloh (1972d) found that *O. kuwanai* responded preferentially to white and blue panels in the field while *Apanteles laeviceps*, a parasitoid of noctuids, responded to yellow and clear ones.

Responses to humidity, temperature, and light may be at least partially responsible for the spatial distribution of parasitoids in the forest. *B. intermedia*, which prefers hot and dry conditions does not parasitize gypsy moths near ground level in non-defoliated, shady areas, although it often does so in drier and less-shaded, open or defoliated areas (Leonard 1971a, Doane 1971c). Conversely, Schwenke (1958) discovered that *Compsilura concinnata* (Mg.), a polyphagous parasitoid, attacked the noctuid, *Acronycta aceris* L., to a greater extent in clumps of trees than in isolated trees. Evidently this parasitoid prefers the cooler, shaded conditions a clump of trees provides. The same is true for *O. kuwanai*, as it attacked host eggs placed in a woodland much more readily than it did those located in a clearing (Weseloh 1972c). However, Simmons et al. (1975) reported that *I. conquisitor* and various tachinids which attack the spruce budworm had lower rates of parasitism as tree species density increased.

Numerous studies have shown that parasitoids are distributed non-uniformly in the forest with respect to height above ground. This may be a result of differing responses to physical factors, plant life-forms, and/or host abundance. As Table 2 shows, most forest parasitoids are reared in greatest numbers from hosts collected near the tops of trees. A few, however, are more abundant near the base of trees or exhibit no height differentiation.

These rearing studies have been complimented in some cases by more direct behavioral observations. Von Finck (1939) observed that *Parasetigena silvestris* (=*segregata*) males usually fly near the ground, and females in tree crowns. However, in areas heavily infested with its host, *Lymantria monacha* L., flights of female *P. silvestris* occurred near the ground (Niklas 1939). Anderson and Kaya (1973b) found that released *Ooencyrtus ennomophagus* restricted their

TABLE 2   *Variations in percent parasitism of hosts collected at different heights in trees.*

Parasitoid	Host	References
Parasitism Greatest Near Top of Tree		
Apanteles fumiferanae[2]	*Choristoneura fumiferana*	Jaynes 1954, C.A. Miller 1959
A. melanoscelus[2]	*Lymantria dispar*	Tigner et al. 1974
Brachymeria intermedia[4]	*L. dispar*	Weseloh 1972c
Ooencyrtus ennomophagus[3] (=*clisiocampae*)	*Ennomos subsignarius*	Anderson and Kaya 1973a
Telenomus coelodasidis[5]	*Heterocampa guttivitta*	Allen 1972
Trichogramma minutum[6]	*H. guttivitta*	Allen 1972
Bessa harveyi[7]	*Pristiphora erichsonii* (Htg.)	Monteith 1960
Coeloides brunneri[2]	*Dendroctonus pseudotsugae*	Ryan and Rudinsky 1962
Various parasitoids	Scolytidae	Berisford et al. 1971
Parasitism Uniform		
Ooencyrtus kuwanai[3]	*L. dispar*	Weseloh 1972c
Glypta fumiferanae (Viereck)[1]	*C. fumiferana*	Jaynes 1954
Telenomus alsophilae[5]	*E. subsignarius*	Anderson and Kaya 1973a
Parasitism Greatest Near Bottom of Tree		
Compsilura concinnata[7]	*L. dispar*	Tigner et al. 1974, Barbosa et al. 1975
Various parasitoids	*Recurvaria milleri* Busch	McLeod 1951

[1] Ichneumonidae, [2] Braconidae, [3] Encyrtidae, [4] Chalcididae, [5] Scelionidae,

[6] Trichogrammatidae, [7] Tachinidae

ovipositional activities to the upper parts of trees and in natural populations were caught on sticky panels mostly near the tops of trees (Kaya and Anderson 1974b). *Apanteles melanoscelus* and *O. kuwanai* were also primarily caught on sticky panels above ground level (Weseloh 1972c). The results for *Ooencyrtus* were contradictory to the percent parasitism data where no height differences occurred, and may be because flight activity, as measured by panels, is not host related (i.e. it may be for dispersion). In the same study, *Apanteles laeviceps*, a parasitoid of cutworms, was caught overwhelmingly on panels nearest the ground.

As seen from the above, the distribution of parasitoids in the forest varies considerably depending on the species involved. In perhaps no case is a single parasitoid uniformly distributed over all the various microhabitats contained in a forest. Each parasitoid species must, therefore, be considered individually, even those which attack the same host. If such is not done, serious errors in sampling and evaluation procedures could occur.

NEEDS FOR FUTURE WORK

A variety of studies on behavior of forest insect parasitoids have been carried out, but work in many areas needs to be expanded. Studies on mating behavior have hinted at the presence of sex pheromones. Research to determine how these pheromones influence mating and over what distances they act should be carried out. The information derived would be useful for more efficient laboratory rearing and field releases.

Another topic in need of study is that of responses of parasitoids to alternate food sources and how these responses change with age. Investigations show that parasitoids prefer some nectar sources over others, but the mechanisms of such preference are unknown. Odor, color, or life-form of plants could cause a directed orientation of parasitoids to plants, or a random process could operate. Depending on the orientation mechanism parasitoids would be more or less efficient at finding alternate food sources, and thus in controlling their hosts. These unknowns need to be investigated before additional progress can be made in understanding the distribution of parasitoids in the forest.

Numerous references show that parasitoids restrict their activities to only parts of the forest habitat, but this fact has been ignored in routine sampling work more in forests than in any other habitat. Probably this is so because the upper portions of a forest are difficult to sample. The importance of this behavior should not be underestimated, however, as the majority of forest parasitoids which attack economically-important forest pests are most active in the upper crown. Biased estimates of parasitoid effectiveness are obtained by sampling host insects only near ground level. At the very least, vertical activity profiles of parasitoids should be obtained. More complete data on influences of host food plants and other biotic and physical factors would also be helpful for establishing efficient and unbiased sampling procedures for parasitoids.

Chapter 9

Pheromones of Lepidopterous Insects

W. L. Roelofs, J. R. Miller, and T. C. Baker[1]

Department of Entomology
New York State Agricultural Experiment Station
Geneva, New York 14456

INTRODUCTION

A decade has passed since I (W. L. R.) joined the New York State Agricultural Experiment Station, and in that time it has become obvious to me that the Experiment Stations play an important role in agriculture. They not only serve as a unique bridge between "ivory tower" research and grower extension services, but also encourage activities on both ends of this bridge. Thus, basic studies can be directed toward and brought along a continuum to the very practical end. In China university professors are required to work several months a year in the fields or factories to keep in touch with the needs of the masses. Laboratory researchers at Experiment Stations can get this feeling for reality without deserting the research programs by working very closely with colleagues who conduct research on the experimental farms and with individual growers.

In the insect pheromone area, the bridge between basic research and its application has been a very busy two-way street. Findings obtained in the laboratory are brought to the field, and data from the field reveal that more research is required in the laboratory. At first, pheromone research was held up until instrumentation became sufficiently sophisticated to allow chemists to identify pheromone compounds. In the course of this work it became obvious that the chemistry was dependent on good behavioral analyses in the laboratory

[1] Present address: Department of Entomology, Pesticide Research Center, Michigan State University, East Lansing, Michigan 48824.

and, particularly, in the field. When the pheromone components were identified, it was found that their use in the field was not straight-forward. Every species seemed to have its own optimum release rate, component ratio, trap design, trap placement, etc. Once a good attractant trap was developed by the combined efforts of chemists and entomologists, other questions arose, such as: 1) how does trap catch reflect population density; can it relate to the necessity of the timing of insecticide applications? 2) can the trap be economically used at a density that will suppress a pest population? 3) can pheromones be used to disrupt mating by atmospheric permeation; if so, what would be the most effective disruptant when dispersed throughout the field—the natural pheromone blend or just one of the pheromone components? and 4) what is the most economical way of dispersing the disruptant in the air to obtain the appropriate concentration for an entire insect flight?

These questions can be answered only by the coordinated efforts of chemists, biologists, economic entomologists, ecologists, and industry. Further development of the promising disruption technique may depend on more detailed knowledge of how pheromones are perceived and how they modify behavior. In this paper we wish to describe some of the efforts that we have made to define the individual roles of pheromone components. This will be the basis for a general survey of related pheromone blends, and will lead to a discussion on a current speculative hypothesis on the origin of pheromones.

Last year at the Cornell Centennial Symposium (Roelofs 1975) I described some of the studies that were carried out on our research animal, the redbanded leafroller moth (RBLR), *Argyrotaenia velutinana* (Wlkr.). Briefly, we have: 1) followed with light and electron microscopy the development of the female sex phermone gland through the pupal and adult stages; 2) defined the chemistry of the pheromone components; 3) conducted various male behavioral tests with the pheromone in the laboratory and the field; 4) studied electroantennogram responses to the pheromone components; and 5) conducted field studies on the use of the pheromone in monitoring insect abundance, mass trapping for control, and in male orientation and mating disruption tests. The next step was to define the role of each pheromone component, with the anticipation that more knowledge of their behavioral effects would help develop better mating disruption programs.

PHEROMONE COMPONENTS OF THE REDBANDED LEAFROLLER

The pheromone components are a mixture of *cis*-11-tetradecenyl acetate (c11-14:Ac), *trans*-11-tetradecenyl acetate (t11-14:Ac), and dodecyl acetate (12:Ac) (Fig. 1) (Roelofs et al. 1975). In field trapping studies, a definite ratio of ca. 8% t11-14:Ac in c11-14:Ac gave the best catches, and the addition of dodecyl acetate in a 3:2 or 2:1 ratio to the 14-carbon components resulted in up

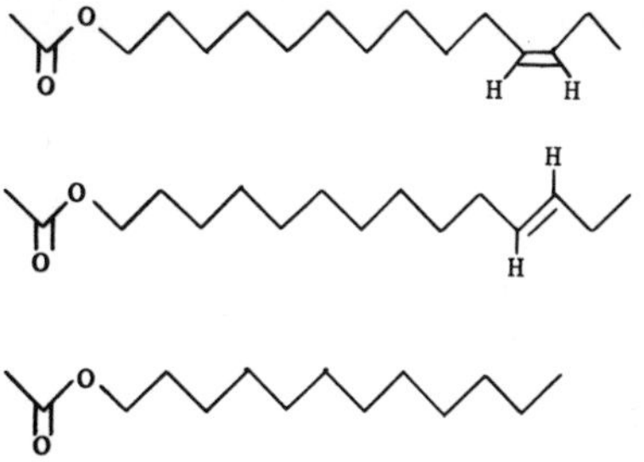

cis-11-14:Ac (92%)

trans-11-14:Ac (8%)

12:Ac (150-200%)

FIGURE 1 *Pheromone components of the redbanded leafroller moth.*

to 10-fold increases in trap catch. It would appear that dodecyl acetate is a potent synergist of attractancy, since it does not attract males by itself. However, counting the number of males caught in a trap does not reveal anything about the behavior that has occurred prior to their capture. To understand better the behavior effected by each component, the compounds were tested separately and in combination in electroantennogram studies, in laboratory stimulation and orientation behavioral assays, and in field behavioral observations (Baker 1975, Baker et al. 1976).

Field Behavioral Studies

Field studies with the pheromone components provide some interesting insights into the behavior effected by each. In one experiment the components were used alone and in various combinations in wicks placed in traps of various sizes (Fig. 2). The only treatments capturing more than two males were the 92:8 mixture of c11- and t11-14:Ac, and the mixture containing all three chemicals (Table 1). The presence of 12:Ac was most important with small traps, which require insects to orient very closely to the pheromone source before they can land. The table top traps captured the males almost at the periphery of the trap and showed only a two-fold increase with 12:Ac. These results indicate that dodecyl acetate is important only for close-range behavior, and that the correct blend of pheromone components is much more important when using the small traps.

Observations were made as males approached non-sticky table tops and Pherocon traps. In approaches to the table tops, males could be observed from as far away as 15 m. The males flew in low to the ground and landed periodically in the grass as they approached the pheromone source. Characteristic behavior exhibited on landing was antennal preening, followed immediately by wing fanning, walking up to the top of the grass blade, and flight. When finally in the vicinity of the table top, a male usually spent many seconds casting at the edge of the metal surface before landing. Observations of 108 males (Table 2) showed

FIGURE 2 *(Top) Table top trap used with sticky surface to trap redbanded leafroller males, and used with a non-sticky surface to observe male behavioral responses to chemicals positioned in the center. (Bottom left) Pherocon^R IC trap. (Bottom right) Sectar I trap. Bottom traps are from Zoecon Corp. (Palo Alto, CA).*

the importance of 12:Ac in effecting close-range responses. With 12:Ac present, there was a significant increase in the number of males landing, in wing fanning, and in walking close to the pheromone source. Since there was no significant difference in the number of males approaching the table tops for the two treatments, the data show that 12:Ac does not "synergize" long-distance "attractancy", but rather elicits close-range responses.

These results were supported further by observing males approaching a non-sticky Pherocon trap. In this situation, males slowed their forward progress

TABLE 1 *The effect of 12:Ac on male RBLR captures with various trap sizes*

Type of trap	Mean no. males captured/trap		Ratio of males caught without/with 12:Ac
	Att.[a]	Att. + 12:Ac[a]	
Table top, 60 cm radius	9.7	19.7	1:2.0
Pherocon IC, 14 cm radius	2.7	14.7	1:5.4
Sectar traps, 7.6 cm radius	2.0	24.6	1:12.3

[a]Attractant (Att.) = c11-14:Ac/t11-14:Ac (92:8), 10 mg; in second treatment 12:Ac, 15 mg.

as they neared the trap edge and engaged in short distance vertical or horizontal casting for as long as 17 sec before attempting to land. The males rarely flew directly into the trap, but landed somewhere on an outside surface and then walked into the trap while fanning. Again, treatments with and without 12:Ac brought an equivalent percentage of males to within 0.5 m of the trap (Table 3). The presence of 12:Ac, however, caused 100% of the males approaching the trap to land whereas only 31% of the approaching males landed with the treatment not emitting 12:Ac. With the 12:Ac, all of the males that landed also engaged in wing-fanning behavior and entered the trap. It is obvious from the data that 12:Ac effected large trap-catch increases in previous field studies because it caused many more males to land and to enter the trap.

Laboratory Behavioral Studies

In the field, no significant differences were found in the frequency or duration of wing fanning between the two treatments (without and with 12:Ac) once males had landed on the trap surfaces. This indicated that the close-range

TABLE 2 *Behavioral observations of RBLR males to table top pheromone sources*

Male behavior	Att.[a]	Att. + 12:Ac[a]
No. males observed	41	67
% approaching to 0.5 m	70.7	82.1 NS
% landing on table	19.0	71.6 **
% fanning while walking	26.8	56.7 **
% approaching to 10 cm of dispenser	17.1	52.2 ***

[a]Attractant (Att.) = c11-14:Ac/t11-14:Ac (92:8), 10 mg; in second treatment 12:Ac, 15 mg.
  **$p < 0.01$
  ***$p < 0.001$

TABLE 3 *Behavioral observations of RBLR males to non-sticky Pherocon traps*

Male behavior	Att.[a]	Att. + 12:Ac[b]
No. of males observed	49	40
% approach to 0.5 m	85.7	87.5 NS
% landing on trap	26.5	87.5 ***
% males entering trap	20.4	87.5 ***
% males touching dispenser	14.3	62.5 ***

[a]Attractant (Att.) = c11-14:Ac/t11-14:Ac (92:8), 10 mg.
[b]12:Ac, 15 mg.
***$p < 0.001$

behavioral modification effected by 12:Ac occurs primarily while the male is in flight. In the overall sequence of precopulatory responses, 12:Ac appears to be important in getting males, which are casting about the pheromone source, to land. Since we could not duplicate this casting flight in our present laboratory stimulation and orientation behavioral tests, it was difficult to observe any behavioral effects attributable to 12:Ac in the laboratory. It did become obvious, however, that any behavioral modifications effected by the pheromone components are dependent on the quantity and quality of the stimulus. For example, at the 2 ng level (Fig. 3), 12:Ac did not elicit any response from RBLR males, whereas a 92:8 mixture of c11-14:Ac/t11-14:Ac, with or without 12:Ac, produced ca. 75% stimulation. It would appear that t11-14:Ac is inhibitory to these responses when present in percentages above 8% since the responses rapidly decrease as the amount of t11-14:Ac increases. Further studies, however, show that this is more likely caused by the differences in threshold levels needed to elicit responses by each mixture. Data (Fig. 4) from a dose-response series show that even pure t11-14:Ac can elicit good wing-fanning responses if present at high enough dosages. Again, the threshold of response was lowest for the 8% mixture. The dosage of 8% mixture needed to produce 50% wing fanning was 100 times less than that required with pure c11-14:Ac and 10,000 times less than that required with pure t11-14:Ac.

The third component, 12:Ac, was added to treatments of pure t11-14:Ac, pure c11-14:Ac, and the 8% mixture in stimulation and orientation bioassay tubes. Dosages of each treatment that elicited less than 50% wing fanning in previous studies did not elicit very different stimulation or orientation responses even though 12:Ac was added (Fig. 5). At higher dosages of the various treatments, 12:Ac was effective in maintaining throughout the 60 sec. period the initial high level of wing fanning produced by the pure c11-14:Ac and by the 8% mixture treatments. Without 12:Ac, wing fanning dropped in 30 sec. to ca. half the initial level.

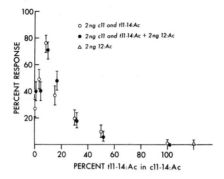

FIGURE 3 *Laboratory activation responses of redbanded leafroller males to pheromone component mixtures.*

In brief, RBLR male behavioral studies both in the laboratory and in the field revealed that these insects are very sensitive to a definite ratio of c11-14:Ac/t11-14:Ac components and that this ratio is needed to elicit and sustain the long-distance precopulatory flight. They also revealed that an additional component, 12:Ac, is used to effect close-range behavior once the moth has undergone the appropriate preceding precopulatory behavior.

Male Orientation Disruption

Since the long-distance components, c11-14:Ac and t11-14:Ac, are used in a 92:8 ratio, the question arises as to whether it would be better to disrupt male orientation with the minor component, t11-14:Ac, or with the correct pheromone blend. To answer this question, plots (0.25 ha each) in a vineyard

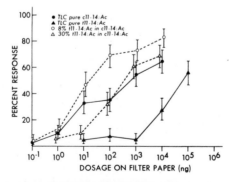

FIGURE 4 *Male redbanded leafroller wing fanning responses to pheromone components in box olfactometers.*

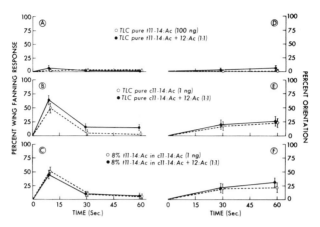

FIGURE 5   *Male redbanded leafroller wing fanning and orientation responses to pheromone components in glass tube olfactometers.*

were treated with microencapsulated (Pennwalt formulation) c11-14:Ac/ t11-14:Ac mixtures in 89:11, 50:50 and 0:100 ratios. The three replicates of treated plots and their corresponding check plots were monitored with RBLR pheromone traps. The results (Table 4) (Roelofs et al. 1976a) indicate that the natural pheromone blend, 89:11, is the most effective disruptant, and the minor component, t11-14:Ac, is the least effective. Based on the laboratory behavioral observations, the disruption data could be interpreted as follows: The threshold for response is the lowest for the 89:11 mixture and the highest for t11-14:Ac.

TABLE 4   *Disruption of communication of male RBLR moths*

Treatment c11-14:Ac to t11-14:Ac	x̄ males/plot[a]	x̄% disruption[b]
89:11	1.0 d	98 a
Check	49.0 a	
50:50	4.6 c	89 b
Check	43.7 a	
0:100	13.0 b	67 c
Check	39.3 a	

[a]Means followed by an uncommon letter differ at the 5% level according to an analysis of variance of the number of males per plot transformed to $\sqrt{x + 0.5}$ and Duncan's new multiple range test.

[b]Percentages followed by an uncommon letter differ at the 5% level according to an analysis of variance of the percentages of disruption per plot transformed to the arcsin $\sqrt{\text{percentage}}$ and Duncan's new multiple range test.

The concentration of disruptant used in this test may not have been high enough to strongly affect the behavioral response with t11-14:Ac, whereas the 89:11 mixture concentration may have been above the threshold level for response with a resulting disruptant effect.

Pheromone Components of Other Leafrollers

The above discussion of the redbanded leafroller pheromone shows that the males are attuned to a particular combination of components. This is particularly important in maintaining specificity in the field in the presence of other species utilizing the same components. A review of pheromones of some other leafrollers (Table 5) shows that a number of species use their own particular ratio of c11-14:Ac/t11-14:Ac as their pheromone. Some other species use a very definite ratio of the positional isomers c11-14:Ac and c9-14:Ac, while others use a mixture of functional group analogs. In all cases reported, the female produces the components in approximately the same ratio that optimally attracts males in the field. Thus, it appears that the females emit a very precise

TABLE 5   *Pheromone blends of leafrollers (Tortricidae: Tortricinae)*

	Pheromone components			
	14:Ac's			
Species	*cis*-11	*trans*-11	Other components	Reference
1 Obliquebanded leafroller	92%	8%		Roelofs and Tette 1970
2 Redbanded leafroller	92	8	12:Ac (200%)	Roelofs et al. 1975
3 Fruittree leafroller	70	30	12:Ac (400)	Roelofs et al. 1974
4 Fruittree tortrix	50	50		Persoons et al. 1974
5 Omnivorous leafroller	12	88		Hill and Roelofs 1975
6 *Clepsis spectrana*	90	-	c9-14:Ac (10)	Minks et al. 1973
7 European leafroller	85	-	c11-14:OH (15)	Roelofs et al. 1976b
8 Smaller tea tortrix	35	-	c9-14:Ac (65)	Tamaki et al. 1971a
9 Orange tortrix	30	-	c11-14:ALD (70)	Hill et al. 1975
10 Summerfruit tortrix	10	-	c9-14:Ac (90)	Meijer et al. 1972
				Tamaki et al. 1971b
11 Tufted apple bud moth	-	50	t11-14:OH (50)	Hill et al. 1974

1 *Choristoneura rosaceana* (Harris)
2 *Argyrotaenia velutinana* (Wlkr.)
3 *Archips argyrospilus* (Wlkr.)
4 *Archips podana* Scopoli
5 *Playnota stultana* Walsingham
6 *C. spectrana* (Treitschke)
7 *Archips rosanus* L.
8 *Adoxophyes fasciata* Walsingham
9 *Argyrotaenia citrana* (Fernald)
10 *Adoxophyes orana* (Fischer von Roeslerstamm)
11 *Platynota idaeusalis* (Wlkr.)

blend of chemicals to which the corresponding males are particularly sensitive. The origin of these chemicals and their variability within a species' pheromone is the subject of a current speculative hypothesis that has received much publicity in the lay press. The next section will discuss some of the research we have conducted on the oak leafroller moth, *Archips semiferanus* (Wlkr.), the insect that was involved in the development of the hypothesis.

SEX PHEROMONE OF THE OAK LEAFROLLER

Previous reports (Hendry et al. 1974, 1975a) on the oak leafroller (OLR) suggested that this moth was different from the other leafrollers because it utilized *cis*-10-tetradecenyl acetate (c10-14:Ac) as a major pheromone component along with at least 17 other monounsaturated 14-carbon acetate isomers in its pheromone system. These reports were of interest to us because the electroantennogram (EAG) responses of male OLR moths to various standards (Hendry et al. 1975b) did not support c10-14:Ac as the major component, and the large number of suggested pheromone components was inconsistent with the specific blends of other leafrollers. Further interest was generated when it was reported (Hendry et al. 1975c) that: 1) the OLR females did not produce pheromone if reared on semisynthetic diet without oak leaves; 2) the males appeared to be attracted to various 14-carbon acetate isomers at distinctly different times during the flight period, leading to the speculation that the oak leafroller was evolving subgroups on different species of oak; and 3) different 14-carbon acetate isomers were found in varying composition in leaves of several oak species suggesting that the subgroups were deriving their particular pheromone from the leaves on which the larvae had fed. These reports had implications for the general field of pheromones, so we investigated the pheromone of this "unusual" leafroller.

Pheromone Components in Female OLR

OLR eggs were obtained from Moshannon State Forest, Pa. and the larvae successfully reared on a pinto bean-based artificial medium (Shorey and Hale 1965) without addition of oak leaves or oak extract (Miller et al. 1976). OLR larvae and pupae also were collected from the foliage of oak trees within a natural infestation of OLR on Boone Mountain, 3 mi. north of Penfield in Elk County, Pa. Efforts were concentrated on obtaining specimens from chesnut (*Quercus prinus* L.), black (*Q. velutina* Lam.), and white (*Q. alba* L.) oaks. Leaves from the appropriate species were used in the laboratory to feed 5th instar larvae until pupation.

The abdominal tips of 2- to 3-day-old females 4 h into scotophase (16:8 LD) were extracted by soaking in methylene chloride. GLC analyses on an XF-1150 column (Fig. 6) showed that extracts from oak-reared females

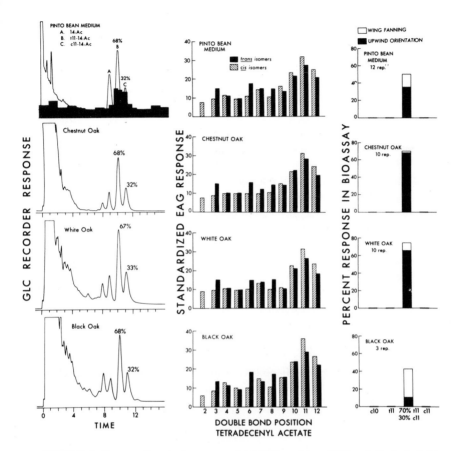

FIGURE 6 *Comparative a) pheromone gland GLC analyses, EAG activity is shaded in the pinto bean tracings; b) male antennal responses, and c) laboratory behavioral responses of oak leafrollers reared on a pinto bean diet, black oak leaves, white oak leaves, and chestnut oak leaves.*

produced the same three peaks (A, B, and C) as found with extracts from medium-reared females. These three components of all extracts showed the following similarities: a) identical GLC retention times; b) virtually identical ratios—the ratios of peak A to peaks B and C varied from 15 to 30%, but the B:C ratio was constant at $\bar{x} = 67:33$ or $68:32$; and c) presence in total quantities of 35-50 ng per individual.

EAG assay of 1-min collections of crude extract effluent from a nonpolar GLC column (OV-1) revealed only one area of EAG activity, which coincided with the retention times of 14-carbon acetates and included the retention times of all three components A, B and C. EAG-active material from OV-1 was collected in 1-min fractions from XF-1150 with subsequent EAG assay. This showed that only components B and C elicited good antennal responses with the minute quantities involved in these extract aliquots (Fig. 6). The three components A, B and C had CLC retention times identical to those of tetradecenyl acetate, *trans*-11-tetradecenyl acetate and *cis*-11-tetradecenyl acetate on OV-1 and on XF-1150 columns (Miller et al. 1976). Saponification of the three components produced products with retention times identical to those of the corresponding alcohols on XF-1150, and treatment of the hydrolysis products with acetyl chloride gave products with the original component retention times on XF-1150.

Although the predominant pheromone components from the various female extracts appeared to be *trans*-11- and *cis*-11-tetradecenyl acetates, special efforts were made to determine if any of the other reported 14-carbon acetate isomers were present. Crude abdominal tip extract was separated by AgNO₃- silica gel TLC and the plates scraped in three bands corresponding to saturated-, *trans*-, and *cis*-compounds. GLC analysis (XF-1150) of each band revealed a single peak corresponding to components A, B and C, respectively, and no evidence of any other 14-carbon acetate isomers. Additionally, the 14-carbon acetate fraction from OV-1 of each type of female extract was subjected to microozonolysis. Each extract produced a large peak on OV-1 corresponding to 11-acetoxyunde-canal, and another large peak corresponding to the unozonized tetradecenyl acetate (Fig. 7). These data confirmed the assigned Δ-11-tetradecenyl acetate structures for components B and C, and also showed that there were no detectable amounts (<1%) of the other positional isomers (Fig. 7).

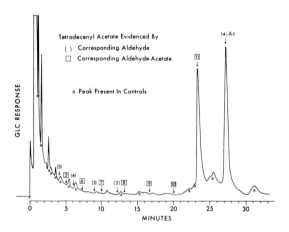

FIGURE 7 *Microozonolysis products on OV-1 of female abdominal tip extract from pinto bean diet-reared oak leafrollers.*

Male OLR Responses to Pheromone Components

EAG profiles were obtained for newly-emerged OLR males from the various oaks and the artificial medium (Fig. 6). Throughout the various series of 10- to 16-carbon acetates, alcohols and aldehydes, the four "types" of OLR males all responded similarly, with the greatest antennal responses elicited by the pheromone components, *cis*-11 and *trans*-11-tetradecenyl acetates.

The various 'types' of OLR males were used also in laboratory excitation and orientation bioassays (Baker et al. 1976, Miller et al. 1976). Again, the specificity of response was similar among all 'types', with only a 70:30 ratio of *trans:cis* mixture of Δ-11-tetradecenyl acetates eliciting responses in a series that included *cis*-10-, *cis*-11- and *trans*-11-tetradecenyl acetates (Fig. 6). The responses of the black oak males are shown to be lower than those shown for the other 'types', but this is attributed to the lack of these males for adequate replication, rather than a statistically different specificity.

The most important data, however, on the biological activity of the pheromone components are from field studies. To test the specificity of the OLR males in Pennsylvania to various ratios of the identified pheromone components and to other isomers previously reported to be pheromone components, we used the small Sectar and Pherocon IC traps (Fig. 2). As noted above with the redbanded leafroller studies, the smaller traps require a more precise blending of the pheromone to lure the males closer to the odor source and to get them to enter the traps. The treatments were replicated between 4–10 times for the various tests, and, more importantly, traps were re-randomized every night in most tests to average out possible population gradients and "hot spots" of OLR adults in the forest.

Specificity of OLR males for a blend of *trans*-11- and *cis*-11-tetradecenyl acetate is dramatically shown in Table 6. The *cis*-4- and *cis*-10-tetradecenyl acetates, as well as the individual pheromone components *cis*-11- and *trans*-11-tetradecenyl acetates did not attract any males, whereas a 7:3 mixture of the latter two compounds attracted 744 males in 2 days. Data from live female pairs show that the synthetic pheromone blend is as attractive as live females, and also show that males responded to all three "types" of OLR females in this test period.

Several other field attractancy tests (Miller et al. 1976) indicated that 1 mg of the pheromone blend on a rubber septum was more attractive to OLR males than lower quantities, and that 10 mg of the blend in polyethylene caps (used for many other leafrollers) was not attractive. Addition of tetradecenyl acetate, identified from OLR abdominal tips, did not increase trap catch, and decreased trap catch when present at >25% of the mixture. A series of *trans*-11/*cis*-11 mixtures was field tested to determine the specificity for the 67:33 ratio found in female tips. The data (Fig. 8) showed a surprisingly narrow range of attractive

TABLE 6   *Male oak leafroller attractancy studies, July 5-6, 1975*

Treatment[a]	x̄ males/trap
cis-4-tetradecenyl acetate	0
cis-10-tetradecenyl acetate	0
cis-11-tetradecenyl acetate	0
trans-11/*cis*-11 (7:3)	124.2
(3-day-old) virgin females	
3 pairs from white oak	81.0
2 pairs from black oak	60.0
1 pair from chestnut oak	120.0

[a]Synthetic treatments were 1 mg chemical on a rubber septum; 6 replicates rerandomized daily.

ratios, with a significant difference obtained between ratios of 66:34 and 70:30. This narrow range of male responsiveness, along with the unvarying component ratios in the females, underscore the lack of pheromonal variation of oak leafrollers in Pennsylvania and further negate the possibility that some oak leafroller populations are evolving quite different pheromone systems in this area. At the conclusion of the 1975 field tests conducted in a very light OLR infestation, 4,242 oak leafroller males had been attracted to the pheromone

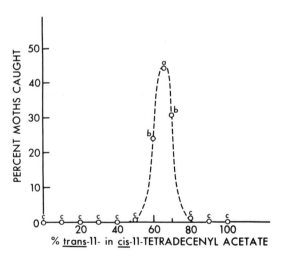

FIGURE 8 *Field attractancy test for oak leafroller males with varying ratios of t11- and c11-14:Ac. The test was conducted from July 6-16, 1975 using Sectar I traps spaced 15-20 m apart. The 6 replicates were re-randomized each day between July 8-11. Mean for the treatments marked by the same letter were not significantly different at the 5% level.*

blend of *trans*-11/*cis*-11 (7:3), and 0 males had been caught in traps baited with the series of individual isomers.

SUMMARY

The oak leafroller study showed that this species is similar to the other leafrollers. It can be reared successfully on diets in the laboratory, it utilizes a specific blend of pheromone components that are common to the other leafrollers, the pheromone components elicit the greatest EAG responses, the blend elicits the greatest laboratory behavioral responses, and the blend is as attractive in the field as virgin females.

Pheromones, therefore, have been shown to be important in reproductive isolation of a complex of sympatric leafrollers. Individual pheromone components are used in precise ratios to effect this specificity. As shown for the redbanded leafroller, additional components are sometimes used to mediate close-range behavior. Knowledge of these pheromone components and the behavioral responses mediated by them is increasingly important as efforts are directed toward the manipulation of pheromone communication for insect control.

Chapter 10

Flight and Mating Behavior of the Gypsy Moth

Charles C. Doane

Department of Entomology
The Connecticut Agricultural Experiment Station
New Haven, Connecticut 06504

INTRODUCTION

It long has been known that males of Lepidoptera could be attracted to unmated females of the same species by a sense of smell. Cuvier (1832) mentioned that naturalists found male moths attracted to caged females in houses "by a very fine sense of smell". Perhaps, for very much longer, man was using this knowledge in a practical way. Cuvier described a practice of Chinese silk proprietors who knew that male moths were guided to the females by a sense of smell. They used this knowledge to their advantage by tying virgin *Bombyx* females of two wild species by threads to rings which were then hung outside to attract wild males for mating.

Forbush and Fernald (1896) suggested the possibility of attracting gypsy moth males, *Lymantria dispar* L., to traps in attempts to reduce their numbers. Collins and Potts (1932) began systematic attempts to trace the source of the gypsy moth attractant with the hope of isolating, identifying and producing the chemical synthetically. They soon realized that nothing was known of the behavior of male moths and began a study of distances males fly in locating the virgin female.

The need to thoroughly define male and female mating behavior has continued to be of paramount value in investigations of pheromones for control of populations. Studies of behavior have tended to follow, rather than precede, efforts to develop pheromones for practical control. Dr. Wellington's comment that, "Entomologists tend to ignore behavior until it gets in the way" is especially apropos of pheromone research with the gypsy moth.

Conversely, failures in development of pheromones for control have given impetus to research on behavior. Indeed, the misidentification of the natural pheromone of the gypsy moth and designation of the chemical, 12-acetoxy-1-hydroxy-9-octadecene, as gyplure, the synthetic attractant (Jacobson 1960, 1962), was partly due to lack of sophistication in testing materials for activity against the male moth (Block 1960). Gypsy moth males were held by the wings with clothespins, a technique developed by Minnich (1922), which allowed them to do little more than move their antennae and legs. Even if significant, this behavior represented a minimal part of the behavioral repertoire of the gypsy moth and could not properly measure the attractive qualities of a pheromone. Although gyplure failed in the field (Doane 1961, Godwin and Hastings 1961), it led to a study of normal mating behavior of the gypsy moth (Doane 1968a). With the isolation, identification and synthesis of disparlure (cis-7,8-epoxy-2-methyloctadecane) by Bierl et al. (1970) and subsequent attempts to disrupt mating (Beroza et al. 1971b, 1973, 1974a, Stevens and Beroza 1972), the study of behavior became increasingly valuable in assessing the results of field studies. In spite of this, many aspects of mating behavior in the gypsy moth still require clarification. The following discussion is a synthesis of observations made on the gypsy moth over a period of years and of pertinent literature on the gypsy moth and other lepidopterous species.

MALE MATING BEHAVIOR

A number of recent reviews and papers demonstrate the range of diversity of behavioral patterns mediated by pheromones (Shorey 1970, 1973, 1974). Roelofs and Comeau (1971) have shown the need for exacting field study to confirm whether or not single chemicals or blends of several can, in fact, reproduce the hierarchy of male behavior normally elicited by the female (Roelofs and Cardé 1974, Cardé et al. 1975a). An exhaustive study of timed sequential steps, such as that made of *Grapholitha molesta* (Busck) (Cardé et al. 1975a) or the comprehensive study of mating behavior of *Trichoplusia ni* (Hübner) (Shorey 1974) must still be undertaken with the gypsy moth. I have taken particular care to restrict interpretation of male gypsy moth behavior only in response to the natural pheromone produced by the female moth and not to various production runs or formulations of disparlure, as these may vary in their effects on the gypsy moth (see Granett Chapter 11).

Mating in Sparse Populations

The term, sparse population, is somewhat vague, but is used here to define a female moth density of less than 10/ha. At some still-unknown distance downwind from a pheromone source, a threshold concentration of pheromone initiates male response. Schwinck (1954, 1955, 1958) investigated male response in several moth species, including *Bombyx mori* (L.) and *L. dispar*, and attempted to establish, at least for long distance orientation, the sequence of behavioral steps produced by increasing concentration of pheromone. At distances of up to 900 m, a threshold concentration of pheromone elicited excitation, wing fluttering and initiation of flight. Schwinck postulated that at these distances a positive anemotaxis was the main orientation mechanism. Collins and Potts (1932) using 12 to 15 virgin female gypsy moths as an odor source found that a few marked males released from as far as 3720 m downwind were trapped but that usually males were trapped from distances of less than 800 m. Based on this study of the gypsy moth, Bossert and Wilson (1963) developed formulae indicating that at optimum wind speed of 100 cm/sec males would not be attracted for more than 4560 m downwind. They pointed out that at these great distances no male could possibly detect a concentration gradient. Only the anemotactic response would serve to direct the male upwind and eventually into the vicinity of the pheromone source.

Within a few meters of the pheromone source, the gypsy moth enters the next behavioral step. Males exhibiting casting behavior may be recognized by the relatively slow, slightly zigzag forward flight with the body held at an angle of about 45° to the horizontal plane and the antennae directed upward with the broad sides forward (Doane 1968a, Doane and Cardé 1973). Wingbeat tends to be rapid and steady. Schneider (1964) hypothesized that this form of flight would tend to move air past the antennae more efficiently. Many species of Lepidoptera exhibit this zigzag or casting flight. This behavior, defined as forward flight with lateral sinusoidal oscillations as the insect moves upwind, has been recently reviewed (Shorey 1973, Farkas and Shorey 1974). As the pheromone is carried downwind it forms an elongate, non-uniform, filamentous plume that is roughly cone-shaped. The filaments readily change shape, break up, and radiate out from the longitudinal axis while they are being carried downwind. The mechanism employed by male moths following this aerial trail (a term coined by Butler 1970), has been assumed anemotactic (Kennedy 1965, Butler 1967, Shorey 1970) although the possibility of insects using chemoklino-taxis and chemotropotaxis where a relatively steep gradient exists close to the odor source cannot be ruled out (Farkas and Shorey 1972, 1974, Kennedy and Marsh 1974).

Recently, the nature of locomotion in, and location of, the aerial trail by moths has been clarified by Kennedy and Marsh (1974). Males of *Anagasta kuehniella* (Zeller), *Cadra cautella* (Walker) and *Plodia interpunctella* (Hübner) flying upwind toward a female releasing pheromone were guided anemotactically by optomotor reactions to the ground pattern. The optomotor response was so strong that the male reduced its air speed if the floor pattern was moving in the downwind direction and was thus carried downwind and away from the pheromone source. Kennedy and Marsh also demonstrated in convincing fashion that casting or zigzag flight is also governed by optomotor anemotaxis and that deviation from a longitudinal axis is variable and dependent on whether the air space in the wind stream is continuously permeated with pheromone. Sudden cessation of the odor stimulus caused the orienting moth to deviate from the upwind direction until the zigzags of its trail were perpendicular to the wind. In effect, the sudden loss of pheromone reset the moth's anemotactic angle, causing it to begin sharp right and left turns that increased to turns of 180°. Such behavior in nature would increase the chances of a male locating the aerial trail or in locating new puffs in the discontinuous trail as they move downwind. It may be seen from the work of Kennedy and Marsh (1974) that the moth utilizes a fixed optomotor speed. This is maintained in the moth making sharp right and left turns but its forward speed toward the pheromone source is almost halted. This right-left turning would keep the moth in position until new puffs in the aerial trail move past its position.

The literature on actual behavior of male moths in long-distance response to pheromone is understandably scanty. Schwinck (1958) described this movement in males as "long-distance unoriented runs." Probably the optomotor response is the major factor in enabling the moth moving upwind, but it is not clear whether there is also some zigzag flight, or, at least, forward flight at some angle to the wind. Studies of anemotaxis have been within a few meters of the pheromone source and it may be that only after the moth reaches a certain threshold concentration near the pheromone source that it ceases long-distance, undirected anemotactic flight and begins to cast. However, Doane (1968a) noted that males on long-distance approach appeared to be flying at a slight angle to the wind. As they passed a meter or so downwind from calling females, they were observed to turn into the pheromone plume and approach with a typical zigzag flight. Perhaps males on long-distance flight may not fly directly upwind but may either fly at a single angle to the wind in one direction or in long sinusoidal curves. Collins and Potts (1932) noted that in some cases males came to traps at right angles from the point of release as well as upwind.

Gypsy moth males tend to fly near the ground when on long-distance oriented flight or when casting. This behavior would allow the male to remain in visual contact with the ground as optomotor anemotaxis would require. Granett (1974) has shown that most males are trapped between 0.5 and 1.5 m above the ground. Cardé et al. (1975b) found that casting males approached an attractant array situated 1.8 m above ground at an average height of 1 m.

Response to Hidden Females. As the male continues its forward progress to the pheromone source, it finally slows its advance and begins hovering just downwind—usually within a half meter of the female (Doane and Cardé 1973). Reduction of flight speed as concentration of pheromone increases near the source, or chemo-orthokinesis (Fraenkel and Gunn 1961), is known in the introduced pine sawfly, *Diprion similis* (Hartig) (Casida et al. 1963) and in *A.*

kuehniella (Traynier 1968). Male moths of *Pectinophora gossypiella* (Saunders) exposed to a high concentration of pheromone will reduce their flight speed and land (Farkas et al. 1974). Wing beat in the hovering gypsy moth remains rapid and the body angle is maintained at roughly 45° to the horizontal plane. At this point a series of behavioral steps ensue, some of which grade imperceptibly into the next. In tests with the female hidden from sight in a cylindrical screen cage (Doane 1968a, Doane and Cardé 1973), the male hovered a few seconds and then began tarsal-touching while flying or hovering. In this stage, the male flew close to the cage, periodically touching it with its tarsi. Males spent most of their time at or near the downwind end of the cage, but would also investigate its other parts several times. Some would go to the upwind end of the cage, out of the pheromone trail, where they would search for a short time and then fly quickly back downwind a half meter or less below the odor source and repeat the approach to the cage. The flying tarsal-touching behavior was often followed by walking/fanning in which the male walks over a surface while fanning its wings at apparently the same wing beat rate but with a much lower amplitude. Landing on the cage for search usually followed several searches by flying with tarsal-touching. In the next step from walking/fanning, the moth further decreases the wing beat to wing vibration and crawls into crevices, under leaves, and other obstructions in search of the female.

None of the sequences for males searching for a hidden pheromone source has been timed. These data should be obtained for comparison with behavior of males in disparlure-treated plots where some of the sequential steps may be recognized in greatly reduced or distorted form (Granett and Doane 1975). Males unsuccessful in finding the female at a pheromone source did not continue to search indefinitely. Mean search time for males searching alone was an average of 20 sec after which males ended searching behavior. With termination of close-range searching, the male abruptly flew away. Flight attitude changed abruptly. The body was held more horizontally than when searching and forward flight was rapid and usually upward and across the path of the wind until the male was lost from sight (Doane 1968a, Doane and Cardé 1973). None of these males was ever seen to slow and begin searching again.

The same non-searching condition can also be elicited by aggressive wing-touching between two or more males searching at a pheromone source with the female hidden from sight. Two males in competition attacked one another within 4.3 sec, after which one or both usually terminated searching. The same effect could be obtained by flicking the wings of the male with a wooden applicator or pencil. In all cases behavior after termination of close-range searching appeared to be identical. Males flew rapidly upward and away and were never observed to resume searching again. This "turned off" behavior is of interest because we suspect that even though a male might encounter a receptive female the male would not attempt to mate. There are indications that an equivalent condition may be elicited by artificial means. Behavior of males seen in plots following treatment with a formulation of disparlure (Granett and Doane 1975) was reminiscent of behavior after termination of search. Males on the outside of plots were searching as normal while those on the inside flew upward and away until lost from sight. While these results are at odds with those of others, it would appear that certain combinations or compositions of disparlure formulations may produce a form of non-searching or "turned off" behavior (Granett Chapter 11). Abrupt termination of close-range searching also has been observed in *G. molesta* in which no return to searching was observed before the males flew from sight (Cardé et al. 1975a).

Response to Exposed Females. When the female is in an exposed position, visible to the approaching male, the sequence of behavioral events proceeds more quickly. These tend to blend together or are shorter in duration than with a hidden female (Doane 1968a). The approaching male, after slowing its forward progress often quickly locates the female by sight and there is little flying with tarsal touching or walking/fanning behavior. After a few seconds, the male lands near the female and moves to her with fanning and walking, touches the female, and after a brief inspection with touching, settles beside her. The receptive female then ceases calling and raises her wings slightly. The male arches his abdomen laterally under the wings of the female to begin copulation, and the male and female then become quiescent.

Vision plays an important role in mating of the gypsy moth as well as in some other Lepidoptera. Gypsy moth males tended to locate a non-calling female in a pheromone trail downwind from an odor source, but tended to ignore a non-calling female a few inches upwind from the source (Doane 1968a). Brown (1974) found that males are highly sensitive to ultraviolet. Virgin females tend to rest on brighter areas of the trunk (Doane 1968a). Brown found that the female may provide visual cues as a highly reflective ultraviolet patch against the dark bark of the tree and possibly further response may be elicited by the specific pattern of the ultraviolet reflection presented by the female. This does not preclude the possibility of further visual cues as the male approaches the female. Further evidence that gypsy moth males see well is that in competition at a pheromone source they will commonly attack one another from distances of at least 0.5 m (Doane and Cardé 1973). It is interesting, in terms of ultraviolet, that the gypsy moth is a day flier with a diel rhythm of activity from 0900 to 2000 hrs (Cardé et al. 1974).

Shorey and Gaston (1970) found that males of *T. ni*, when stimulated by female sex pheromone, often utilize visual cues from the female in their approach. Males presented with the most attractive models, one on each side and 2 cm away from the source, produced orientation to the models 56% of the time against 44% for the pheromone source. Copulatory attempts directed at the model averaged 86% vs. only 14% toward the source. Both orientation and copulatory attempts associated with models were invariably directed toward the lower apex. The two most attractive models were dried females placed head up with wings folded or partly open. It is interesting that this night-flying species also employs sight as part of its close-range searching behavior. Traynier (1968) found that males of *A. kuehniella*, in the presence of pheromone, attempted to mate with other males and with clay models.

Mating in Dense Populations

Behavior of males in dense populations is obviously different from that in sparse populations and indicates that males are capable of alternate strategies in mate finding. The various patterns one may observe in dense populations are complicated and need more study, but certain generalizations are possible. Males do not need to undergo long-distance anemotactic orientation when there is a high pheromone background in the air space. Early behavioral responses are simply not relevant and males appear to adopt a surface-searching technique in locating and mating with females. Shorey (1970) noted that different concentrations of pheromone will elicit different behavioral sequences or different steps in the sequence. Low concentrations are sufficient to induce early steps such as antennal or wing expansion and initiation of flight while high concentrations would induce such late-sequence steps as copulatory behavior. This has been demonstrated experimentally in *B. mori* (Schwinck 1955) and *A. kuehniella* (Traynier 1968).

Thus, gypsy moth males in dense populations search surfaces at ground level, including rocks, foliage and surface litter, and up and down tree trunks, limbs, and foliage. Holbrook et al. (1960) and Stevens and Beroza (1972) found decreased catches of moths in traps positioned high. Granett (1974) caught the greatest number of males in traps at 0.5 and 1.5 m above ground and fewer at 3 m or higher. Further discrimination in height of trap to catch was made by Cardé et al. (1975b). Three times as many males were caught in traps 10-20 cm above ground compared to traps at 1 m above ground.

Males are also strongly drawn to tree trunks in dense populations. Granett (1974) caught many more males in traps hung at 0.5 m from trunks compared with those hung at 1, 3, and 10 m. He also found that more moths were caught in traps hung near trees with 32-38 cm dbh than in traps hung from either smaller or larger trees. Cardé et al. (1975b) noted that vertical flight within ca 1 m of tree trunks is a male searching behavior in dense populations. Thus, there is evidence that males are surface searchers in these dense populations and tend to stay close to such surfaces during periods of activity.

While sight is important in males searching in sparse populations, as discussed earlier, it is a major factor in males searching in dense populations. Weseloh (1972d) noted that gypsy moths oriented to dark objects such as trees where females were likely to be located. He found that male moths were most strongly attracted to dark colored panels of red, black and blue and least to light-colored or clear panels. Brown (1974) noted that the gypsy moth is unable to perceive blue and black as colors, but would respond to the contrast of these dark objects presented against the ultraviolet of the sky. Mazokhin-Porshnyakov (1969) observed that perception of objects and ability to distinguish one object from another depends on differences in their reflective properties and noted that trees and poles present landmark silhouettes against the ultraviolet background of the sky.

Recently, Richerson et al. (1976a,b) proposed that males in dense populations orient directly to trees and other vertical objects and then search for females. They found that more released males were caught at trees in plots with a density of 72 virgin females per 0.2 ha plot than in plots with 32 or fewer virgin female gypsy moths. However, even with 5 females per plot they observed no anemotactic response by the males and, therefore, concluded that gypsy moth males are unable to orient by anemotaxis, even in sparse populations (Richerson et al. 1976a). While this may be true, in part, in dense populations it would seem premature to eliminate anemotaxis as a mate-finding strategy in sparse or even in moderate populations, especially in view of considerable evidence to the contrary (Schwinck 1955, 1958, Doane 1968a, Doane and Cardé 1973, Farkas and Shorey 1974). Behavior of males in a dense population raises the possibility that there may be a kind of "natural disruption of communication" in operation in the gypsy moth. If this is true it would suggest that the male moth has been able to adapt to the problem, and it infers that disruption by use of an attractant may not be completely successful.

More research should be done on problems of population quality and mating behavior in the gypsy moth. Shorey (1974) has discussed effects of environmental and physiological factors on sex pheromone behavior. Marked changes favoring males may occur in the sex ratio of gypsy moth adults in dense populations (Campbell 1963c). Bobb (1964, 1972) found that the females of the Virginia-pine sawfly, *Neodiprion pratti* (Dyar), release relatively high levels of pheromone during the beginning of an outbreak but little at greatest density or during decline of the population. Crowding may result in sawfly females that have a tendency to release less pheromone. Leonard (1974) discussed his work showing that crowding in the gypsy moth larval population will result in marked behavioral changes in the succeeding generation.

We have observed during several seasons that, in dense populations, gypsy moth males searching surfaces often show a curious inability to mate. In one instance, three virgin females placed under observation on tree trunks called for a period of 2 hr and although many males passed within a few cm of each female, none attempted to mate. Richerson et al. (1976b) noted that up to 2/3 of the males were not likely to mate with virgin or calling females even if they crawled over or passed within a few cm of them. Granett (1974) observed that the number of males flying in a given air space may have little relationship to the likelihood or rate of mating. The ability of the male to find and mate with a female was estimated by the reciprocal of the time elapsed before virgin females mated during the natural gypsy moth flight and was defined as "male mating potential." In a given population, this condition could also be influenced by such factors as the capacity of the female to attract and mate.

FEMALE MATING BEHAVIOR

Virgin female gypsy moths attract males by assuming a characteristic position and release pheromone by rhythmic protrusion and retraction of the last abdominal segments (Doane 1968a). Cardé et al. (1974) found that males actually determine diel mating rhythms since they are attracted only during part of the time that females release pheromone. Males were attracted between 0900-2000 hrs with greatest numbers between 1100-1500 hrs. There was evidence that the diel period is now longer than earlier reported in North America or presently from Europe where the nun moth, *Lymantria monacha* (L.) responds to the same pheromone but mates at night (Görnitz 1949). Cardé et al. (1974) suggested that here, in the absence of the nun moth, the gypsy moth has evolved a longer activity period. Richerson and Cameron (1974) measured the greatest release of pheromone in the female between 0800-1600 hrs.

Virgin female moths are somewhat positively phototrophic and may move to the more sunny locations on the trunk, but many mate close to the location where they emerge (Doane 1968a). Chances of a female mating in a dense population, where sight is important, would be better in a bright location where she would present an ultraviolet silhouette to the searching male (Brown 1974). Females are ready to mate within 2 hr of eclosion (Forbush and Fernald 1896, Block 1960, Doane 1968a) and are maximally attractive for about 3 days, after which their attractiveness decreases rapidly (Collins and Potts 1932, Holbrook et al. 1960, Richerson and Cameron 1974). The attractive period is related to their behavior and physiological state. The females are least excitable during the first and second days following eclosion. After this they become increasingly nervous and during periods of activity do not call and are unlikely to mate (Doane 1968a). Mortality increases sharply after the third day. Holbrook et al. (1960) found 3% mortality between 16 and 24 hrs after eclosion and 28% from 64-72 hrs. Such females tend to respond abnormally and are unreliable subjects for behavioral study.

After mating, females become active and are negatively phototrophic. Mated females do not attract males but in the presence of pheromone from another source they may attempt to mate (Doane 1968a). A recently mated female will actively resist mating again by moving away from males attempting to copulate. Egg laying begins within 1 hr after copulation, and during this process, females are not easily disturbed. Eggs are deposited normally in one mass after which the female dies. Multiple mating appears common in the male (Forbush and Fernald 1896, Richerson et al. 1976b), but multiple mating of the female is infrequent in nature (Forbush and Fernald 1896, Taylor 1967, Doane 1968a). Taylor obtained 10% remating of females in cages while Richerson et al. (1976b), using caged females and males, obtained less than 10% mating.

Flight of females was noted early (Forbush and Fernald 1896) and was considered rare. Recent observations confirm this view (Sandquist et al. 1973) for some forms, but races or species of gypsy moths in some parts of the world may fly well (Leonard 1974).

THE PHEROMONE SYSTEM

Finally, the exact nature of the chemicals mediating normal mating behavior in the gypsy moth male is still open to investigation. Recent studies indicate that disparlure is, by far, the most attractive epoxide both for the nun moth and the gypsy moth (Schönherr 1972a, Schneider et al. 1974). It would appear that disparlure is a group-specific pheromone for the *Lymantria-Porthetria* genus since all species tested to date have reacted to it (Schneider et al. 1974, Boness 1975). The nun moth and gypsy moth are widely sympatric in Europe and Asia, but the species are isolated by differing behavioral and temporal patterns including both seasonal and diel periodicity in mating activity (Ambros 1938, 1940, Nolte 1940, Cardé et al. 1974) and by differing temperature requirements for activity (Collins and Potts 1932, Boness 1975). Although a number of multiple component pheromone systems have been identified (Roelofs and Cardé 1974), there are others that apparently utilize single chemical systems in which sight plays a major role. Benz (1973) and Benz and von Salis (1973) found that in the larch bud moth, *Zeiraphera diniana* (=*griseana*) (Gn.), a single chemical acts only as a far-distance attractant while near-distance orientation of the males to the females is strictly by vision. Most interesting is the recent work of Iwaki et al. (1974) which indicates that the discrepancy in attraction between the natural system in the gypsy moth and the synthetic preparations may exist in optically defined disparlure. Their preliminary laboratory trials suggest that the natural pheromone may be the (+) enantiomer. The racemic sample was less stimulatory while the (-) enantiomer produced least response in male Japanese gypsy moths. These data implicate a chiral receptor system in the olfactory organs of the males.

In conclusion, it would appear that the gypsy moth utilizes a single pheromone system and that, in the presence of the pheromone, sight plays an important role in the location of the female. Male mating behavior is adaptive to conditions imposed in sparse and dense populations of adults and males may be able to adopt several behavioral strategies in locating females.

Chapter 11

A Pheromone for Managing Gypsy Moth Populations

J. Granett[1]

Department of Entomology
The Connecticut Agricultural Experiment Station
New Haven, Connecticut 06504

INTRODUCTION

Pheromones of numerous economically important insect species have been studied during the past decade for use in control and monitoring. This research has been motivated by several factors. Pheromones used to directly control insects would be environmentally safe and compatible with other control agents. Also, techniques for monitoring insect populations using pheromones tend to be extremely efficient. Several recent reviews have dealt with these aspects of pheromone use (Jacobson 1972, Shorey 1973, Birch 1974).

A pheromone of the gypsy moth (*Lymantria dispar* L.) has particular utility and potential. It has been used extensively in traps for monitoring populations and has been tested as a control agent. Reviews and proposals on this work have been published (Beroza and Knipling 1972, Leonard 1974, Cameron 1974). Herein I shall expand upon the scope of past reviews on the use of the gypsy moth pheromone for monitoring and control and suggest directions this research might take. I will address myself to the applied aspects of this problem and will discuss the basic research when it directly pertains to the problem of control.

HISTORY

Virgin female gypsy moths attract males to traps (Forbush and Fernald 1896). Based on this phenomenon, female-baited traps were utilized in survey

---

[1] Present address: Department of Entomology, University of Maine, Orono 04473.

work as early as 1913 (Collins and Potts 1932). Because of difficulties in using live females, female abdominal tips which bear the pheromone glands were used as bait and then solvent extracts of the tips were used. The extracts were later chemically treated for greater potency and durability (Burgess 1950). Early attempts to characterize the active components of the extracts were unsuccessful (Collins and Potts 1932, Haller et al. 1944). A chemical structure and the name gyplure for the actual attractant were proposed in 1960 (Jacobson et al. 1960); however, field work proved this material to be inactive (Doane 1961, Godwin and Hastings 1961) and the structure was later retracted (Jacobson et al. 1970). Bierl et al. (1970) proposed a new structure, cis-7,8-epoxy-2-methyloctadecane and the name disparlure for the pheromone, and in field tests it was attractive to gypsy moth males. Since 1970, accelerated research efforts on the use of disparlure have included work on trapping for survey, mass trapping for control, and atmospheric permeation of the pheromone for control.

GYPSY MOTH TRAPPING

Trap Design

Various traps have been used to survey populations of gypsy moths, to trap males for population control, and to assay the results of atmospheric permeation experiments for control. The gypsy moth trap used by Forbush and Fernald (1896) was made from crossed pieces of wood placed over a horizontal floor piece. The trap was covered with an adhesive substance to hold the moths attracted by a caged virgin female. Collins and Potts (1932) used cylinders covered internally with an adhesive and with concave funnel-ends. Holbrook et al. (1960) tested a series of sticky traps and reported on the application of a paper-cup trap. Its efficiency was low; only 1/10 to 1/3 of the moths attracted to it were caught (Richerson et al. 1976b). The 3M Sectar® trap (later available from Zoecon Corp., Palo Alto, California) was a foldable sticky trap commercially available in several forms and was used in a number of experimental situations. The delta trap, a modification of the foldable sticky trap described by Beroza et al. (1975), was used throughout the 1975 gypsy moth season in all USDA affiliated survey work. It caught only 16% of attracted males when hung horizontally. Traps oriented vertically were twice as efficient but did not approach the efficiency of an open sticky panel (Maestro, manuscript in preparation). Such flat panels covered with an adhesive substance and positioned against trees have long been used in Europe (Maksimović 1959). All sticky traps have limited quantitative use because they become clogged with moths and wing scales and require either replacement or cleaning.

Recently a trap was developed that did not depend on a sticky surface to hold moths (Granett 1973). The trap had concave funnel-ends with baffles and contained a slow-release dichlorvos disc. This trap could hold more than 1800 moths and thus could be used quantitatively even in dense population areas. Trap catch was correlated with *male mating-potential* defined as the ability of male moths to find and mate with females (Granett 1974). In a pheromone context this concept is useful to determine whether a field treatment has altered behavior or reduced male searching-activity sufficiently to effect insect control.

Bait

In order to be effective in the field, attractiveness of bait in gypsy moth traps must be competitive with that of a virgin female. One to 6 μg disparlure with trioctanoin added to retard evaporation was equivalent in attractiveness to one laboratory-reared female (Beroza et al. 1971a, b). Similarly, a trap containing 10 μg of the same disparlure formulation was only somewhat better than a trap baited with a laboratory-reared female (Stevens and Beroza 1972). The actual disparlure emission rate from a laboratory-reared female was about 5 ng/30 min and similar to that emitted from a trap wick baited with 10 μg disparlure (10 ng/30 min) (Richerson and Cameron 1974). Also, the laboratory females did not exhibit a diel periodicity. These values were considerably different from emissions from a field-collected female which produced a single peak averaging greater than 800 ng/30 min once in her life. These results would indicate that laboratory-reared females are not suitable as substitutes for field-collected females. These values for disparlure may not represent the pheromone output of females. In field tests with natural populations, amounts of disparlure-bait as high as 1 mg (no trioctanoin) were not as attractive as a hidden, field-collected, virgin female (Cardé et al. 1974). Reasons for this disparity are unknown. Activity of another chemical or blend of some additional substance with disparlure may be necessary to equal a female's attractiveness. Naturally occurring blends have been found to be common in other insects (Cardé et al. 1975a, Mitchell 1975). Components of the blend may function differently, with each component triggering a different behavioral response. More research is needed on analogues of the gypsy moth pheromone to find whether such components do exist naturally and to determine their effects.

A second possibility involves optical isomers (Iwaki et al. 1974). The optically pure (+) isomer of disparlure was about 1000 times more attractive than the racemic mixture (i.e. 1:1 ratio) to Japanese gypsy moth males. If the female is able to produce one of the optical isomers preferentially and males detect them at some ratio other than 1:1, the greater catch when female-baits are used may be explained. Although use of the optically pure (+) isomer for control work is not presently feasible because of its cost, use in traps to assay results of control tests may be desirable considering its 1000-fold greater attractiveness.

A related problem concerns "high-potency traps." Beroza et al. (1974a, 1975) claimed that traps baited with 20 mg disparlure should be more attractive than a native female. Although a dose-response up to 1000 μg has been reported (Beroza et al. 1971a), such results have not been obtained consistently (Schneider et al. 1974, Radovan 1975). The inferiority of disparlure when compared directly with field-collected females would also indicate that a high-potency trap may not be feasible with our present knowledge of the gypsy moth sex attractant. Although optically pure isomers may be more active than racemic disparlure, tests have not been conducted against American gypsy moths.

Trap catch may not be proportional to the level of disparlure bait. Traps baited with more than 5 cm² disparlure-impregnated Hercon® wicks (Beroza et al. 1974b) caught fewer moths than traps baited with lesser amounts (C. Schwalbe, personal communication). It is not known whether this decrease was due to a disparlure contaminant or to an overwhelming of moths with high amounts of disparlure. Similarly, pheromone-releasing stations evaporating 0.1 mg disparlure/day did not elicit orientation to the station, although moths were attracted into the area (Cardé et al. 1975b).

Mass Trapping for Control

Mass trapping to reduce male populations and thereby affect female fertility was described in a model (Knipling and McGuire 1966). The formulae made assumptions concerning levels of male and female numbers over time, mating potential, and relative attractiveness of males to traps. The model shows that if enough traps are utilized for a given female population, males, by chance, will be attracted to traps more frequently than to females. If this situation is extended to the extreme, the females will remain unmated, thus lowering the population of the succeeding generation.

Field tests were first attempted by Forbush and Fernald (1896) with virgin females as bait, and resulted in trapping of many males, but fertility of native females was unaffected. Two mass trapping experiments using disparlure as bait were reported by Cameron (1973). In 1971, 300 traps were placed in a 16-ha block and male moths released. Virgin females (hereinafter termed monitor-females) were then deployed in the treated and control blocks to determine whether male mating-potential had decreased sufficiently to cause these monitor-females to remain unmated. The results showed a non-statistical reduction in the fertilization rate. In the 1972 experiment, traps containing a 500 μg disparlure-bait were air-dropped over 100 ha test blocks having several densities and dispersions of artifically placed males and females. Only 1 out of 12 tests showed a slight, but significant, reduction in mating. Traps air-dropped for 2 consecutive years in an isolated natural infestation also failed to "eradicate" the gypsy moths.

The disparlure was mixed with the trap adhesive so the bait was subject to aging and release rates were low (Cameron 1973, Beroza et al. 1973). Because of faulty traps, these tests, therefore, must be considered inconclusive in determining whether mass trapping has potential for gypsy moth control.

In similarly designed tests, more efficient traps baited with 500 μg disparlure were air-dropped in 16 ha plots where 300 laboratory-reared males were released. Depressed catches in monitor-traps containing 10 μg disparlure were obtained. Recovery of males was relatively low, with 10% of the released males being recovered in the control plots and less than 1% in the treated plots (Beroza et al. 1973). Results here would appear to give information on male preferences between the two levels of disparlure (500 μg vs. 10 μg) in the traps and bear little relationship to what would happen if native females were present. No monitor-females were used in these experiments.

Control strategies have been proposed for use of gypsy moth traps. One uses traps to treat isolated, newly-established populations. A related strategy would be to use traps, probably in conjunction with other reduction treatments, in sparse areas as a barrier to prevent spread of the infestation. Based on the Knipling and McGuire (1966) model, large numbers of traps would be necessary for even low populations. Traps are costly to make and distribute and might be objectionable from a litter standpoint. With the additional problems of trap design and bait it seems unlikely that traps will be developed in the near future for direct gypsy moth control. Attempts have been made to test the feasibility of these strategies. An insecticide treatment was used to reduce the gypsy moth population before introduction of disparlure traps. The results were not conclusive because of the low adult populations and a collapsing population especially in the non-treated area (Beroza et al. 1975).

ATMOSPHERIC PERMEATION

The second method for using a pheromone for gypsy moth control requires treating large areas so that the atmosphere within the forest becomes permeated with pheromone. Communication between males and females is affected and males are unable to find females. The mechanism of this disruption is unknown. One possibility is that the artificial pheromone sources compete with females much as baited traps compete with females for the attention of the males. A second possibility is that the males become habituated to the high level of pheromone present and cease to respond to it. A third possibility is that the artificially high pheromone level causes an abnormal behavioral response in the male. Either the males become overly stimulated and are therefore not able to find the females (Richerson et al. 1976a), or the behavioral response is completely abnormal such that at high concentrations the pheromone does not elicit proper orientation in the male (Granett and Doane 1975, manuscript in preparation). It is also possible that some component of the pheromone formulation is synergistic with disparlure or is functioning as an inhibitor.

Field Experiments

There has been much field research with disparlure involving atmospheric permeation (Table 1). In evaluating the results from these tests, variations in the experimental designs must be considered. The male populations in all the early tests (1−4) were artificial; either the males were released as adults or distributed while pupae. The rationale for using such artificial populations has been (1) tests could be conducted outside of the natural gypsy moth flight season; (2) artificial populations could be maintained and assayed at low levels; and (3) the population could be controlled relatively accurately.

Such tests did yield useful information on formulations and rates of application. In test 1 (Table 1) trap catches were depressed. The second test described the use of microcapsules as slow release formulations for atmospheric permeation. Such formulations included a sticker which allowed vertical distribution of the disparlure. Disruption by the disparlure continued for up to 2 months. This was considerably longer than in test 9 where no slow-releaser was used. In that test infertility of monitor-females had decreased to less than 10% in 2 weeks. In test 3, several application rates were tried; however, no statistical conclusions on a dose-response were drawn.

Natural populations were used in tests 5 through 9. Test 5 was the first in which a natural population was suppressed. Mating in the field was reduced for at least a part of the season and there was a reduction from the expected egg mass count. Further experiments (test 7) showed a dose-response; 5 g disparlure/ha reduced mating of tethered females by about half; 20 g/ha depressed mating about 97%. Based on this work the authors concluded that disparlure was a feasible tool for areas with sparse adult populations. Although no fixed definition of a sparse population can be given, a population that produces 10 or fewer egg masses/ha has been considered sparse.

Test 6 was designed to evaluate disparlure in both sparse and dense populations in 1 ha plots sprayed from the ground with a mistblower. Male mating-potential was depressed 97−98%. Based on these data, disparlure is a potential control tool irrespective of population size. The results suggest that 1 ha plots may be better suited for formulation work than larger plots.

A behavioral aspect of test 6 was the observed absence of male moths within the treated plots, although they were present outside of the treated areas, sometimes in high numbers. Apparently the treatment was repellent to the males. Further investigations of gypsy moth behavior under conditions of disparlure treatment (test 8) showed that differences in behavioral patterns between control and disparlure-sprayed plots occurred. However, the high degree of mating-potential depression reported in test 6 was not duplicated. There are conflicting accounts of male behavior in treated plots. Richerson et al. (1976a, b) observed that males are stimulated to search tree trunks to a greater degree in treated than in control plots. They interpret their results as indicating that disparlure will not be an effective control agent in dense populations. A decrease in male orientation to verticals was observed in test 8.

Since it should be possible to routinely achieve the degree of mating control recorded in test 6, the inconsistencies encountered in the several years' work indicate definite problems in the utilization of disparlure for control.

Assays

The first problem centers around how best to measure efficacy in a disparlure-sprayed plot. Generally, such parameters have been used as male captures in disparlure- or female-baited traps, mating of monitor-females, and counts of egg masses after the flight-season. The relative functioning and efficacy of various trap designs and baits was discussed in preceding sections under "Gypsy Moth Trapping."

Monitor-females to assay efficacy have been used in most tests of atmospheric-permeation because they take into account visual cues the males might use in mating (Doane 1968a, Brown 1974) and because the pheromone emitted is genuine. After a period of time in the plot the females are brought back into the laboratory. They are checked for the presence of sperm or the fertility of eggs is determined. In the field, females frequently are lost through predation or because they leave the site. Several techniques have been used to overcome this loss. Females may be placed on trees under burlap bands (Schwalbe et al. 1974) or they may be tethered to trees (Richerson et al. 1976a). Use of opened paper bags for resting sites and field exposure of females for only 48h increased recovery to 94% in control plots and 78% in treated plots (Granett and Doane 1975).

Traps and monitor-females are ideal for measuring depression in the male mating-potential through the season; however, these methods are only an indirect determination of what is occurring with the native females. Direct measures, such as egg mass counts, must be made to determine whether populations are increasing or decreasing. Gypsy moth egg masses are frequently hidden under bark flaps, in tree-holes and under rocks in the duff; therefore, counts are only estimates of the egg population. However, tests in very low populations create problems of interpretation in this regard, especially if eradication is the aim of the treatment. If no egg masses are found in a treated area it may be possible to say that numbers decreased from an untreated area; however, it is impossible to say, based solely on egg mass counts, traps, and monitor-females that a population has been reduced to nothing. Before disparlure can be said to be an eradicant in sparse populations, a different test must be devised, i.e. a test involving several insect generations in which there is no chance of reinfestation from the surrounding areas.

TABLE 1 *Tests of atmospheric permeation using disparlure for gypsy moth control*

Test	Plot size	Male population	Assays	Disparlure/ha	Carrier	Reference
1	40 acres	released, lab-reared	disparlure- and female-baited traps	0.02 g/acre	paper	Stevens and Beroza 1972
2	16 ha	released, lab-reared	disparlure- and female-baited traps	1.8-11.1 g/ha	cork, gelatin and nylon capsules, molecular sieve	Beroza et al. 1973
3	100 ha	released, field-collected	monitor females	5-25 g/ha	cork, nylon capsules	Cameron 1973
4	16 ha	released, field-collected	monitor females	2.5-15 g/ha	gelatin capsules	Cameron et al. 1974 Schwalbe et al. 1974
5	60 km²	sparse, native	disparlure- and female-baited traps, monitor females, egg mass counts	5 g/ha	gelatin capsules	Beroza et al. 1974a
6	1 ha	sparse and dense, native	disparlure-baited traps, monitor females	18 g/ha	gelatin capsules	Granett and Doane 1975
7	2.6 km²	sparse, native	disparlure- and female-baited traps, tethered females, egg mass counts	5-20 g/ha	gelatin capsules	Beroza et al. 1975

| 8 | 1 ha | dense, native | behavior, disparlure-baited traps, monitor females | 0.5-20 g/ha | nylon capsules | Granett and Doane, manuscript in preparation |
| 9 | 0.25 ha | dense, native | disparlure-baited traps, monitor females | 0.2 g/ha | petrol | Bedny and Kovalev 1975 |

Formulations and Pheromone Chemistry

A second major problem in atmospheric permeation tests with disparlure is the formulation and pheromone chemical used. To date, relatively few formulations have been field tested and no published field data are available on emission rates of those formulations, comparative longevity, effects of rain and sun, proper stickers, distribution of spray particles, and total quantities of lure emitted. Such data are necessary for a rational choice of formulations to be used.

The proper chemical to be used in atmospheric permeation work is also open to question. Amounts of trans-isomer in the disparlure used to date have varied from 3 to 15%. Non-epoxy contaminants have also varied. Different batches and formulations resulted in behavioral- and control-differences between spray plots and controls. It may be possible that isomers of disparlure are not the only materials which are active. A blend of isomers and analogues may be necessary for such tests to work. Blends found active as attractants may not be active in atmospheric permeation tests, and vice versa. The possibility of a chemical other than the natural pheromone being better in an atmospheric permeation control procedure was suggested for the olefin precursor of disparlure, 2-methyl-cis-7-octadecene (Cardé et al. 1973). Field tests did not show this material to be as good a disruptant as disparlure when used alone or at one blend ratio with disparlure (Cameron et al. 1975, Cardé et al. 1975b). Modification of male behavior was also observed.

CONTROL STRATEGY

Much work in basic and applied research will be needed before atmospheric permeation with a pheromone, analogue, or blend becomes a control tool. However, it should be evident from the positive tests that this method has potential. Assuming that the aforementioned problems eventually will be solved, important questions will be: How should we use this method for population control? Can it be used as a barrier to prevent spread or to eliminate an isolated population? Can it be used to reduce populations as an insecticide would be used prior to damage in dense populations? Or, can it be used in an incipient out-break to prevent spread of the infestation by 1st instar dispersal?

Beroza and Knipling (1972) and Beroza et al. (1974a) suggested that disparlure had potential only in sparse populations. They proposed a barrier zone using insecticides and disparlure to prevent spread of the gypsy moth out of the northeastern United States and to eliminate spot infestations outside of this area. The barrier would cover thousands of square miles and be sprayed with insecticides prior to disparlure treatment.

Such a program would seem potentially dangerous to the environment and not politically feasible or desirable, especially in light of current laws, public attitudes and the large areas involved. The cost of establishing and maintaining a barrier zone would be considerable, and as the area infested by the gypsy moth increased, costs would escalate. Treatment of such large areas annually would be necessary even if the barrier were to remain static. If the barrier were moved northeastwardly as proposed, all northeastern states would eventually have to be treated. The treatment would have to continue even in non-outbreak years and be maintained indefinitely or until the gypsy moth were eliminated from North America. Vehicular traffic and movement of plant materials would have to be monitored to prevent spread outside the barrier.

The second possibility, treatment of isolated spot infestations, is also under consideration. Here, too, as presently conceived, insecticide sprays would precede disparlure treatment. Large blocks would have to be treated completely with the insecticide. Again, there would be great potential for environmental damage. Residents of newly-infested areas would probably oppose insecticide treatment before damage occurred; sprays over large areas are rarely sanctioned even when gypsy moth damage is grossly evident.

The reduction in male mating-potential in dense populations in test 6 (Table 1) suggests an alternative strategy for pheromone use. One theory on how a gypsy moth outbreak occurs is that the population first builds in small loci, and in response to the population stresses of density and food limitation, the succeeding year newly-hatched larvae disperse out of the area on silk threads in the thermal air currents (Leonard 1971c). If atmospheric permeation were developed for control, the pheromone could be sprayed on these loci immediately following the first defoliation and prevent the spread of the outbreak to surrounding areas. This strategy would require accurate monitoring of populations and rapid treatment after a defoliated area was found. The aim of treatment would not be to eliminate the population completely, but merely to reduce numbers to non-outbreak levels that could be maintained by the normal biological restraints. Because the pheromone is non-toxic, these biological restraints would not be injured by the treatment.

A related strategy for a pheromone in high populations would be to use it in the manner of an insecticide. A county-sized area could be sprayed to reduce populations the year after treatment. Fairly large blocks would have to be treated because of possible blow-in of 1st instar larvae. Such sprays could be used to prevent damage by treating an area while the population is incipient or to prevent a second year of damage. Considerably less biology and survey work would be required for this usage since the pheromone would be used merely as a safe insect control agent. Hopefully, opposition to the size of the area sprayed would be minimal because of the innocuous nature of the spray and because of the obvious gypsy moth damage that had already occurred to the forest areas.

The advantage of using pheromone for gypsy moth control relates to its safety and specificity. Since it is not a poison, none of the fauna other than the gypsy moth would be directly affected. Use during the adult stage would essentially eliminate indirect effects it might have on the parasitoid populations until the succeeding year. Pheromone should also be compatible with other control agents. Beroza and Knipling (1972) and Beroza et al. (1974a) suggested use of disparlure with insecticides and biological control agents. Initial testing has been done (Beroza et al. 1975). Integrated control procedures with selective insecticides, insect growth regulators, bacterial and viral agents, and parasitoids should also be considered.

Disparlure is currently a survey tool and may eventually be developed for use in control programs. When this occurs, we should consider the feasibility of a regional integrated gypsy moth management program using disparlure and other safe control tools. The technical knowledge on the prevention of gypsy moth damage using insecticides has long been available; with the development of environmentally acceptable control agents such as disparlure, gypsy moth management may become feasible on a larger scale.

Chapter 12

Attractant Pheromone of the European Elm Bark Beetle (*Scolytus multistriatus*): Isolation, Identification, Synthesis, and Utilization Studies

G. N. Lanier,[1] R. M. Silverstein[2] and J. W. Peacock[3]

[1,2] *Departments of Forest Entomology and Chemistry, respectively, State University of New York, College of Environmental Science and Forestry, Syracuse 13210.*
[3] *USDA Forest Service, Northeastern Forest Experiment Station, Delaware, Ohio 43015.*

INTRODUCTION

The European elm bark beetle, *Scolytus multistriatus* (Marsham), breeds in weakened or dying elms (*Ulmus* spp.). Moribund host material emits volatiles that attract both male and female beetles (Meyer and Norris 1967, Peacock et al. 1971). Successful tunneling by virgin females into the inner bark results in a greatly accelerated rate of attraction of beetles to the breeding site.

Studies initiated in 1969 and completed in 1970 showed that this increased attraction is in response to a pheromone produced by tunneling virgin females (Peacock et al. 1971). When beetles arrive at the source of attraction, females initiate additional galleries while males scurry over the bark locating and inseminating tunneling females. Individual males typically mate several females (Bartels and Lanier 1974). Once mated, females terminate pheromone release (Elliott et al. 1975) and attraction to the breeding site declines.

The potency of the attraction of virgin females boring in elm logs suggested that the pheromones involved might be used to manipulate populations of the European elm bark beetle and thereby reduce incidence of *Ceratocystis ulmi* (Buis.) C. Moreau, causative agent of Dutch elm disease (DED) which is vectored by this important pest. In 1970 we initiated efforts to mass-produce, isolate, identify, and synthesize the chemical attractants.

Because it had yielded the pheromone or pheromone components for other scolytids (Silverstein 1970, Vité 1970, Borden and Stokkink 1971), frass (boring dust plus fecal pellets) produced by virgin female beetles boring in elm logs was

149

initially used as a source of attractant chemicals. We built special frass collectors to obtain several kilos of frass from 250,000 virgin females.

Using a laboratory olfactometer (Borden et al. 1968), we showed in early 1971 that frass and benzene or pentane extracts of frass would elicit an attractant-excitant response from walking male beetles (Peacock et al. 1973). Subsequent chemical fractionation of these extracts yielded several fractions that were active in the laboratory. However, in field tests in 1971 and 1972, neither frass nor any extracts or lab-active fractions attracted in-flight beetles. Consequently, other techniques for the collection of attractant volatiles were investigated.

The extraction of beetle and host-produced volatiles from the air with Porapak Q provided a simple and efficient means for collection and concentration of the attractant volatiles. Charcoal-filtered air was drawn over logs infested with virgin female beetles and then through a glass column containing the Porapak. The collection period began 72 hrs after infestation and continued for 168 hrs, which corresponded to the period when (1) virgin females are most attractive in the field (Peacock et al. 1971), and (2) frass from females is most active in laboratory olfactometers (Peacock et al. 1973). The volatiles extracted from the Porapak with hexane stimulated beetles in the lab and were attractive to in-flight beetles in the field (Peacock et al. 1975).

In 1972 we began a large-scale aeration program, which, by 1973, provided enough Porapak extract for the chemical characterization of the pheromone. In a typical 5 week period, aeration of 60,000 female beetles yielded an extract containing approximately 10^7 beetle hrs of attractant (amount of attractant produced by one beetle in 1 hr). Successive fractionation by GLC and bioassay yielded several fractions that were individually stimulating to beetles; greater activity was recorded when certain fractions were assayed in combination. Field studies during 1973 confirmed that a combination of three fractions was as attractive to in-flight beetles as the crude Porapak extract.

Purification of the active fractions and chemical analysis continued during October 1973 through April 1974. Finally, in May 1974, field experiments conducted in Charlotte, North Carolina, confirmed the potent attractiveness of a combination of three pure compounds: 4-methyl-3-heptanol (I), 2,4-dimethyl-5--ethyl-6,8-dioxabicyclo [3.2.1] octane (II), and (-) α-cubebene (III) (Pearce et al. 1975). I and II are beetle-produced pheromone components, while III is a host-produced component. The Charlotte field test also showed that an impure

I

II

III

mixture ("Multilure") containing 99% pure I, crude synthetic II (90%), and cubeb oil (containing 10% III) was as attractive as the mixture of pure I, II, and III. In the following pages we describe 1974 and 1975 field tests to determine if mass trapping of *S. multistriatus* on Multilure-baited traps can reduce the incidence of beetle-vectored DED.

IDENTIFICATION AND SYNTHESIS OF THE PHEROMONE COMPONENTS

(-)-4-Methyl-3-heptanol

Compound I was identified as (-)-4-methyl-3-heptanol by comparison of its MS, IR, and NMR spectra (Fig. 1) with those of a synthetic sample prepared by sodium borohydride reduction of 4-methyl-3-heptanone. With its two chiral centers, the synthetic compound exists as two diastereomers, separable by gas chromatography. The peak of the isolated compound was coincident with that of the diastereomer of shorter retention time on Carbowax 20M. The isolated compound was shown to be a single enantiomer by means of the Mosher derivative and a chiral shift reagent (Plummer et al. 1976). The absolute configuration was not determined. The specific rotation was $[\alpha]_D^{25} - 15°$, c = 6 mg/ml hexane.

Multistriatin

The bicyclic ketal structure of Compound II was assigned on the basis of its spectral data (Fig. 2), its hydrogenolysis products (Pearce et al. 1975), and on the basis of previous experience with analogous compounds isolated from other scolytid beetles (Silverstein 1970). Hydrogenolysis at 260°C with 3% palladium on Chromasorb B (Beroza and Acree 1964) gave the following hydrocarbon products (ratio):

(2.3)   (3.3)   (1.0)

A nonsterospecific synthesis of multistriatin (Pearce et al. 1975, 1976) gave four isomers on GLC fractionation in the following proportions: $\alpha,\beta,\gamma,\delta$; 34:1:7:58. The α-isomer corresponded to the biologically active compound; the β-isomer was also found in the extract from Porapak Q, but it was virtually inactive. (In the preliminary report by Pearce et al. (1975), the multistriatin isomer referred to as β in the synthesis scheme is now referred to as δ. The confusion resulted from the belated finding that the naturally occurring β-compound had isomerized to the δ-compound on standing in $CDCl_3$ in the NMR tube.)

multistriatin
$\alpha:\beta:\gamma:\delta = 34:1:7:58$

The relative stereochemistry of the four multistriatin isomers was described by Gore et al. (1975) as follows:

These assignments are based on chemical and spectrometric data. The following stereospecific synthetic approach provided direct chemical evidence for the stereochemistry at C-2:

Nmr Spectrum

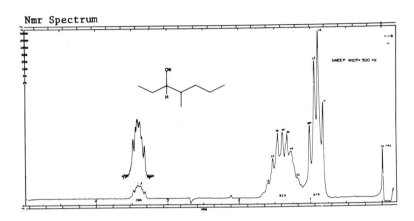

Infrared Spectrum

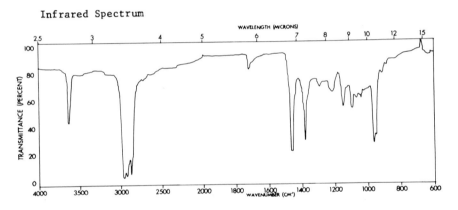

Mass Spectrum

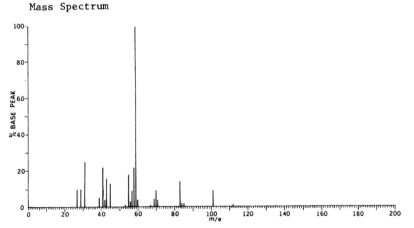

FIGURE 1. *Isolated 4-methyl-3-heptanol: NMR, IR, and Mass spectra.*

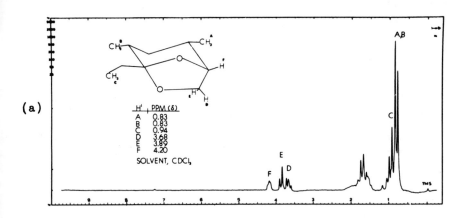

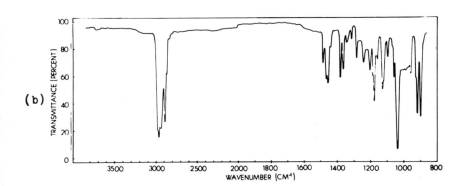

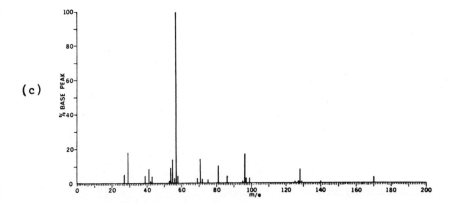

FIGURE 2. *Isolated α-multistriatin: (a) NMR, (b) IR, and (c) Mass spectra.*

Thus the C-2 methyl groups in the α and γ isomers must be in the endo configuration while in the β and δ isomers, they are in the exo configuration. The failure to isolate the β-isomer from the reaction mixture is probably a result of the relative instability of the compound.

Acid catalyzed hydrolysis (1 mg isomer, 0.5 ml 1N H_3PO_4, 0.5 ml THP, reflux 48 hr) of the multistriatin isomers resulted in interconversion of the isomers with the same configuration at C-2; i.e., α ⇌ γ, β ⇌ δ. Epimerization occurs at C-4 via the dihydropyran intermediates.

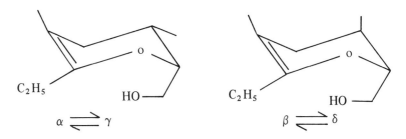

On reproducing the acid equilibrating conditions with D_3PO_4, D-H exchange occurred at C-4 and on the methylene group of the C_2H_5 substituent. This was determined by mass (Gore et al. 1976) and NMR (Gore et al. 1975) spectral data, which verified the assumption of enolization at C-4.

NMR data further confirmed the structural assignments. In all cases, the endo methyl group signals are 0.29-0.44 ppm upfield from the exo methyl group signals.

It now remains to establish the absolute configuration of the multistriatin isomers and to determine the enantiomeric composition of the isolated α-multistriatin, which had been shown to be optically active, $[\alpha]_D^{25} -47°$, c = 1.93 mg/ml hexane.

Use of (S) (+)-2-methyl-3-butenoic acid in the synthesis scheme shown above (Pearce et al. 1975, 1976) gave (2R) (−)-α-multistriatin. This, together with knowledge of the relative stereochemistry, established the absolute configuration of the isolated α-multistriatin as 1S, 2R, 4S, 5R, and the absolute configurations of the other isomers.

The (S) (+)-2-methyl-3-butenoic acid used was 70% optically pure (the (R) (−) acid of 60% purity was also used in a parallel experiment). Each isomer of multistriatin was purified by preparative GLC and shown to be optically active; it is a reasonable assumption that the optical purity of each isomer should be close to that of the starting butenoic acid (see below).

Determination of the optical purity (enantiomeric composition) of the isolated α-multistriatin was attempted via a proton NMR spectrum of the complex with a chiral shift reagent (Stewart et al. 1976). Although the spectrum showed no evidence of the other enantiomer, the small peak separation

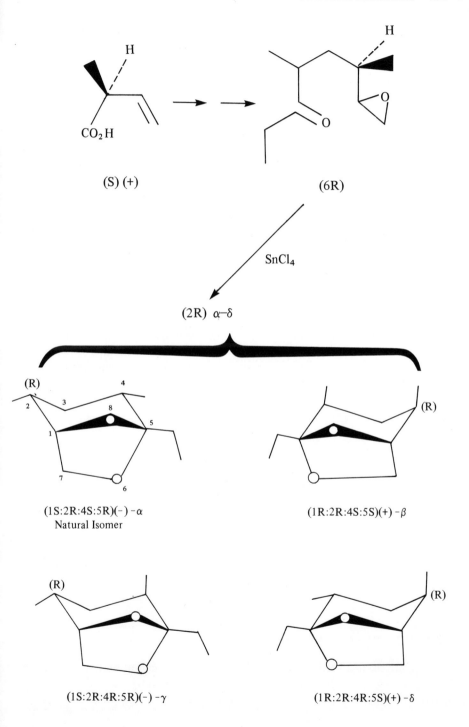

(S) (+)

(6R)

SnCl₄

(2R) α–δ

(1S:2R:4S:5R)(−) –α
Natural Isomer

(1R:2R:4S:5S)(+) –β

(1S:2R:4R:5R)(−) –γ

(1R:2R:4R:5S)(+) –δ

and broadening did not permit unequivocal interpretation. Corroboration was obtained by means of a ^{13}C NMR spectrum of the complex. This technique was not applicable to the small amount of isolated α-multistriatin, but it was applied to the enriched synthetic samples of (+) and (−)-α-multistriatin. By this procedure, the optical purity of synthesized (−)-α-multistriatin was 56% and that of the (+) enantiomer was 47%; thus there was a slight loss in optical purity in the course of the synthesis. Comparison of the specific rotation of the isolated (−) enantiomer (−47°) with the values calculated for the optically pure enantiomers (−47° and +44°) supports the assignment of full enantiomeric purity for the isolated (−)-α-multistriatin.

(−)-α-Cubebene

(−)-α-Cubebene was identified by matching the GLC retention times and the MS, IR, and NMR spectra of the isolated compound (Fig. 3) against those properties of an authentic sample (graciously supplied by Dr. Y. Hirosa, Institute of Food Chemistry, Dojimanaka, Kita-Ku, Osaka, Japan). The structure and absolute stereochemistry had been rigorously determined (see references in Pearce et al. 1975). The specific rotation ($[\alpha]_D^{25}$ −23°, c = 2.0 mg/ml hexane) was in accord with the recorded literature value ($[\alpha]_D^{30}$ −20.0°). Sufficient quantities for field tests were obtained by distillation of cubeb oil (Fritzsche, Dodge, and Olcott, Inc., N. Y.) through a 40-plate spinning band column. The stereochemistry, as defined by previous workers (see above), is represented by the structure:

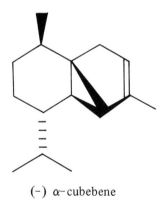

(−) α−cubebene

ATTRACTIVENESS OF THE ISOMERS OF THE BEETLE-PRODUCED PHEROMONE COMPONENTS

Synthesized 4-methyl-3 heptanol (I) consists of a pair of diastereomers, each with two enantiomers. Initial field tests in combination with II and III indicated that the synthetic heptanol was less attractive than an equivalent amount of natural I. A 4X increase in amount of synthetic heptanol resulted in attractiveness equal to that of the mixture containing natural I. These data suggest that, of the four enantiomers in synthetic heptanol, only the naturally occurring (−)-enantiomer is active.

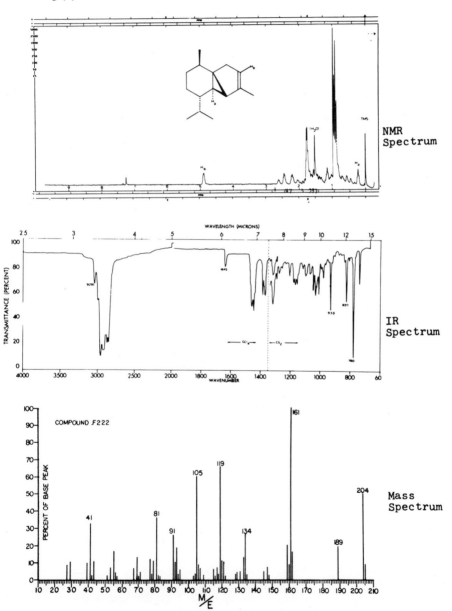

FIGURE 3. *Isolated α-cubebene: NMR, IR, and Mass spectra.*

Multistriatin occurs as four diastereomers, each consisting of two enantiomers. Pearce et al. (1975) found α and β multistriatin in extracts from aeration of beetle-infested logs, but only the α isomer was clearly attractive in the laboratory. Our subsequent bioassays of synthetically produced pure α, β, γ, and δ isomers showed that only the α form of II increased the attractiveness of a mixture of I + III (Table 1). The β, γ, and δ isomers did not reduce the activity of the mixture of I + IIα + III.

The individual enantiomers of a α-multistriatin were not available for comparison. However, the apparent equality of the attractiveness of the synthetic mixture of enantiomers with an equal amount of natural (−) enantiomer suggests that the (+) enantiomer might also be attractive (Table 1).

1974 EVALUATION OF "MULTILURE" IN DETROIT, MICHIGAN

In mid-May 1974, approximately 420 Multilure-baited traps were placed on the bole of healthy American elms (*Ulmus americana* L.) in each of two experimental plots in northeastern Detroit, Michigan. Each plot was 1,000 m on

TABLE 1. *Indices of attraction[a] of* Scolytus multistriatus *to the isomers of multistriatin (I) in combination with I and III*[b]

	Lab Bioassay A[c,d]	Lab Bioassay B	Field Bioassay
I + II	24	17	−
I + III + IIβ	24	24	4
I + III + IIIγ	16	12	2
I + II + IIδ	24	7	6
I + II + IIα	114	107	100
I + III + IIα (N)[e]	100	100	−
I + III + IIα	103	122	−
IIβ			
IIγ			
IIδ			

[a]Index of attraction = No. responding to test/No. responding to standard X 100. Standard is index 100.

[b]Dosages = 50 beetle-hour equivalents (bh) for lab bioassay A, 10 bh for lab bioassay B, and 1500 bh for the field bioassay.

[c]Lab bioassay A, conducted by Peacock in Delaware, Ohio utilized the attractant-arrestant walkway of olfactometer described by Peacock et al. (1973). Lab bioassay B employed a forced air-attractant response. Field test used blower olfactometers.

[d]Lab bioassays measured the number of beetles/25 tested which responded positively in 3 individual trials of each treatment. Field tests, which deployed 4 treatments simultaneously in 5 replicated trials, caught an aggregate of 5,371 beetles.

[e]II$_\alpha$ (N) is natural; all other isomers of II are synthetic.

a side and contained approximately 1,500 healthy elms with an annual DED rate of 5-10%. The traps were pieces of hardware cloth (27.5 x 27.5 cm) coated with Stikem Special® and suspended from the tree bole by wire brackets 3 m above the ground; the Multilure was dispensed from 3 ml polyethylene vials attached in the center of the traps. A small number of unbaited traps or traps baited with females on logs or crude Porapak extract were also placed in each plot for comparison with Multilure.

The results were encouraging. Well over a million beetles were captured in the two plots—roughly 750,000–1,000,000 in one plot (A), 500,000–750,000 in the other (B). Without question, the Multilure-hardware cloth trapping system could annihilate large numbers of in-flight beetles. Moreover, attraction of beetles to Multilure compared favorably with female beetles boring in logs and with the crude attractant extracts.

Although the results of the 1974 tests represented significant progress toward the ultimate goal of reducing beetle-vectored cases of DED through pheromone trapping, it is clear that the destruction of over a million beetles in the trapping areas had little, if any, significant impact on DED (Cuthbert and Peacock unpublished data). Estimates of the beetle population made in December 1974, indicated that approximately 5 million beetles emerged from brood trees within plot A. Thus, the 750,000–1,000,000 beetles trapped represented about 20% of the population emerging within the plot. Studies on trapping technology conducted during 1974 and 1975 indicated that considerable gains could be made by modifying the Detroit system. For example, it was found that the baits used were maximally attractive for only two of the six weeks they were exposed and that different designs of traps were up to seven times more effective than the hardware cloth squares.

EXPERIMENTS TO IMPROVE TRAPPING SYSTEM

Concurrent with mass-trapping studies, a number of smaller-scale experiments designed to optimize the trapping system were conducted in 1974 and 1975 in Detroit and in Syracuse, New York. Aspects such as trap design, size, placement and height were evaluated for their effects on beetle attraction and capture. Other studies evaluated the relative practicality and effectiveness of several commercially-prepared slow-release Multilure baits, the effect of varying ratios of the pheromone components, and the duration of attractiveness of Multilure baits. Also included in the experimentation was a study to determine the efficacy of using insecticide-treated surfaces to replace Stikem-coated traps.

Trap Size

Traps of varying sizes were compared to determine the relationship between trap size and beetle catch. In 1974, hardware cloth squares of 14, 19.5, 27.5 and 38 cm on a side were compared in Detroit while 30.4 and 91.2 cm traps were tested in Syracuse. In Detroit, traps were suspended from brackets affixed at the 3 m level on healthy elms; in Syracuse, traps were hung at 3 m from ropes stretched between poplar (*Populus* sp.) trees. In both areas, attractant baits used were polyethylene vials containing 10^6 beetle-hour-equivalents of Multilure.

The number of beetles trapped increased directly with trap surface area. Densities of beetles on traps of different sizes were virtually identical within trapping areas. For example, the 30.7 and 91.4 cm screens in Syracuse caught 0.091 and 0.089 beetles/sq. cm, respectively.

In 1975, white paper sticky traps affixed like posters to utility poles were tested in Syracuse. Four of our "standard" 45.7 x 66 cm posters were alternated with four "giant" traps 178 cm tall, extending around the circumference of the poles. Standard traps were ca. 3 m above the ground and baited at one of the upper corners with a Multilure-in-Hercon® (see "Studies on controlled release pheromone dispensers") bait. The lower margin of the giant traps was 2.5 m above the ground and the bait was affixed at the trap midpoint.

An aggregate of 125,886 beetles was caught in this experiment, 38,336 or 30% on the four standard traps and 87,550 or 70% on the giant traps.

The mean density of beetles on standard traps was 3.17 beetles/sq. cm while that on giant traps was 1.48. There was no apparent concentration of beetles around the bait on standard traps, but on the giant traps, beetles were modally distributed around the bait in the trap center.

Unlike the tests with hardware cloth squares, increasing size of poster traps increases effectiveness in trapping beetles responding to pheromone baits, but not in numbers directly proportional to the increase in surface area. Our data suggest that a trap covering the circumference of a utility pole for a vertical distance of at least 90 cm would have a good surface area: number-of-beetles-trapped relationship.

Trap Visibility

Tests of hardware cloth traps of different sizes included 91.2 cm square traps of which the edge third or center third was covered with a plywood panel. These traps averaged twice the total catch of the plain screen traps, and beetles were concentrated on the plywood portions. It seemed that beetles used the wooden panels as a landing target, as opposed to being intercepted in flight by the less visible screen.

Further tests using an array of black, white or striped 30.4 cm square panels confirmed the assumption that beetles orient toward, and land on, conspicuous objects in the vicinity of the pheromone source. Hanging opaque panels were four times as effective as screens.

On bright days, in-flight beetles exhibited a preference for hanging black rather than white traps, and for the black sections of black and white striped traps (Lanier unpublished data). In Detroit, 20 white poster traps (25.5 x 55 cm) nailed to the boles of healthy elms caught three times as many beetles as the same number of black traps (Peacock unpublished data). We concluded that it was the contrast, and not the shade (black or white per se), which influenced beetle catches. Against the sky, black was most conspicuous and therefore favored; against the dark bole of an elm, white traps were by far the most obvious. Thus, poster traps used in 1975 mass trapping experiments were white.

Further increasing contrast by adding 20 cm diameter black "bulls-eyes" in the center of 45.7 x 66 cm white poster traps did not result in greater catches than those on plain white traps, but did change the distribution of beetles caught. Density of beetles on the bulls-eyes was 1.405 ± 0.542 (n = 12) times that for the trap as a whole, while density of beetles in a similar area on plain traps was 0.791 ± 0.233 times the density on the trap as a whole. On plain traps, beetles are usually visibly concentrated near the edges of the traps where the contrast is most marked.

Trap Design

Peacock and Cuthbert (unpublished data) compared traps commonly used for pheromone trapping of Lepidoptera with our standard (27.5 x 27.5 cm) hanging hardware cloth trap. Designs included Dixie® cups (coated with Stikem on the inside only, or on both sides), Sectar-I® traps (coated with Stikem on the inside only, or on both sides), and different sizes and shapes of flat cardboard coated on one side with Stikem. Some of these flat cardboard traps were nailed to the bole of elms, others were hung from wire hangers nailed to the bole of the trees. Lanier (unpublished data) compared traps made from 30.4 cm squares of hardware cloth, black and white squares of plywood, black cones 20 and 40 cm long made from plastic-coated cardboard and white 45.7 x 66 cm cardboard affixed like posters to utility poles.

Dixie cups and Sectar traps (whether Stikem-coated inside only, or on both sides) were poor beetle traps. Peacock and Cuthbert (unpublished data) found that hanging or poster type cardboard traps were about equally as effective as screens of the same size. Lanier observed three times larger catches on plywood panels than on screens. This apparent discrepancy may have resulted from the escape of beetles from the cardboard panels following absorption of the Stikem into the cardboard. The small cone was slightly more effective than the screen while the large cone was 6.5 times as effective as the screen. It is believed that convection currents generated by heating of the air inside the cone was a factor in this increased effectiveness. Poster traps, such as those used in 1975 mass trapping, were 3.6 times as effective as the screens used in Detroit the previous year.

Trap Height

The effect of trap height on beetle catch at pheromone baited traps was determined using Multilure-baited hardware cloth traps placed at different levels (3-4 m, 6-8 m, and 10-14 m) on diseased and healthy elms. Beetle catches at the three different heights were determined in both the first and second beetle flight periods in Detroit. On healthy elms, traps at the 3 m level caught 25–60 times as many beetles as traps at the other levels. The situation in diseased elms is remarkably different; traps at the lower level caught more beetles, but the traps at the upper two levels did far better than the traps at similar levels in healthy elms (Cuthbert and Peacock 1975).

Studies on Controlled Release Pheromone Dispensers

Two dispensers, polyethylene vials and macrocapsules (Controlled Release Chemical Corporation, Santa Fe, New Mexico) were evaluated in Detroit during July and August, 1974. Two additional dispensers, Hercon® laminated plastic dispensers (Herculite Protective Fabrics Corp., New York, New York) and Conrel® hollow fiber dispensers (FRL Corp., Dedham, Mass.) were evaluated in Australia in December. The polyethylene vials baited with 10^6 beetle-hour equivalents attracted beetles at significant levels for only 2–3 wks; the other three dispensers gave satisfactory results for 2 mo or longer. Because they were relatively easier to use, available commerically in quantity, and more attractive for a longer period than either the polyethylene vials or macrocapsules, the Hercon and Conrel dispensers were considered to be more suitable for mass-trapping studies involving large numbers of pheromone-baited traps.

During 1975 five different dispensers of three basic types were evaluated. These included improved models of the Conrel and macrocapsule dispensers and three different Hercon laminated plastic dispensers. Twenty of each of these five types were randomly distributed on 100 traps in Detroit. In addition, 20 check traps, dispersed throughout the plot, were baited biweekly with a Conrel dispenser to maintain a constant high level of attractiveness throughout the season. The baits on the 100 test traps were not changed during the experiment while the Stikem-coated papers on all 120 traps were replaced biweekly.

All of the dispensers performed adequately for 2 mo; some remained highly attractive for 120 days and longer (Peacock and Cuthbert unpublished data). However, those dispensers that were attractive for the longest periods (hollow fibers and macrocapsules), were the most difficult to handle, while the easier to use Hercon baits were the least effective for long-term attraction of beetles.

At Syracuse, the duration of attractiveness to Hercon baits was also examined during 1975 by sequential replacement of baits on different traps within replicated (4 times) trap lines. This experiment demonstrated that baits up to 80 days old were as attractive as fresh baits, even though lab analysis showed the elution rates of pheromone do decrease in an inverse logarithmic manner. The discrepancy between elution and relative attractiveness indicates that baits were initially releasing pheromone at a rate higher than that which results in maximum catches.

Dose-mixture Experiments

The attractiveness of various doses and mixtures of the three components of Multilure, as measured by the beetle catch on Stikem-coated traps, was evaluated in Detroit during 1975. Traps were placed 3 m high on the bole of healthy elms that were about 35 m apart. The various combinations of components (the heptanol, multistriatin, and cubebene) in Conrel dispensers were assigned at random to traps. After 2 wks field exposure, the traps were removed, the beetles were counted and samples of beetles from all traps were sexed.

The results indicate that beetles can detect small (less than 2-fold) changes in the ratio of components. The dose of multistriatin (M) released, particularly in relation to the dose of the heptanol (H), appears to be most important in determining trap catches. The release rate of M should not exceed the release rate of H; if the release of M exceeds the release of H, or if it exceeds about 300 μg/day, catches are strongly depressed. On the other hand, increased dose of H appears to increase catches in direct proportion to dose, at least up to about 400 μg/day. Similarly, catches are directly dependent on the dose of cubebene, although a doubling of the dose only increased catches about 25 to 50% (Cuthbert unpublished data).

Evaluation of Insecticide—Pheromone Traps

Studies were initiated in 1975 to determine the effectiveness of insecticide treated surfaces as a possible replacement for Stikem-coated traps. The contact toxicity of a number of insecticides was determined by exposing walking beetles for various lengths of time to insecticide-treated panels after periods of field weathering of the panels. Preliminary results indicate that methoxychlor is the best of the candidates tested because: (1) field exposure tests suggest it has the longest residual effectiveness (16 wks), and (2) contact with the insecticide treated panels for only 5 sec results in beetle mortality exceeding 90% within 24 hr after exposure. Concurrent field studies showed that at least 58% of the beetles attracted to a pheromone bait remain in the vicinity of the bait for 5 sec or longer (Barger unpublished data).

The results of these studies suggest that methoxychlor-treated surfaces could replace Stikem-coated surfaces as lethal traps for bark beetles attracted to pheromone baits. A larger-scale field study to test the hypothesis is planned for 1976.

Trap Exposure and Beetle Catches

Data from trap lines in various trap design tests conducted at Syracuse during 1975 were analyzed to determine the relationship between the degree of exposure (openness) of the traps and beetle catches. These numerical results are integrated with observations from trap-out experiments in Hamilton, Clinton and Hinerwadel's Grove, New York.

In all of our experiments, traps which were completely unobscured caught the most beetles. For example, in Hamilton the two most effective traps were on utility poles between the street and a parking lot. At Hinerwadel's, traps on utility poles and affixed to a cyclone fence caught three times the average catch per trap. Traps on trees with high crowns were clearly more effective than traps shaded by foliage.

The quantified data show that of traps on utility poles, those with 100% exposure caught two times the number of beetles caught on traps with >50<100% exposure and three times the numbers taken on traps <50% exposed.

It is clear that trap placement is a major consideration in a trap-out program. Visually obscured traps may have the detrimental effect of attracting beetles they do not catch.

EXPERIMENTS ON DISPERSAL AND RECAPTURE OF *SCOLYTUS MULTISTRIATUS* ON MULTILURE-BAITED TRAPS

During 1975 an experiment designed to increase our knowledge of flight range, dispersal, and recapture of the European elm bark beetle was conducted in a large (1200 m by 1600 m) limestone quarry near Jamesville, New York. Specific objectives were as follows:

    1. Study the flight and response of *S. multistriatus* including:
        a) Relationship of trap catches to proximity of beetle source.
        b) Direction of flight with respect to wind.
        c) Launching of flight from the brood source.
    2. Determine the trapping efficiency of pheromone-baited traps.

Beetle source was logs from naturally infested elms hauled into the limestone quarry on May 2. The logs had been incubated in a glasshouse so that beetles would be ready to emerge prior to the natural population. The quarry itself contains scattered juvenile elms in old quarried areas. A few of these had died from DED, but we were not able to find any trees currently infested by beetles within the test periphery. Elms and elm bark beetles were present outside the test area and within 400 m of some of the traps in the outside ring.

Traps consisted of 45.5 x 66 cm cardboard fashioned into a cylinder and painted so that two 11.4 cm black stripes alternated with unpainted white cardboard. These cylinders were supported about 1.5 m above ground by nailing them to one leg of a tripod. Traps were baited on May 10 with Multilure-in-Hercon dispensers. The release rate approximated that of 2000 virgin females.

Traps were arranged in five concentric circles surrounding the brood logs as follows:

Circle	No. Traps	Distance (m) from source	Arc distance (m) apart
A	3	20	20
B	3	100	200
C	6	200	200
D	12	400	200
E	18	600	200

Beetles were removed from all traps and counted on May 19, May 27–28 and on June 4. Brood logs were removed after the count was completed on May 28. Traps were dismantled on June 4. Emergence of wild beetles, as detected by monitoring traps in the Jamesville area and in Syracuse, began on May 22.

The number of beetles emerging from the brood logs during the test period was estimated by counting the emergence holes on a circumferential section of each log equal to 10% of the total length of the log. These sections were covered with thick latex paint at the time the traps were baited (May 10) so that holes made by beetles emerging during the test period could be differentiated from those of beetles emerging prior to the test. Exact limits of the sample area were delineated by rubber bands stretched around the logs.

Recovering of Beetles from the Brood Source

The aggregate catch for the experiment was approximately 32,000 beetles. Of these, 1,286 were recovered on May 19 when only beetles from our brood source were in flight. The catch of May 27–28, consisting of a mixture of quarry and wild beetles, totaled 5,057. The 25,894 beetles counted on June 4 are considered to be wild beetles drawn into the quarry by our pheromone baits (Table 2). This impressive influx of wild beetles shows that immigration will be a major consideration in any trap-out program.

The total recovery of quarry beetles was estimated to be 2,989 or 10.3% of the estimated total emergence of 29,000. This figure is considered to be a minimum estimate of potentially attacking beetles because it does not correct for emergence holes made by beetle-sized parasites and post emergence mortality. Ground spiders that congregated on our log pile presumably preyed on newly emerged beetles; swallows and predaceous flies in the area may have killed significant numbers of in-flight beetles.

Distribution of Beetles on the Traps

With the exception of one trap which was inadvertently left unbaited until May 19, beetles were found on every trap at each count. Differences in catch between circles were pronounced as were differences in catches on individual traps within circles.

TABLE 2. *Summary of* Scolytus multistriatus *captured in the quarry experiment*

Trap Circle	Distance from Center	Number of Traps	May 19*		May 27–28		June 4	
			Total	Beetles/ Trap	Total	Beetles/ Trap	Total	Beetles/ Trap
A	20 m	3	495	165.0	788	262.7	1,061	353.7
B	100 m	3	30	10.0	88	29.3	349	116.3
C	200 m	6	95	15.8	278	46.3	2,358	393.0
D	400 m	12	230	19.2	1,043	86.9	5,461	455.1
E	600 m	18	436	24.22	2,860	158.9	16,665	925.8
		42	1,286	30.6	5,057	120.4	25,894	608.2

*Sources of beetles were as follows: May 19–quarry; May 27–28– mixture of quarry and wild; June 4–wild.

Wild beetles were concentrated on traps on the northwestern periphery. This distribution coincides with a concentration of elms on the hill sloping toward Limestone Creek, west of the quarry. Once well inside the quarry, wild beetles apparently distributed themselves in a manner similar to quarry beetles.

The largest proportions of quarry beetles were caught on the innermost (A, 20 m) and outer (D, 400 m; E, 600 m) circles. Similar behavior was observed in Colorado in 1974 by Dr. Wayne Brewer (pers. commun.). These results appear to be related to the refractory period of *S. multistriatus* in laboratory bioassays; few newly emergent beetles respond to pheromone, but beetles conditioned by 12 hr of activity are highly responsive.

S. multistriatus probably undergoes a dispersal flight during which it is not responsive to odors. After sufficient exercise, the threshold for odor response decreases. Our results indicate that net dispersal distance of 400 m or more is usual. Previous estimates of 304 m considerably understate the flight capacity of *S. multistriatus*.

Influence of Wind Direction

Winds within the quarry were considerably more intense and more pervasive than in the surrounding countryside. Prevailing winds were from the west and northwest, although gusts came from various directions.

Upwind orientation is apparent by large catches on a trap immediately west of the brood logs. Traps in the upwind section of the D and E circles were also more effective than corresponding traps in downwind or quarter-wind sections. However, the overall effect of wind on beetle catches was not as great as would be anticipated if it is assumed that beetles usually locate an attractant source by flying upwind to it.

A likely explanation for the near equality of trap catches of quarry beetles is that beetles simply do not fly when it is windy. For several hours, we observed newly emerged beetles crawling over brood logs. Very few beetles attempted to launch themselves while wind perceptible to the observer (GNL) was blowing. During periodic quiet periods, beetles came out of bark fissures and sheltered logs to open areas from which they quickly launched. When air movement resumed, beetles promptly withdrew. Observations at the quarry and considerable experience trapping beetles in Syracuse and elsewhere confirm that beetles also respond to pheromone-baited traps only during quiet periods. Peak catches invariably occurred during the late afternoon of hot days and during still, overcast days.

ATTRACTION OF NON-TARGET INSECTS

In Germany, Multilure-baited traps caught, in addition to high numbers of *S. multistriatus*, low numbers of *Scolytus scolytus* Fabricius and *Scolytus laevis* (Chap.) (Vité et al. 1976).

During 1975 a study compared the numbers and species of non-target insects captured on pheromone-baited and unbaited traps. Comparisons were based on biweekly catches from May–October on 40 traps (10 baited on healthy elms, 10 unbaited on healthy elms, 10 baited on non-elms, and 10 unbaited on non-elms) at Washington, D.C., Detroit, Michigan, and Ft. Collins, Colorado. These studies are supplemented by observations at Syracuse and Hamilton.

Evaluation of the Detroit catches indicates that certain hymenopterous parasitoids of *S. multistriatus* are attracted by Multilure. Other non-target species appeared to be captured in equal numbers on baited and unbaited traps (Kennedy unpublished data). The analyses of comparative catches are incomplete for other localities but observations of traps on utility poles in Syracuse and Hamilton implicate the attractiveness of Multilure to the species listed below:

Enoclerus nigripes (Say) (Coleoptera: Cleridae)–predator of *Scolytus multistriatus* and other bark beetles.

Platysoma lecontei Marseal (Coleoptera: Histeridae)–general predator associated with trees colonized by bark beetles.

Xiphydria maculata Say (Hymenoptera: Siricidae)–wood borer in moribund elms.

Entedon leucogramma (Ratzeburg) (Hymenoptera: Eulophidae)–introduced parasitoid of *S. multistriatus*.

Cheiropachus colon (L.) (Hymenoptera: Pteromalidae)–introduced parasitoid of *S. multistriatus*.

Scolytus sulcatus LeConte (Coleoptera: Scolytidae)–bark beetle which feeds on apple, black cherry and elm.

SURVEY AND DETECTION

Pheromone-baited sticky traps have been used successfully to delineate the distribution of *S. multistriatus*. During 1974 and 1975 beetles were detected for the first time in several counties in California and Oregon. Catches at traps in Cass County, North Dakota represented a new state record, as did catches at several locations in Arizona. Trap catches have indicated that beetles are present in New Brunswick, Canada. Conversely, lack of *S. multistriatus* on traps in Clinton, New York and Orono, Maine indicated that local DED control programs need not be concerned with this vector. The pheromone trapping system also has been used successfully for beetle detection and survey in Australia, the Netherlands and Germany.

1975 MASS TRAPPING STUDIES

The mass trapping of elm bark beetles on Multilure-baited traps as a strategy for reducing Dutch elm disease was evaluated during 1975 in several localities encompassing a variety of situations and trapping strategies (Table 3). Major efforts were invested at Detroit, Ft. Collins, and Hamilton. Hinerwadel's Grove,

TABLE 3. *Localities of mass-trapping* Scolytus multistriatus *during 1975*

Locality	Area (hectares)	Trap deployment	Total Numbers of: Elms[a]	Traps	Beetles killed	Incidence of DED (%)[b] 1974	1975
Detroit, Michigan	520	Grid	2,800	1,100	3,800,000	4.3	7.4
Ft. Collins, Colorado	1,350	Grid	3,545	2,200	1,440,000	3.5	2.8
Hamilton, New York	260	Grid	660[c]	330	395,700	ca. 25	Not determined
Evanston, Illinois	2,200	Diffuse grid	18,000	88	542,500	4.1	1.8
Washington, D.C.	515	Diffuse grid	3,000	50	190,000	2.0	2.5
Syracuse, New York	400	Groups	168	79	815,579	22.2	6.7
Hamilton College, New York	25	Fence	109	30	133,750	39.7	41.5
Hinerwadel's Grove, No. Syracuse	4	Fence	26	11	96,125	7.1	0
University of Delaware, Newark	70	Fence	180	21	36,971	4.4	0

[a]American and European elms only; the DED resistant Asian elms are not included in this figure.

[b]Rate of DED is expressed as the percent of the healthy trees newly infested during the year, based upon symptoms visible during the late summer. Infections judged to be via root grade are excluded.

[c]An approximately equal number of elms occurred in wooded areas and on farm land at the periphery of the populated area.

and the campuses of University of Delaware and Hamiton College were chosen to explore the use of pheromone traps to prevent immigration of fungus-carrying beetles. Trapping in Evanston, Illinois and Washington, D.C. was designed for survey, while the Syracuse results are byproducts of tests for improvement of trap efficiency.

The traps used in all areas (except some of the different designs evaluated in Syracuse) were 45 x 66 cm sheets of white double poly-coated paper, covered on one side with Stikem Special and nailed or stapled to the bole of street trees or utility poles at a height of approximately 3 m. Baits consisting of Multilure dispensed from Hercon laminated plastic and Conrel hollow fiber were attached to the center of each trap. These devices were chosen because of their performance in 1974 dispenser tests. Each type was designed to release 100 μg of the heptanol, 100 μg multistriatin, and 400 μg cubebene per day for 120–180 days. At Detroit and Ft. Collins, equal numbers of each type were used; elsewhere, the Hercon dispenser was used exclusively.

Traps were deployed about 30–50 m apart in a grid pattern in Detroit, Ft. Collins and Hamilton. In tests at Hinerwadel's, University of Delaware and Hamilton College, traps were picketed around the periphery of the elms to be protected. In Syracuse, traps were placed in scattered clusters, while at Washington, D.C. and Evanston, traps were spaced at 400–800 m intervals.

Table 3 summarizes for each area the data on acreage, number of traps used, total beetles caught, and incidence of DED. For a more complete evaluation, the results are discussed by areas.

Detroit

The Detroit study provided an evaluation of mass trapping in an area with an exceedingly high beetle population, both within the trapping plot and in the surrounding area.

An estimated 3.8 million beetles were captured at the 1,100 traps during the period May 15–October 15, 1975; 1.5 million were trapped during the first flight period (May 15–July 15); 2.3 million during the second period. Significantly more beetles were captured at traps around the periphery (the outside 150 m of the plot) than in the interior of the study area. This result indicates immigration of beetles from outside the test area—a situation that could lead to increased twig-crotch-feeding and higher DED levels inside the trapping area if all of the incoming beetles are not captured. A preliminary count of diseased trees in the plot showed new beetle-vectored incidence of DED (7.3%) was higher than that in nearby check plots (4.3%) and that the level of disease within the test plot increased during 1975 (Table 3). We attribute this increase to the influx of beetles from areas outside the plot.

Ft. Collins

Fort Collins was chosen as a study site because of its relatively low beetle population, and because the beetle population outside of the city was considered insignificant. The entire city was gridded with 2,200 traps which caught an aggregate of 1,490,000 beetles—190,000 during the first flight period and 1,300,000 during the second flight period.

DED rates within the city dropped from 3.5% in 1974 to 2.8% in 1975. Incidence of DED in the nearby town of Loveland was 4.1% in 1974 and 3.8% in 1975.

Hamilton

It was apparent during the early stage of this test that Hamilton was a poor choice for testing mass trapping of the European elm bark beetle to control DED. The other known beetle vector of the disease, the native elm bark beetle *Hylurgopinus rufipes* (Eichhoff), was dominant in this area. Except for the Colgate University Campus, sanitation had been neglected since 1974, and unregulated wooded areas at the periphery of the village were a source of abundant beetles (mostly native).

An aggregate of 396,000 European elm bark beetles was taken on 330 traps within the village and the Colgate Campus. DED rates have not been assessed. However, the beetle catch is thought to be meaningless in view of the predominance of the native elm bark beetle. This species was taken on some traps, but it was not clear if it was attracted by Multilure.

Syracuse

DED had swept through Syracuse, causing the virtual extinction of elms in most parts of the city by 1971. Remnant elms in the test area were scattered street and yard trees.

Traps arranged in scattered lines for our trap design experiments caught an aggregate of 816,000 beetles. This was 63% of the estimated 1.3 million beetles from the eight brood trees within the area; immigration is thought to be virtually nil.

Seven of the 105 elms healthy in June showed new beetle-vectored DED infections (an eighth tree was infected by root graft). The infection rate (6.7%) was considerably lower than that experienced in 1974 (22.2%) (Table 3). However, we do not conclude that this decrease was a result of mass trapping. Other variables such as improved sanitation and natural ebbing of the epidemic may have been factors in the decline.

Hamilton College, University of Delaware and Hinerwadel's Grove

In each of these areas, traps were picketed at 30–100 m intervals around the area to be protected.

At the onset of the experiment, success at Hamilton College was viewed as unlikely, owing to the intense DED epidemic in the surrounding area and the abundance of *H. rufipes*. It is obvious from the disease rates (41.5% in 1975 vs. 39.7% in 1974) that our expectations were realized.

Elms within the grounds of the University of Delaware and Hinerwadel's Grove are isolated groves that were believed to be completely free of elm bark beetle broods. Beetles captured on traps surrounding these areas originated in unknown brood sources 750 m or further from the traps. In contrast to norms established from 1961–1974, no new infections were identified in either area.

We view this lack of new incidence of DED as extremely encouraging but not necessarily a result of mass-trapping elm bark beetles. The sample size is small and the excellent elm care practiced in both areas could be responsible for the observed lack of DED.

Evanston and Washington

Excellent sanitation and prophylactic methoxychlor sprays have kept DED at low levels in the city of Evanston and the Capitol Grounds in Washington, D.C. The widely-spaced (400–800 m) pheromone-baited traps were deployed in these areas for the survey of beetle population only. However, the declines in DED rate within these areas (Table 3) warrant consideration of the possible contribution of beetle trapping.

CONCLUSIONS

The attractant pheromone of the European elm bark beetle consists of three components, two of which are produced by the virgin female beetle, and one by the host tree. A crude mixture of the synthesized attractive components (Multilure) is potent enough to be effective in the manipulation of populations of the European elm bark beetle. Our methods of utilizing the pheromone have to date been relatively primitive.

The effective range of pheromone baits appears to be considerably greater than had been anticipated at the onset of mass trapping experiments. Traps deployed in 40–50 m grids in Detroit, Ft. Collins and Hamilton were too densely spaced and/or too potent. Many of the beetles stimulated were probably unable to orient to the traps due to the pervasiveness of pheromone in the area.

In Detroit, more beetles were attracted into the trapping area than were caught. The same grid system did not have a negative effect in Ft. Collins where there was no appreciable source of immigrating beetles. Decreasing trap density and optimizing the size and the positioning of traps will result in a considerable favorable change in the ratio of number of beetles stimulated/number of beetles killed.

Mass trapping seems unlikely to have an appreciable effect in extreme epidemic situations such as that experienced at Hamilton, New York. The maximum effectiveness of this technique will probably be realized in areas where both the numbers of brood trees and competing pheromone sources are low. Hence, mass trapping may be a synergistic component of a DED program including sanitation and other techniques.

The reduction in the rate of DED in Ft. Collins, Syracuse, University of Delaware, Evanston and Hinerwadel's is currently viewed as coincident with, but not necessarily a result of, mass trapping. Continued tests during 1976 should provide additional information on the effectiveness of pheromone trapping *S. multistriatus* to control DED.

ACKNOWLEDGMENT

The elm bark beetle study was supported by the U. S. Forest Service, the Elm Research Institute, the Rockefeller Foundation, and the College of Environmental Science and Forestry. The other participants in the study were G. T. Pearce, W. E. Gore, R. A. Cuthbert, J. B. Simeone, and W. W. Jones. Mass trapping studies in the various areas were aided by the following on-site cooperators: Dale Bray, University of Delaware; John Laut and Wayne Brewer, Ft. Collins; Dennis W. Ceplecha, Evanston; James Sherald, Washington; Craig Grant, Detroit. We thank Mr. John P. Hansel, Executive Director of the Elm Research Institute, for his help and encouragement.

Chapter 13

Estimating Peak Concentrations of Pheromones in the Forest

Donald E. Aylor

Department of Ecology and Climatology
The Connecticut Agricultural Experiment Station
New Haven, Connecticut 06504

INTRODUCTION

Although knowledge of the average concentration, obtained by averaging at a point during some long time, of a substance dispersing in the atmosphere is sometimes sufficient, many phenomena depend more on peak concentrations lasting only briefly. For example, gaseous pollutants that harm vegetation only after hours at a low concentration will quickly damage it at a high concentration (Heck et al. 1966, Thomas 1961). Likewise, moths respond faster to pheromone the higher the concentration, e.g., the response per unit time of *Trichoplusia ni* (Hübner) (Lepidoptera: Noctuidae) males is markedly faster in greater pheromone concentration (Mayer 1973). This faster response has also been observed in gypsy moth *Lymantria dispar* L. (Granett, personal communication) and is illustrated in Fig. 1.

Most calculations of pheromone dispersion have employed time-average diffusion equations (Bossert and Wilson 1963, Wright 1958) that average fluctuations in pheromone concentration. So far, concentration fluctuations only have been related qualitatively to searching (e.g., Wright 1958, Farkas and Shorey 1972). Mayer's and Granett's results suggest that knowledge of the instantaneous or peak concentration would help predict the response of male moths to a pheromone outdoors.

Herein, I shall review the basis of the commonly used average diffusion equation and discuss the differences between this and relative diffusion appropriate for shorter times. This analysis will relate the turbulence in a forest

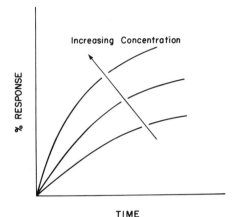

FIGURE 1. *The percent of male moths responding to a pheromone after a given time of exposure increases with the concentration in the air.*

to instantaneous or peak concentrations and to average concentrations of pheromone emitted from a single point source. Implications of this to short range flight to a female or trap will be discussed.

CHARACTERISTICS OF TURBULENCE

Turbulence is defined in terms of observable properties of the flow and is not a property of the fluid as is viscosity. Turbulent flows are random, dissipative, continuous, three-dimensional, nonlinear, occur at large Reynolds numbers, and are diffusive (Tennekes and Lumley 1972). Here we are most concerned with the diffusivity of turbulence which causes rapid mixing of mass, momentum and heat.

While molecular diffusion is characterized by random molecular movements with an average length of the molecular mean free path, turbulent diffusion in the atmosphere is characterized by random movements of masses of fluid through distances that are a billion times or more longer than the molecular mean free path. Thus, in most atmospheric flows, turbulence swamps molecular diffusion.

A fundamental feature of turbulence is that it consists of parcels of fluid or eddies of all sizes from a fraction of a centimeter to many meters, all undergoing simultaneous random movements. This intermingling of such a range of sizes gives atmospheric turbulence its evolutionary or explosive character (Richardson 1926, Csanady 1973), with the *rate* of diffusion of a cloud of material dispersing in the atmosphere actually increasing with time of travel. This explosive growth rate, standing in sharp contrast to the constant or declining rate of growth of the

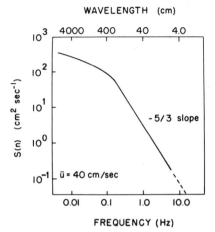

FIGURE 2. *A ficticious power spectrum for the longitudinal wind speed inside the forest. Here S(n) is the power spectral density at frequency n, and the −5/3 regime extends from eddy sizes of about 3 m down to 1 cm or less. In the example, $n^{5/3} S(n)$ is approximately equal to 3 throughout this regime.*

time-average outline of a continuous plume, is the signal characteristic of relative diffusion (Batchelor 1952, Csanady 1973) and is essential to analysis of instantaneous concentrations.

Another important feature of turbulence is the way that the energy of the flow is passed down to smaller and smaller eddies and ultimately dissipated by viscosity as heat. The distribution of turbulent energy within this continuous range of fluid parcel or eddy sizes in a given flow is usually determined by analyzing the time-series of wind passing a fixed point (see Chapter 6 in Tennekes and Lumley 1972) and obtaining the power spectrum (Fig. 2) of the turbulent energy. Over a sizable range of eddies this energy transfer process tends to adjust the flow toward isotropy and gives on the spectrum graph (Fig. 2) an extended region, called the inertial subrange, where the energy per unit frequency decays like the −5/3 power of frequency. For further details the reader is referred to text books on turbulence (e.g. Pasquill 1962, Tennekes and Lumley 1972).

Spectral analysis can help specify diffusion inside a forest. In particular, if an extended −5/3 region exists, then a theory (Batchelor 1952) for diffusion of a cloud of a substance relative to its center of mass can help estimate concentrations. Moreover, power spectra reveal the rate of eddy-energy transfer (Lumley and Panofsky 1964), which is related to the typical size of the small, dissipative eddies. The size of these smallest eddies gives an upper limit of cloud sizes for which molecular diffusion is important (Csanady 1973). Typically, in the atmosphere, this size is a centimeter or less.

AVERAGE CONCENTRATION

The equations generally used to describe the concentration $\overline{N}$ (g/cm^3) of pheromone downwind in the x direction, for the steady emission of pheromone at a rate Q (g/sec) (Bossert and Wilson 1963, Wright 1958, Sower et al. 1973, Farkas and Shorey 1974) have been of the time-average Gaussian form (Gifford 1968)

$$\overline{N}(x, y, z) = \frac{Q}{2\,\pi\,S_y\,S_z\,\overline{u}} \exp\left[-\left(\frac{y^2}{2\,S_y^2} + \frac{z^2}{2\,S_z^2}\right)\right]. \quad (1)$$

Here S_z and S_y are the standard deviations of cloud dimensions in the vertical z and cross-wind y directions and $\overline{u}$ (cm/sec) is the average horizontal wind speed. The S's are functions of x. Figure 3 illustrates the effect of averaging over time on the plume outline and concentration distribution within the plume. The familiar form of equation (1) (Sutton 1947) is readily obtained by letting

$$S_y = \tfrac{1}{2}\,C_y\,x^{(2-n)/2}$$
$$\quad (2)$$
$$S_z = \tfrac{1}{2}\,C_z\,x^{(2-n)/2}$$

Reference should be made to the original paper for specification of the constants C_y, C_z, and n. For atmospheric stability other than neutral, recourse is usually taken to experimental values of S (Gifford 1968).

Whatever representation for S is chosen, the concentrations predicted by eqn. (1) are averages over a suitably long time T. In other words, a sample is

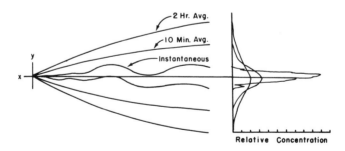

FIGURE 3. *The approximate outline (left) and cross-plume distribution of concentration (right) of a smoke plume observed instantaneously, as in a snapshot, or integrated over time, as in a time exposure lasting 10 min and 2 hr redrawn from Meteorology and Atomic Energy (Anon, 1968b). Increasing fluctuations in the wind during longer observations decrease the average concentration in a composite sample collected at a fixed point with time of averaging.*

taken continuously at a fixed point in space for a period T, and the concentration of this composite sample is $\overline{N}$. The question of how long to sample must be answered by experiment (Gifford 1960). As remarked in the introduction, moth behavior may be influenced by brief or peak concentrations of pheromone. To determine the disparity between the brief peak and the average concentration requires a further discussion of the stochastic nature of atmospheric flows.

FLUCTUATIONS IN CONCENTRATION

Turbulent dispersion depends on the random, but continuous, movements of fluid, which we recognize from a fixed vantage point as fluctations in speed and direction. The idea that a wide range of lengths or eddy sizes enter into turbulent dispersion was introduced earlier. A simple model showing how a cloud of pheromone is dispersed by eddies of various sizes is shown in Fig. 4. Eddies much larger than the puff of pheromone essentially transport the puff as a whole and cause it to meander, while eddies much smaller than the puff tend to readjust concentration gradients within the puff but disperse it little. Eddies about the size of the puff reduce the concentration most effectively. Only after

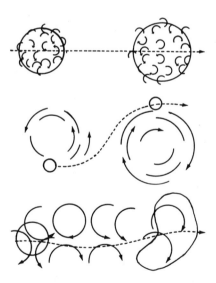

FIGURE 4. *Idealized dispersion redrawn from Meteorology and Atomic Energy (Anon. 1968b). In eddies smaller than the puff, the puff grows slowly and concentration decreases slowly (top). Eddies larger than the puff transport it intact and concentration is reduced little (middle). Finally, eddies about the size of the puff tear the puff apart and rapidly diminish concentration (bottom). In the atmosphere all eddy sizes act simultaneously.*

a sufficiently long travel time will the puff grow as large as the largest eddies and meandering cease. It is the large eddies that cause the familiar looping of chimney plumes observed during unstable atmospheric conditions, and large scale transport also causes the lateral meandering in the forest that will be discussed in the next section.

Meandering causes major disparities between peak and average concentrations. Figures 3 and 4 show that, because of meandering, a sampler fixed in space will often experience zero concentration as the cloud wafts about. Thus, this meandering greatly reduces the average concentration obtained from a composite of a continuous sample at a fixed point. Clearly, a much greater average concentration would be sensed by a sampler moving with, and thus always in, the puff than a fixed sensor.

Diffusion with respect to a coordinate system moving with the center of the plume is termed "relative diffusion" (Batchelor 1952, Csanady 1973). Relative diffusion does not follow the same laws as does the absolute diffusion relative to the ground (Taylor 1920), which produces the average diffusion of eqn. (1). Using the similarity theory of homogeneous turbulence (Pasquill 1962), Batchelor (1952) considered the relative separation of two particles and predicted that where the $-5/3$ law holds the average standard deviation $\overline{Y}$ of cloud size grows with diffusion time t according to

$$\overline{Y} \propto t^{3/2} \tag{3}$$

Note that this relationship expresses a *rate* of cloud growth $d\overline{Y}/dt = t^{1/2}$ that increases with time, a feature seen in diffusion of smoke in the atmosphere (Gifford 1957). This explosive rate of growth is in marked contrast to absolute diffusion where, after an initial period while the growth rate is constant, the rate of growth of the plume decreases with time or distance from the source (Taylor 1920). The history of diffusion from a point source is governed by three regimes: a brief initial period of molecular diffusion while growth increases with the square root $t^{1/2}$ of diffusion time, followed by an evolutionary phase while growth increases as $t^{3/2}$ and finally, after the cloud grows large compared to the inertial subrange of eddies, growth occurs just as in the final phase of absolute diffusion (Csanady 1973).

It must be emphasized that the overbar on the $\overline{Y}$ in eqn. (3) designates an ensemble average taken to smooth the distribution. This averaging, however, has been performed on a collection of puffs relative to the puff center and *not* relative to a fixed point in space as for the standard deviations S_y and S_z in eqn. (1). This is a fundamental difference between "relative" and "absolute" diffusion. Referring again to Fig. 4, we see that eddies smaller than the puff cause a disorderly distribution of material within the puff. Although eventually the smallest eddies and molecular diffusion tend to smooth out the distribution, eddies smaller than the current size of the puff cause random distortions of the puff, leaving regions of low, or even zero, concentration intermingled with regions of high concentration (Corrsin 1961). Although a beginning has been made (Csanady 1973), there is still little theoretical guidance for predicting variation in concentration within a puff.

It is observed experimentally that, although the distribution of material within a given puff is disorderly, an average of many puffs produces a cross-puff distribution that is approximately Gaussian (see Figs. 4.1 and 4.2 in Csanady 1973). While concentration fluctuations due to turbulence on the scale of the puff can account for ratios of instantaneous peak to average concentrations (P/A) of 2 to 3 (Csanady 1973), meandering can account for P/A ratios of as much as 50 (Gifford 1960). Gifford (1959) described a fluctuating plume by considering its time average variance S^2 (akin to S_y^2 and S_z^2 in eqn. 1) as the sum of the variance Y^2 of the relative diffusion of an average puff and the variance D^2 of the meandering plume centerline about a fixed axis

$$\overline{S^2(t)} = \overline{Y^2(t)} + \overline{D^2(t)} \tag{4}$$

Thus, the time-average or absolute diffusion is caused by diffusion relative to the puff center plus meandering of the center caused by motions much larger than the puff. The ratio (P/A) of peak to average concentration is then:

$$\frac{P}{A} = \frac{\overline{Y^2} + \overline{D^2}}{\overline{Y^2}} \exp\left[\frac{y^2}{2(\overline{Y^2} + \overline{D^2})} + \frac{z^2}{2(\overline{Y^2} + \overline{D^2})}\right] \tag{5}$$

In the atmosphere, the first term on the right hand side of eqn. (5) varies between 1 and 5 while the exponential term, which has a positive sign, contributes greatly to P/A away from the mean plume axis.

Since Gifford's results were derived for stationary, homogeneous turbulence in the free atmosphere, they surely do not apply in the forest. However, the separation of meandering from relative diffusion gives important insight for experiments. This separation is especially important for the lateral fluctuations in the forest stem space where meandering is most likely not due to the large scale portion of a homogeneous turbulent spectrum but is probably more deterministic than stochastic.

DIFFUSION IN THE FOREST STEM SPACE

So far, little quantitative information about diffusion in the forest exists, particularly about peak concentrations. Information that does exist (e.g. Raynor et al. in press, Fritschen et al. 1970) underscores the large effect of heterogeneous vegetation and ground on dispersion. The remainder of this discussion is restricted to the space beneath the canopy down to the soil since gypsy moths tend to fly near the ground (Doane Chapter 10) and the stem space is where pheromone-baited traps attract the most male moths (Holbrook et al. 1960, Granett 1974, Doane Chapter 10).

Sufficiently far in from the windward edge of a uniform forest, i.e., about 15 canopy heights (Meroney 1968), the wind in the stem space is mainly a result of the downward transport of momentum. Several models of momentum transport above and within plant canopies (e.g., Tang 1970, Cionco 1965) stress that the considerable aerodynamic drag on the vegetative elements rapidly depletes momentum and thus greatly slows wind through the canopy. Indeed, winds inside the forest are often so light that they cannot be measured accurately with conventional instruments. The remainder of this discussion will focus on dispersion in the light winds that occur often in Connecticut forests during the summer.

Heterogeneity of the forest modifies the wind inside directly and mechanically and also indirectly through shading the sun (Brown et al. 1969). First, the irregularity or roughness of the canopy top enhances turbulence and thus vertical exchange of momentum and mass. Canopy permeability influences vertical exchange locally where the wind penetrates openings. Horizontal permeability of the canopy and undergrowth channels horizontal air motion in the stem space. Although uneven heating inside the forest causes horizontal differences in temperature and density of air that could drive slight breezes of about 10 cm/sec (Bergen 1974), the channeling of wind by heterogeneities in the canopy is apparently more important for causing variations in wind among the stems (Raynor et al. in press, Brown et al. 1969).

Vertical air temperature gradients in the forest also affect the turbulence. The canopy of a mature forest is the major source and sink of radiant heat. Consequently, during a bright day the canopy will warm more than the forest floor resulting in a stratified, stable temperature profile or "inversion" in the stem space (Raynor 1971, Hosker et al. 1974, Geiger 1965). For stable stratification and light winds, the variability of the lateral component of the wind is often sizable (see Fig. 4.21 in Lumley and Panofsky 1964). Moreover, temperature inversions reduce turbulent diffusion in the vertical (see Fig. 3.11 in Gifford 1968). However, since theoretical guidance for predicting "relative" diffusion in stratified conditions is lacking, the effects of thermal stratification will not be treated here but must remain for experiment.

Although there are few measurements of turbulent power spectra in the forest, it appears that a $-5/3$ power law may hold over a limited range of frequencies (Allen 1968, Brown et al. 1969, McBean 1968, Shinn 1969). The lower limit of eddy sizes of these measurements range from 40 to 100 cm. Lacking more extensive measurements, we might assume for this discussion, that the $-5/3$ law holds for eddy sizes all the way down to the small, dissipative ones.

Measuring and interpreting turbulent power spectra in the forest are difficult. Turbulence in the forest is assuredly not homogeneous. Turbulence is extremely dissipative, and in the absence of a ready supply of energy from the mean flow, it decays rapidly (Tennekes and Lumley 1972). Thus, we expect turbulence to be patchy inside the forest. Near holes in the canopy, turbulent energy of all scales should be great. As this turbulence is convected along under the canopy it will decay. Moreover, any stable thermal stratification of the air will speed this decay (Csanady 1973). As the flow moves among the stems, more turbulence is created by vortices shed from stems. However, since the wind speed profile in the stem space is often quite invariable with height (Brown et al. 1969), the usual processes of vortex stretching (Tennekes and Lumley 1972), which passes energy from lower to higher frequencies and establishes isotropy, are not expected to be as effective as in a more sheared flow. Thus, in a forest, turbulence is not likely to be homogeneous or isotropic.

Often, in the forest, a plume of smoke will be observed to meander widely but diffuse relatively little until it encounters a region near a canopy opening where mixing is great and the concentration of the diffusing material drops dramatically (e.g. Fritschen et al. 1970). Wide lateral meandering has also been observed for plumes released near the floor of model canopies in a wind tunnel (Meroney 1968). In contrast, 30-minute average concentrations of particles released inside a pine forest indicated that vertical dispersion increased at a faster rate away from the source than lateral dispersion and that exchange through the canopy was considerable (Raynor et al. in press). Clearly, few generalities can yet be made about turbulence in the forest. However, for my purpose of emphasizing the importance of a mechanistic approach to dispersion in the forest, an illustrative calculation for restrictive conditions in the forest will be presented.

AN ILLUSTRATIVE EXAMPLE AND A SUGGESTED EXPERIMENT

To determine whether and how a particular moth will respond, both the concentration of pheromone and the time of exposure to pheromone should be known. A brief exposure to a high concentration may or may not elicit the same response as a longer exposure to a low concentration. In particular, a moth may bypass behavioral steps when exposed to a high enough concentration (Doane Chapter 10). Also, Roelofs et al. discuss in Chapter 9 the importance of the chemical composition of the pheromone mixture, stressing the requirement for a specific component for trapping leaf roller moths once they are near the trap. A similar phenomenon may be important for short range "homing" to the female. Therefore, an illustrative example is given using some ideas of this chapter to estimate the maximum concentration within 10 m of a pheromone source.

First, the turbulence in the forest must be characterized. Because the light winds in the stem space are often uniform with height (Tang 1970), usual methods for determining turbulent diffusion from profiles (Lumley and Panofsky 1964) are not reliable. Despite serious limitations, forest turbulence can probably best be characterized by power spectra. The one-dimensional fictitious spectrum of Fig. 2 represents turbulence with an inertial subrange for eddies from about 300 cm to less than 1 cm. The scant measurements that exist suggest that the $-5/3$ regime may fail in the forest for eddies as large as 40 to 100 cm (e.g., Allen 1968, Brown et al. 1969). At present, frequencies of about 4 Hz seem to be the limit of resolution for turbulence measurements within canopies (Shaw et al. 1974). This is one reason why the curve in Fig. 2 is extended as a dashed line. Another reason is that I am postulating a $-5/3$ law where it probably does not hold.

The first two regimes of relative diffusion (see heading "Fluctuations in Concentration") are considered: 1) molecular diffusion until the cloud of pheromone released from a point grows to about the size of the smallest eddy and 2) the evolutionary growth described by $\overline{Y^2} \propto t^3$. Meandering is excluded by referring the concentration to the instantaneous puff center. Finally, the predicted concentration is compared with a time-average referred to a fixed mean plume axis.

Before proceeding to calculate the peak concentration within 10 m of a source, the validity of starting with a point source of pheromone should be qualified. A female moth emitting pheromone while resting on a tree trunk cannot, of course, be considered a point source, particularly nearby. In its early stages relative diffusion is sensitive to the initial size of the diffusing cloud (Batchelor 1952), and this problem will ultimately require solution. To predict the actual initial size of the pheromone cloud requires an analysis of the aerodynamics near the trunk and is not discussed further here.

Assuming a molecular diffusivity K for disparlure (cis-7, 8-expoxy-2 methyloctadecane) of about 0.05 cm^2/sec, one calculates from Fick's law that the standard deviation of the puff grows to about 1 cm in

$$t = \frac{(1\,\text{cm})^2}{2K} = 10 \text{ sec}$$

In this time and in an average 40 cm/sec wind, the puff would travel about 4 m, and the maximum concentration at the center of the puff would be about (see Eqn. 1.49 Csanady 1973)

$$N = \frac{Q}{4\,\pi\,\bar{u}\,Kt} \simeq 4 \times 10^{-3}\,Q$$

g/cm^3 where Q is the steady rate of emission of pheromone in g/sec. If the smallest eddy in the $-5/3$ range were 0.1 cm instead of 1 cm then t would be 0.1 sec, and molecular diffusion would be entirely negligible.

Later, the standard deviation of the puff, diffusing in a homogeneous, isotropic field of turbulence, is given by (see Eqn. 4.34 Csanady 1973)

$$\bar{Y} \simeq A \, e^{1/2} (t - t_o)^{3/2}$$

where A is a constant of order 1 and t_o is the effective time origin for this second phase of diffusion. The rate of eddy-energy transfer can be estimated from the power spectrum, Fig. 2 by (Lumley and Panofsky 1964)

$$ae^{2/3} \simeq \bar{u} \, S(n) \left[\frac{n}{\bar{u}} \right]^{5/3}$$

From Fig. 2, $n^{5/3} \, S(n)$ is a constant in the inertial subrange equal to about 3. The constant a is about $0.47/(2\pi)^{2/3}$ (Lumley and Panofsky 1964). Therefore, with $\bar{u} = 40$ cm/sec we find that $e \simeq 2.5$ cm^2/sec^3, and ignoring the small initial (relative to t_o) size of the puff

$$\bar{Y} \simeq 1.6 \, (t - t_o)^{3/2}.$$

Thus, if the initial period of molecular diffusion lasted 10 sec or about 4 m and the second phase of diffusion lasted 15 sec the standard deviation of the puff after traveling for 25 sec, or a total distance of about 10 m, would be

$$\bar{Y} \simeq 1.6 \, (25 - 10)^{3/2} \simeq 1 \, m$$

The maximum concentration at the center of the puff would be roughly

$$N_{max} \simeq \frac{Q}{2 \, \pi \, \bar{Y^2} \, \bar{u}} \simeq 4 \times 10^{-7} \, Q \, .$$

Remember that $\bar{Y}$ refers to an ensemble average, and concentration fluctuations within the puff have been ignored (see heading "Fluctuations in Concentration"). Now I compare this estimate of N_{max} to a time-average, using eqn. (1). Taking experimental standard deviations for the time-average plume at 10 m from the source of 8 m cross-wind and 2 m vertically (Raynor et al. in press) the maximum average concentration on the mean plume axis is only about 1/16 of the N_{max} estimated at the instantaneous puff center. This comparison cannot be carried far because, as already noted, the conditions required for eqn. (3) to hold have not been established in the forest.

Finally, I suggest an experiment utilizing a bioassay that might help establish the value of the present approach. First, the concentration C_1 of pheromone eliciting a specific response, e.g., rapid wing-fanning by the male moth, in a time T_1, would be quantified for a species. These moths, restricted by a flow-through cage, would then be kept in the pheromone plume for a time T_1

at a fixed radial distance from the source. The meanderings of the plume could be made visible by an inert tracer. The response of the moths would reveal the maximum distance X_1 where a concentration greater than or equal to C_1 was maintained for T_1. In addition, a distance X_a for which the average concentration would equal C_1 can also be determined from an appropriate average of concurrent wind measurements. It is postulated here that, within 10 m, or so, of the source, X_1 will likely exceed X_a substantially, thus establishing the importance of considering brief, peak concentrations rather than averages.

SUMMARY

Although often used to predict pheromone concentration in a forest or close to a pheromone source, Sutton's diffusion equation is not appropriate for predicting moth behavior in these situations because moths can respond quickly to pheromone while Sutton's equation predicts *average* concentrations. These averages through time can often be only a few percent of maximum or peak concentrations. Moreover, ventilation inside a forest is unique and is not readily analyzed by existing theory. An analysis of these turbulent flows suggests a separation of the effects of large- and small-scale motions of the atmosphere on diffusion. This kind of separation is inspired by the fluctuating plume model of Gifford; however, the complex micro-meteorological conditions in the forest render even this model inapplicable. Nevertheless, an illustrative calculation is presented for the peak concentration of pheromone emitted from a point source in the forest. The shortcomings of the calculation are discussed, and an experiment is suggested.

IV

BIOLOGICAL-AND
INTEGRATED CONTROL

Chapter 14

Theory Underlying Introduction of Exotic Parasitoids

P. S. Messenger

Department of Entomological Sciences
University of California
Berkeley, California 94720

INTRODUCTION

Biological control is the regulation of the densities of plant and animal populations through the lethal actions of natural enemies, parasitoids, predators and pathogens. When the regulated species is a pest, biological control has been and can be used in many cases as an effective means of control.

Many phytophagous insects are pests because (a) they attack plants of value to man (crop plants, forests, ornamentals), and (b) they occur in high, damaging numbers. Often in such cases the high pest densities occur because of the absence of effective natural enemies. Such is particularly so where the pest insect is an immigrant. Many of the principal pests of agricultural crops or ornamental plants in the United States are such invader species. A notorious example is the gypsy moth, *Lymantria dispar* L. A logical approach to the control of such pests is to search for and to import one or more of their natural enemies.

The rationale described above has been used as the basis for a long series of attempts to control many plant pests. Many of these attempts have led to remarkable successes; the classic case of the cottony cushion scale, *Icerya purchasi* Maskell, on citrus in California in 1890, controlled by the predatory vedalia beetle, *Rodolia cardinalis* (Mulsant), introduced from Australia, is a leading example. On a world-wide basis more than 120 different species of insect pests and weeds have been reduced to more or less satisfactory levels of abundance through the use of imported natural enemies since 1890 (DeBach 1971, van den Bosch and Messenger 1973).

191

Not all bona fide attempts to apply biological control have led to successful results. Indeed, the rate of failure probably amounts to three out of four attempts. Some of these failures are due to technical weaknesses in the application of the method. Some are due to ecological limitations on the part of the natural enemies involved (van den Bosch and Messenger 1973), or to the fact that the target pest species is abundant not because of lack of natural enemies, but because of agricultural practices that influence the nature, abundance and susceptibility of the attacked plant. The gypsy moth is an example where biological control has thus far failed (Hoy, Chapter 15). Other examples against which intensive efforts to apply biological control have been made include the European corn borer, *Ostrinia nubilalis* (Hübner), the oriental fruit moth, *Grapholitha molesta* (Busck), and the cotton boll weevil, *Anthonomus grandis* Boheman.

The question is, does the practice of biological control have a theoretical basis? It has been contended by some that the practice is essentially empirical; that attempts to apply biological control are pragmatic, and hence that the rate of success is as much a consequence of biological accident as of careful, planned application of effort based on ecological theory or principles.

It is the contention of this paper that biological control does have a basis in ecological theory, and that many of the current practices of specialists in the application of biological controls can be defended on theoretical grounds. Indeed, a case can even be made that certain aspects of ecological theory have been derived from the results of biological control.

THEORETICAL CONCEPTS UNDERLYING BIOLOGICAL CONTROL

The fundamental concept underlying biological control is that of the *natural control of population numbers*, often described by the term "balance of nature." Other theoretical considerations subsumed by this fundamental concept include the regulation of population numbers by density-dependent mortality factors, the competition between species utilizing the same ecological resource, the specificity and stability of trophic relations among species within communities, and the self-sustaining, self-limiting, reciprocal interaction that occurs between host and parasitoid or predator and prey.

Natural Control of Abundance

All species have the ability to increase their numbers through the process of reproduction, but no species does so without limit (Huffaker and Messenger 1964, Huffaker et al. 1971). The restrictions on unlimited population growth are contained within the environment in which the population exists. Many of the environmental factors that can influence population growth or set limits to ultimate population size are listed in Fig. 1. In fact, any environmental factor

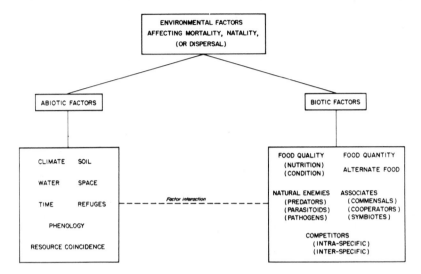

FIGURE 1. *Environmental factors affecting the abundance of insect populations.*

that affects the mortality (or survival) or natality of the population, or that influences the movement (dispersal) of organisms into or out of the habitat, contributes to the natural control of numbers. In Fig. 1, the environmental factors that influence population numbers are classified as abiotic (physical) or biotic (living or organic).

The fact that many factors are present and acting together to affect mortality, natality, or dispersal in any habitat of a population, makes difficult the study and analysis of population size. The difficulty is compounded when it is realized that many environmental factors interact among themselves. Thus, both climate (temperature, humidity, light, precipitation, wind) and natural enemies (parasitoids, predators, pathogens) can cause mortality or suppress natality of an insect population. Further, climate can influence the activity and hence the lethal impact of natural enemies on the target population (Messenger 1970, 1971).

In Fig. 1, the environmental factors affecting the natural control of population numbers are arranged as though there is something intrinsically different about the action or importance of abiotic and biotic factors. In fact, the concept of natural control of numbers is based on the way that population size (density) itself influences the action of environmental factors. In Fig. 2, the environmental factors are listed not only according to whether they are abiotic or biotic in nature, but also according to whether they have the property or properties of varying in their action in relation to the density of the population being limited. Only density-dependent mortality factors can regulate the numbers of populations, that is, maintain them at some characteristic level of

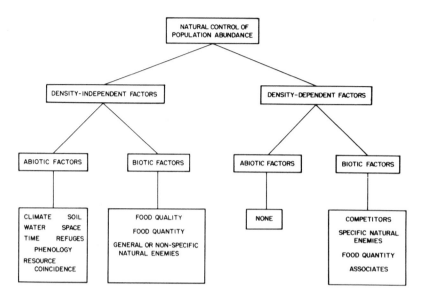

FIGURE 2. *Environmental factors influencing the natural control of abundance of insect populations.*

abundance (Nicholson 1954, Huffaker 1958). Natural enemies can exhibit the property of density-dependence, although in some circumstances a particular natural enemy may not. Other members of the same population, acting as intraspecific competitors, always have the property of density-dependence (Milne 1957). Physical factors, their intensity of action on mortality or natality not being altered by the size of the target population, are density-independent factors, never density-dependent.

It is to be noted that certain biotic factors may act as either density-dependent or density-independent, such as food quantity, or certain kinds of natural enemies. Food quantity can be limiting or regulative only when it is in short supply; other factors can restrain a population such that competition for food never becomes controlling. Non-specific natural enemies will not act as dependable population regulators so long as alternate hosts or prey are also present; though this does not mean that non-specific or general parasitoids or predators cannot play a useful role in the biological control of insect pests (see Ehler and van den Bosch 1974). Specific natural enemies can act as density-dependent regulatory factors of populations, though other environmental factors may interfere with, preclude, or modify such action (van den Bosch and Messenger 1973, Messenger et al. 1976).

Density-dependent Mortality

A density-dependent mortality factor is one whose mortality or "killing power" increases as the host population increases, and decreases as the host population decreases. More precisely, the proportion, or percentage of hosts killed must increase or decrease with increase or decrease in host density. For a natural enemy to act this way, the searching enemy must find and kill (or oviposit in) more hosts, proportionately, as the density of the latter rises, and vice versa.

In Fig. 3, block diagram (A) illustrates the mechanism of density-dependent mortality. When the enemy removes hosts or prey promptly, that is, within the period of one host or prey generation, no or very little time-lag occurs between attack and host or prey density change. As each prey is removed, prey population density declines, and subsequent predator-prey contacts become fewer simply because prey are scarcer. Such a promptly responding mortality factor is commonly called a direct density-dependent mortality factor. For a parasitoid to act as a direct density-dependent factor, since the act of parasitism does not immediately remove hosts from the scene, it must be able to complete at least two generations to one of the host.

However, most natural enemies, because of developmental time-lags, are unable to complete their life cycles so much more rapidly than the host or prey, and thus there is a generational time-lag. This means that there is a numerical lag between host and enemy population numbers. This is indicated in Fig. 3, block diagram (B). Because of this delay in numerical response of enemy to host, such mortality is described as delayed-density-dependent mortality. Such a property has fundamental importance in the way natural enemies affect host populations, and, as shall be described later, deep importance for the development of a theory of biological control.

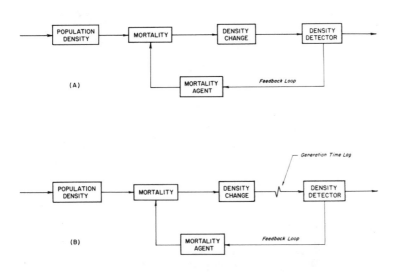

FIGURE 3. *Schematic diagram of the mechanism of density-dependent mortality.*

The Ecosystem Framework

When we consider the potentialities for "classical biological control," or the importation and colonization of exotic natural enemies for control of immigrant pests, in relation to the concept of natural control, it is perhaps best to do so in the context of the ecosystem. The ecosystem, of course, is the community of interacting plant and animal species together with the physical habitat containing them. Figure 4 is a diagrammatic representation of an ecosystem designed specifically to emphasize the position or role of natural enemies. While it may not appear so at first glance, all of the environmental factors listed in Figs. 1 and 2 can be assigned directly or indirectly to one or more features of Fig. 4. Climate, soil, water, plants or insects as food, preferred and alternate

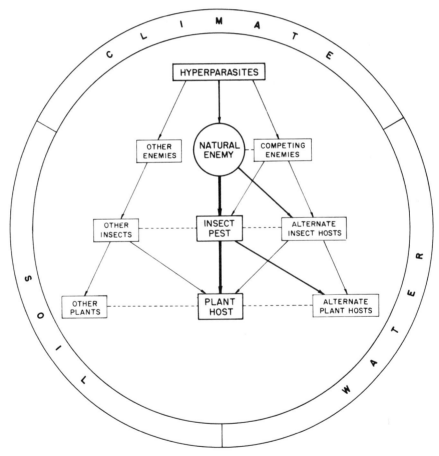

FIGURE 4. *Schematic diagram of the ecosystem framework within which reside an insect pest and its natural enemies.*

hosts, associates and competitors may be directly inferred. Space, time, refuges, phenology, resource coincidence, food quality and quantity may be indirectly inferred. The important aspect of Fig. 4 is that it provides a structural connection among the components and factors listed in Figs. 1 and 2. This structural dimension is important in considering further the theoretical basis for biological control.

In Fig. 4, where solid lines show trophic relations and dashed lines possible competitive interactions, the target insect under consideration for biological control, denoted as the "insect pest," is visualized as existing in its native habitat. It, of course, is shown associated with (attacking) its definitive plant host. In many cases of classical biological control this plant host will be the same as, or closely related to, the host plant attacked by the pest in the target region, although this need not be so. Alternate host plants that may serve as food for the target insect, as well as other plants, are depicted, as are other phytophagous insect species which feed upon these plants. Natural enemies that attack the target insect are also shown; these will be either host specific, or will attack alternate host insects as well. More than one natural enemy species is shown attacking the target insect, which is the usual situation for most phytophagous insects in their native habitats. There may (and usually will) be other natural enemy species occurring in the same community, though these will be associated with other hosts than the target host. Thus it is mandatory in searches for exotic natural enemies that host relations be carefully ascertained. Many failures in biological control work have been due to the importation and attempted establishment of natural enemy species that were not effectively associated with the definitive pest species. And, finally, the various natural enemy species will in turn have their own natural enemies, which, when the latter are themselves parasitoids, are depicted by the designation, hyperparasites.

Now, in relation to the indigenous or native ecosystem of the pest species, as depicted in Fig. 4, consider the ecosystem occupied by the pest in the invaded region, diagrammed in the upper part of Fig. 5. The unlabeled boxes in the "source ecosystem" are the same as those labeled in Fig. 4. For the invaded or "receptor ecosystem," only the host plant and the pest insect populations are shown. For oligophagous or polyphagous pest species, only the target or crop plant is shown. No "source natural enemies" are shown, nor are any of the other indigenous or source plant or insect species. Of course, this need not necessarily be so in every case of an immigrant pest insect, but it often is, and it serves to focus the discussion on what next occurs in programs of biological control.

It is this lack of adapted natural enemies, depicted in the "receptor ecosystem" of the invaded region, that is claimed to be the reason why the immigrant pest insect attains such high, destructive densities. This does not mean that natural enemies native to the receptor habitat do not sometimes attack the immigrant pest. Often they do, but usually such enemies are poorly adapted to

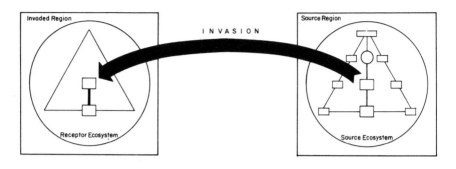

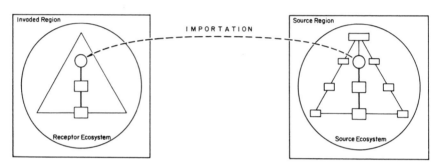

FIGURE 5. *Schematic diagram of the environmental circumstance involved in the invasion of a pest insect into a new region and the subsequent establishment of its natural enemies for biological control purposes.*

such new hosts and are consequently ineffective in restraining the latter.

To initiate a program of classical biological control, the search for and importation of one or more exotic natural enemy species existing in the source region must be carried out. This is diagrammed in the lower part of Fig. 5. Again, the receptor ecosystem is purposely diagrammed as simple, as will be the case in most invaded agro-ecosystems. It may be that the receptor ecosystem is actually too much simplified, such that other plant or host insect resources required by the natural enemy (pollen and nectar sources, alternate hosts) are absent. Such deficiencies have been known to be the cause of some past failures of biological control, or reduced effectiveness of certain established exotic natural enemies (Clausen 1956, Messenger et al. 1976).

The Impact of Imported Natural Enemies

The above discussion, then, describes the ecological or theoretical framework for the application of biological control to immigrant pest insects. As indicated in the beginning of this paper, a long list of examples exists that testifies to the practicality of the technique. Three quantitative examples are illustrated in Fig. 6. Population densities of the target pests before and after the successful introduction of the indicated effective natural enemies are shown. One example refers to a weed, the Klamath weed, *Hypericum perforatum* L. (data from Huffaker 1967). A second example concerns the olive scale, *Parlatoria oleae* (Colv.), against which two effective parasitic species were used (data from DeBach et al. 1971). The third example is that of the walnut aphid, *Chromaphis juglandicola* (Kalt.) successfully controlled by a climatically adapted

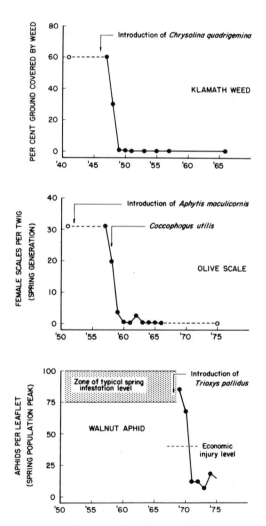

FIGURE 6. *Illustrations of the quantitative impact of the importation and establishment of effective natural enemies for the control of insect pests and weeds.*

strain of the parasite, *Trioxys pallidus* (Haliday) (data from Michelbacher and Ortega 1958, Sluss 1967, Frazer and van den Bosch 1973, and Messenger 1975). When the introduced natural enemy or enemies prove to be effective control agents, the results are dramatic. Financial savings from reduced pest control costs are equally rewarding.

HOST-PARASITE POPULATION MODELS

The fact that a logical case for biological control can be made, based on the re-establishment of natural controls as well as practical experience, does not constitute the full development of the theoretical basis for natural enemy action. The construction of mathematical models that presumably mimic the interactions and consequences of natural enemy actions extends the theoretical basis for biological control in a most insightful way. Indeed, some of these models, constructed for other reasons, serve to reinforce or explain a number of conclusions and assumptions of practitioners of biological control relative to what constitutes an effective natural enemy (or the most effective one, given a choice of several), and what constitutes the most efficient way to proceed towards the attainment of effective biological control. Among the properties of a natural enemy deemed to be important for giving effective control are (DeBach 1964a, 1971):

(a) it should act in a density-dependent way,
(b) it should be host specific, or substantially so,
(c) it should have a high searching ability for hosts,
(d) it should have a high reproductive capacity relative to the host pest,
(e) it should be tolerant to the same environmental conditions as the host.

There are several other considerations concerning the practice of biological control about which much insight can be gained from population theory and host-parasite models. These concern the importation and use of more than one natural enemy for control of a given pest species. Two aspects of this are involved: (a) the introduction of two or more enemy species that attack the same stage of development of the host (multiple introductions), and (b) the use of several enemy species, each attacking a different stage of the host (sequence theory). There has been debate about whether multiple introductions or the sequence theory are effective strategies for bringing about biological control (see Huffaker et al. 1971). Introductions of several enemies attacking the same host stage bring about competition between enemy species, thus requiring consideration of competitive exclusion, competitive displacement, and competitive coexistence. Introduction of several enemy species to establish a sequence of regulatory agents also involves aspects of competition, though in a less direct way. A review of theoretical population models involving competition, on the one hand, and host-parasite systems on the other, may help the evaluation of these strategies.

Simple Population Models

The exponential growth model, the logistic growth model, and the Lotka-Volterra two-species competition and host-parasite (or predator-prey) models, are well known in the ecological literature (Chapman 1931, Slobodkin 1961, Varley et al. 1974), but suffer from their unrealism. They represent extremely simplified organisms with very short developmental periods, and no time-lags between changes in density and resultant impact on reproduction and survival. They are thus difficult to apply to real situations such as we would like to do in connection with biological control.

Nevertheless, certain of these models have been used to suggest ideas about natural enemy action, or to illustrate certain concepts believed to apply to biological control. They have also served as a theoretical basis on which more realistic host-parasite or competition models have been formulated.

The Exponential Growth Model

This is the simplest population growth model, and refers to the uninhibited increase in numbers of an organism in an unlimiting environment.

$$\frac{dN}{dt} = rN \tag{1}$$

$$N_t = N_o e^{rt} \tag{2}$$

Where dN/dt is the instantaneous growth rate of the population, N is the population size at any instant in time, and r is the intrinsic growth rate of the organism under the conditions of the habitat. The growth constant, r, which is the arithmetic difference between the organism's birth rate and death rate, is a species-specific characteristic. For arthropods r is also affected by other environmental factors, such as temperature, humidity, diet, and so on (see Messenger 1964).

One of the characteristics of an effective natural enemy is that it have a "power of increase" greater than that of its host (see page 200). To the degree that power of increase is reflected in the value of r, this last parameter can be used to evaluate the potential capacity of a natural enemy to suppress its host (Messenger 1964, 1970). Figure 7, taken from Messenger (1970), shows the r values, as affected by mean temperature, of three different species of parasitoids that attack the spotted alfalfa aphid, *Therioaphis trifolii* (Buckton). Experimental studies indicate that only in those zones of temperature where the r

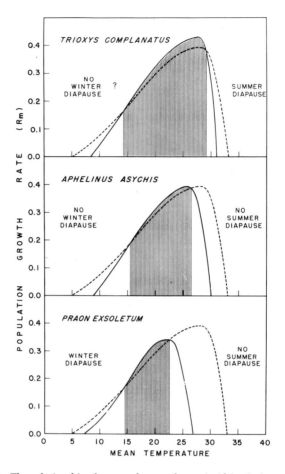

FIGURE 7. *The relationships between host and parasitoid intrinsic rates of numerical increase as affected by fluctuating temperatures. From Messenger (1970).*

values of the parasitoid are higher than those of the host will the parasitoid be able to restrain or suppress a growing population of the host.

The Logistic Growth Model

This is perhaps the simplest population model that includes a limit to growth:

$$\frac{dN}{dt} = rN(\frac{K-N}{K}) \tag{3}$$

where r, again, is the intrinsic rate of natural increase, N is the population size, and K is the maximum number that the population can reach. The growth curve so described is sigmoidal. The integral form of the model:

$$N_t = \frac{K}{1+ae^{-rt}} \tag{4}$$

where the only new symbol, a, is mathematically a constant of integration, and biologically is found from the equation: $\log_e a = rt'$ where t' is the time taken for the population size, N, to reach $K/2$ (see Varley et al. 1974).

Although the logistic growth model is much used in the ecological literature to illustrate limited population growth, and as such enters into the formulation of other population models, such as the Lotka-Volterra competition models (see below), its application to biological control is less apparent. H. S. Smith (1935) concluded that natural enemies could serve as limiting factors restricting the growth of host populations, though he did not show a mechanism for how this could be done. He concluded further that the "equilibrium level," K, imposed on the host population by the enemy, varies with the rate at which parasitism or predation increased with host or prey density, with lower values for K with higher values for the rate of increase of natural enemy action.

Lotka-Volterra Competition Model

In this model two species are presumed to be present initially in a common habitat. Each species population grows alone according to the logistic model. However, each species is also presumed to inhibit or interfere with the other. The negative impact of an individual of one species is greater in respect to the other species population than it is in respect to its own population. The equations for the model are:

$$\frac{dN_1}{dt} = r_1 N_1 \frac{(K_1 - N_1 - \alpha N_2)}{K_1} \tag{5}$$

$$\frac{dN_2}{dt} = r_2 N_2 \frac{(K_2 - N_2 - \beta N_1)}{K_2} \tag{6}$$

where N_1, and N_2 are the population sizes of the two species, r_1 and r_2 their two intrinsic growth rates, K_1 and K_2 their respective equilibrium levels when growing alone, and α and β the respective competition coefficients. Depending on the relative values of K_1, K_2, α and β, there are four possible "outcomes" to competition: (a) either N_1 or N_2 survives while the other is eliminated, depending on the initial density ratios, (b) both survive and coexist, (c) N_1

always survives alone, and (d) N_2 always survives alone. Both Slobodkin (1961) and Varley et al. (1974) provide details.

The theoretical implications of the model are important for biological control. As has already been noted, for many pest species, more than one natural enemy can be found to occur, particularly in native habitats of the pest species. Thus, multiple introductions of natural enemy species is frequently practiced in biological control work. Competitive exclusion (Gause's rule), the prevention of the establishment of a new enemy by the presence of an already established enemy species, or competitive displacement, the elimination of an established enemy species by the introduction of a new one, are often observed in biological control work (DeBach 1966). These results may very well follow as consequences of Lotka-Volterra competition theory. However, the effects of such exclusions or displacements on host population numbers are not predictable from this theory.

On the matter of multiple introductions, H. S. Smith (1929) has contended that the opportunities for (a) establishing a better natural enemy, and (b) getting better "coverage," or geographical distribution through this practice are sufficient reasons to justify this practice. Arguments to the contrary are usually centered on the conclusions that competition between natural enemy species may result in less effective suppression of the host population.

In Fig. 8 is a schematic representation of the results of introducing three different parasite species into California for the control of the spotted alfalfa aphid (see Messenger 1971). Over substantial portions of the State only one or the other of the three parasites occurs. In a central portion, and along much of the coast, there could be some competition where overlap occurs. Invariably, the most effective species, *Trioxys complanatus* Quilis, survives where competition occurs.

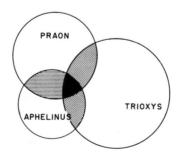

FIGURE 8. *Schematic representation of the geographic distribution and competitive overlap of three parasitoids introduced into California for the biological control of the spotted alfalfa aphid. From Messenger (1971).*

Nicholson-Bailey Model

This model presumes that a parasitic species searches for and attacks a host species, that in each host that is encountered by the parasite an egg is deposited, that any attacked host is not attacked again, and that each attack results in the production of one progeny parasite (Nicholson 1933, Nicholson and Bailey 1935). Host and parasite generations are exactly synchronized. No other mortality than parasitism affects the host population. The model is represented by the following pair of difference equations:

$$N_{t+1} = N_t F e^{-aP}t \tag{7}$$

$$P_{t+1} = N_t(1-e^{-aP}t) \tag{8}$$

where N_t and N_{t+1} are the densities of the host in successive generations, P_t and P_{t+1} are the densities of the parasite in successive generations, F is the host power of increase from one generation to the next, and a is the searching coefficient (area of discovery) of the parasite. In Fig. 9, upper graph, are shown the population densities of successive generations of both host and parasite when the host's power of increase, F, is 5.0 and the parasite's searching coefficient, a, is 0.1.

A number of things can be noted from this example. The host and parasite populations oscillate in numbers, the parasite oscillations lag behind the host oscillations, and the oscillations increase in amplitude. The practical implication of the increasing oscillations is that eventually the system destroys itself by driving to the H=0 or P=0 axis or, contrarily, to such high densities that other environmental resources (space, host food) become limiting.

Nicholson and Bailey (1935), of course, noted this property of their model. They concluded that this results in the localized destruction, or fragmentation (see Huffaker and Messenger 1964), of the host population, with subsequent reinvasion by dispersing hosts from nearby, as yet unparasitized host subpopulations. That this fragmentation must be a universal consequence of the action of parasitic attack of pest insects may be a difficult proposition for economic entomologists to accept in specific cases.

The Nicholson-Bailey model provides that there is a "steady density" of host, and of parasite as well, about which these density oscillations take place:

$$N_s = \frac{\log_e F}{a(F-1)} \tag{9}$$

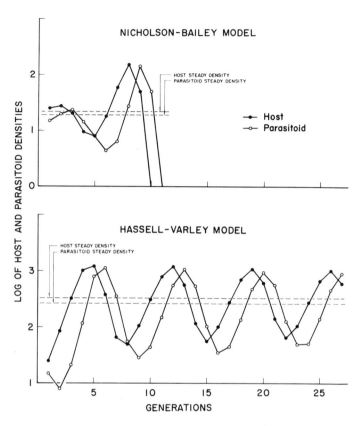

FIGURE 9. *Oscillations of host and parasitoid populations over a sequence of genera-tions in accordance with the Nicholson-Bailey host-parasite model (upper), and the Hassell-Varley model (lower). Host power of increase, 5, parasitoid area of discovery, 0.1, parasi-toid mutual interference constant, 0.5.*

$$P_s = \frac{\log_e F}{a} \tag{10}$$

where N_s and P_s are the respective steady densities of host and parasite populations, and F and a are the host power of increase and parasite searching coefficient, as before. What this means, for biological control specialists, is that (a) the larger is the host power of increase, F, the higher are the steady or equilibrium densities of both host and parasite, and (b) the greater is the parasite searching coefficient, a, the lower are these densities. Hence, given two parasites to choose between for use in biological control, all other things being equal, that parasite with the higher searching capacity for the host in question will give the better host suppressing results.

Another consequence of the Nicholson-Bailey model is that two parasite species attacking the same host population, either at the same stage or in a sequence of stages, cannot coexist. Empirical observation again often provides contrary evidence (see Varley et al. 1974). However, one thing of importance does stand out in this Nicholson-Bailey competition consequence. That parasite with the greater searching capacity (area of discovery) is the survivor in such cases. It also can be shown that the parasite with the higher area of discovery, a, will produce the lower steady density of hosts. This follows from equation (9), above.

Hassell-Varley Model

The fact that, both in nature and in laboratory experiments, the fragmentation result of the Nicholson-Bailey model is not often observed, has led to much conjecture about "dampening factors" (see Huffaker et al. 1971). These are presumed to restrain the tendency for the ever-increasing oscillations required by the model. Such factors may include some form of intra-specific competition on the part of either host or parasite population when these increase to high values, or the action of general predators attracted to the high host populations, or the usage of refuges by hosts when their population becomes low, or the differential dispersal of hosts relative to parasites, and so on.

It remained for Hassell and Varley (1969) to modify the Nicholson-Bailey model by the introduction of an intraspecific, dampening factor with respect to the parasite that provided a major improvement to the host-parasite model. This factor they described as "mutual interference" among searching parasites which takes greater and greater effect as parasite density increases. The modified model is as follows:

$$N_{t+1} = N_t F e^{-Q(P_t)^{1-m}} \tag{11}$$

$$P_{t+1} = N_t (1 - e^{-Q(P_t)^{1-m}}) \tag{12}$$

where Q is the area of discovery or searching coefficient of the parasite when its population density is unity, and m is the mutual interference constant of the parasite. This relation of parasite searching power and density was derived from the observation that a of the Nicholson-Bailey model was not a constant in numerous laboratory experiments, but rather that it varied with parasite density roughly according to the following relation (see also Varley et al. 1974):

$$a = QP^{-m} \tag{13}$$

Figure 9, lower graph, illustrates the output of the Hassell-Varley model when the host F is 5, parasite $a = Q = 0.1$, and $m = 0.5$. The steady densities of host and parasite populations are now:

$$N_s = \left(\frac{\log_e F}{Q}\right)^{\frac{1}{1-m}} \left(\frac{F}{F-1}\right) \tag{14}$$

$$P_s = \left(\frac{\log_e F}{Q}\right)^{\frac{1}{1-m}} \tag{15}$$

Thus it can be seen that, for any given values of F, power of increase, and Q, specific search capacity (Hassell-Varley quest constant), the greater the mutual interference constant, m, is, the higher will be the host steady density. Hence we have the situation that while the occurrence of mutual interference among parasites attacking the same host population introduces stability into the host-parasite system, it also renders the parasite less effective in terms of biological control.

A very interesting further consequence of the Hassell-Varley host-parasite model is that it allows for the stable co-existence of two or more parasites attacking the same host (Hassell and Varley 1969). These parasites can attack the host simultaneously or successively. The magnitudes and relative values of the Q and m values of the two parasites determine whether there shall be coexistence or displacement, and, if coexistence, which parasite shall be the more abundant. Again, the steady density of the host is increased when supporting two enemies than when only supporting one.

We may now be in a position to interpret theoretically the conclusion of DeBach (1964a, 1971) that in most cases of successful biological control, the results are due to the action of a single natural enemy. Table 1 provides examples of pests that have been successfully controlled by principally one natural enemy species.

However, there are several well-known cases of biological control in which at least two natural enemies have contributed collectively to effective biological control. Some of these are listed in Table 2. In the case of the winter moth, *Operophtera brumata* (L.), one of the enemies (*Cyzenis albicans* (Fal.)) is effective at higher host densities, and the second (*Agrypon flaveolatum* (Grav.)) at lower host densities. In the case of the olive scale, *Parlatoria oleae*, one enemy (*Aphytis maculicornis* (Masi)) is effective in the winter and spring host generation, the other (*Coccophagoides utilis* Doutt) in the summer host generation (Huffaker and Kennett 1966).

TABLE 1 Insect pests, the effective biological control of which has been brought about by a single natural enemy species, as indicated

Pest Species	Natural Enemy	Place	Reference
Aleurocanthus spiniferus (Quaint.)	*Prospaltella smithi* Silv.	Japan	Watanabe 1958
Aleurocanthus woglumi Ashby	*Eretmocerus serius* Silv.	Cuba, Jamaica, Costa Rica, Panama	Clausen 1956
Aleurothrixus flocossus (Mask.)	*Amitus spiniferus* (Brethes)	Chile	DeBach 1971
Antonina graminis (Mask.)	*Neodusmetia sangwani* Rao	Texas	Schuster et al. 1971
Aonidiella aurantii (Mask.)	*Aphytis melinus* DeBach	Greece	DeBach et al. 1971
Aonidiella aurantii	*Aphytis melinus*	Turkey	DeBach 1971
Aspidiotus destructor Sign.	*Cryptognatha nodiceps* Marsh.	Fiji	Taylor 1935
Aspidiotus destructor	*Cryptognatha nodiceps*	Principe	Simmonds 1960
Ceroplastes rubens Mask.	*Anicetus beneficus* Ish. & Yam.	Japan	Yasumatsu 1958
Chromaphis juglandicola (Kalt.)	*Trioxys pallidus* (Hal.)	California	van den Bosch and Messenger 1973
Chrysomphalus aonidum (L.)	*Aphytis holoxanthus* DeBach	Israel, Brazil, Peru	DeBach 1971
Eriococcus coriaceus Mask.	*Rhizobius ventralis* (Erich.)	New Zealand	Miller et al. 1936
Gonipterus scutellatus Gyll.	*Anaphoidea nitens* Gir.	South Africa	Tooke 1953
Homona coffearia Nietn.	*Macrocentrus homonae* Nixon	Ceylon	Evans 1952
Hypera postica (Gyll.)	*Bathyplectes curculionis* (Thom.)	Central California	Clausen 1956
Icerya purchasi Mask.	*Chryptochaetum iceryae* (Will.)	Coastal California	DeBach 1971
Icerya purchasi	*Rodolia cardinalis* (Muls.)	Interior California	DeBach 1971
Lepidosaphes beckii (Newm.)	*Aphytis lepidosaphes* Compere	Brazil	DeBach 1971
Levuana iridescens Beth.-Baker	*Bessa remota* (Aldr.)	Fiji	Tothill et al. 1930
Perkinsiella saccharicida Kirk.	*Tytthus mundulus* (Bredd.)	Hawaii	Pemberton 1948
Phenacoccus aceris Sign.	*Allotropa utilis* Mues.	British Columbia	Baird 1958
Planococcus kenyae (LePell.)	*Anagyrus* sp. near *kivuensis*	Kenya	LePelley 1951
Promecotheca coeruleipennis Blanch.	*Pediobius parvulus* Ferr.	Fiji	Taylor 1937
Promecotheca cumingi Baly	*Dimmockia javanica* Ferr.	Ceylon	Fernando 1972
Pseudococcus citriculus Green	*Clausenia purpurea* Ishii	Israel	DeBach 1964a
Pseudococcus comstocki (Kuwa.)	*Pseudaphycus malinus* Gahan	Russia	Kobakhidze 1965
Pseudococcus gahani Green	*Tetracnemus pretiosus* Timb.	California	Clausen 1956
Quadraspidiotus perniciosus (Com.)	*Prospaltella perniciosi* Tower	Switzerland	Mathys and Guignard 1965
Saissetia nigra (Nietn.)	*Metaphycus helvolus* (Comp.)	California	Clausen 1956

TABLE 2 *Insect pests, the effective biological control of which has required the joint action of two natural enemy species*

Pest Species	Natural enemies	Place	Reference
Aonidiella aurantii (Mask.)	*Aphytis melinus* DeBach *Comperiella bifasciata* How.	Interior So. Calif.	DeBach et al. 1971
Aonidiella aurantii	*Aphytis lingnanensis* Comp. *Prospaltella perniciosi* Tow.	Coastal So. Calif.	DeBach et al. 1971
Diprion hercyniae (Hart.)	Virus (polyhedrosis) *Drino bohemica* Mesn.	Canada	Cameron 1972
Operophtera brumata (L.)	*Agrypon flaveolatum* (Grav.) *Cyzenis albicans* (Fall.)	Nova Scotia	Embree 1971
Parlatoria oleae (Colv.)	*Aphytis maculicornis* (Masi) *Coccophagoides utilis* Doutt	California	Huffaker and Kennett 1966

Holling Disc Equation Model

This model refers to the way in which the rate of parasitism or predation of searching natural enemies varies with host density (Holling 1959). It is described as the functional response of the enemy to the host because it refers only to the increase in attack within a natural enemy generation rather than the way enemies change in numbers as a consequence of attack (Solomon 1949). The model is described by the equation:

$$N_A = \frac{a'TN_oP}{1+a'T_hN_o} \tag{16}$$

where N_o is the initial density of hosts, N_A is the number attacked, a' is the coefficient of attack, T is the time available for the parasite to search and attack the hosts, T_h is the time taken by a parasite to "handle" the host, that is, to probe and oviposit in it, and then resume searching, and P is the number of parasites searching.

The more steeply the curve starts out, and the higher it goes before leveling out, the more effective is the natural enemy. Thus, as shown in Fig. 10, the greater the coefficient of attack, a', or the shorter the handling time, T_h, or the longer the total searching time of the parasite, T, the more effective the enemy.

The Holling Disc Equation has been used to evaluate the behavior of certain natural enemies. For example, in the case of the spotted alfalfa aphid parasite, *Praon exsoletum* (Nees), the influence of temperature on its functional response has been measured (Messenger 1968). The results of this study are illustrated in Fig. 11. It can be easily seen that both the coefficient of attack, a', and the handling time, T_h, are functions of temperature. Maximum attacks per hour, $60/T_h$, are also affected by temperature. Comparison of the data in Fig. 11 with those of Fig. 7 show an obvious correlation between range of effective temperatures within which laboratory populations of *P. exsoletum* suppresses growing populations of the host aphid and peak values for the coefficient of attack, a', as determined by the Disc Equation.

SUMMARY

To establish a theoretical basis for the use of exotic natural enemies in the biological control of insect pests, we have started with the concept of natural control of populations, using as a holistic framework the ecosystem concept. Pests are pests for any number of reasons, but for the purposes of this presentation we have singled out those cases where insect pests seem to be so abundant because of the lack of effective natural enemies. This seems to be particularly so in those cases where the pest species itself is of exotic origin.

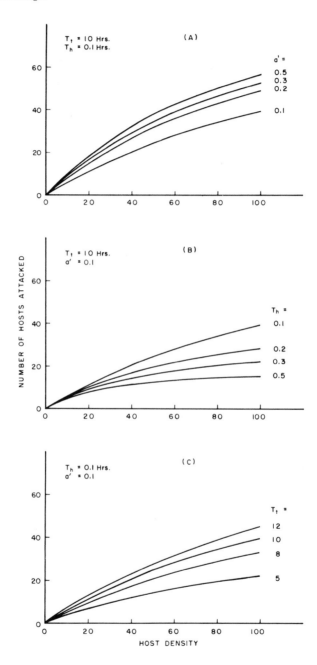

FIGURE 10. *Effects of varying the various parameters of the Holling Disc Equation on the resultant parasite functional response curves. (See text for explanation of symbols.)*

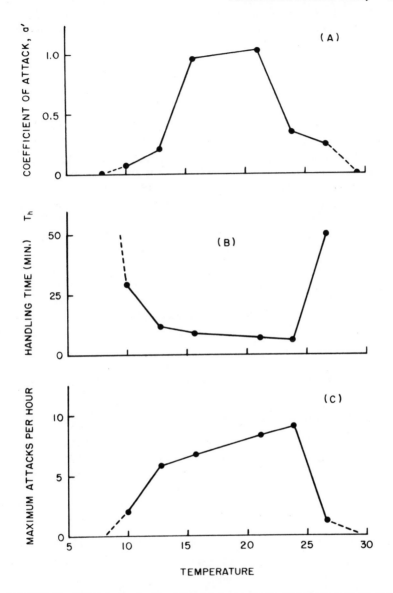

FIGURE 11. *Effect on fluctuating temperatures on the functional response parameters of the parasitoid,* Praon exsoletum, *when attacking its host, the spotted alfalfa aphid,* Therioaphis trifolii. *Data from Messenger (1968).*

With the general idea of natural control of population, we have then focused on the situation where the major control factor or factors in the environment are natural enemies. We have shown from empirical evidence that biological control of immigrant pests can be brought about through the importation and establishment of adapted natural enemies. Then we have explored the various ecological theories underlying population growth, limitation to population growth, the role of natural enemies in limiting or regulating population growth, the theoretical models purporting to describe host-parasite or predator-prey interactions, and competition theory. In each case we have attempted to show either how these theoretical concepts and models help explain the events that often are observed to occur in biological control work, or how work in biological control might be improved or extended by their use.

Because of space limitations we have left out a number of interesting theoretical considerations that concern biological control. There are the additional ideas of M. P. Hassell and R. M. May that extend the host-parasite model by including a host dispersion component, of May and W. W. Murdock concerning diversity and stability in ecosystems, of Murdock on "predator switching," of the phenomenon of superparasitism and its impact on host-parasite interactions (Messenger 1968, Rogers 1972), and of Force (1974) concerning the ideas of r and K selection and parasite life strategies.

Indeed, biological control is an ecological phenomenon. It deals with insect and/or plant populations. Therefore all theoretical concepts concerning population ecology should be considered the domain of biological control theory.

Chapter 15

Establishment of Gypsy Moth Parasitoids in North America: An Evaluation of Possible Reasons for Establishment or Non-Establishment

Marjorie A. Hoy

Department of Entomology
The Connecticut Agricultural Experiment Station
New Haven, Connecticut 06504

Now with the U.S. Forest Service
Northeastern Forest Experiment Station
Hamden, Connecticut 06514

INTRODUCTION

After 70 years of intermittent effort 10 gypsy moth parasitoids became established in North America. The gypsy moth (*Lymantria dispar* L.) parasitoid introduction program is one of the few massive projects in biological control history (Brown 1961) in terms of years and of numbers of personnel involved. The program began in the fall of 1905 and continued until 1914; activity during the interval 1914–1922 was low, but in 1922 a large program resumed and continued until 1933. Extensive parasitoid importation resumed in 1963 and continues (Pschorn-Walcher 1974).

The gypsy moth remains a problem in North America even though a series of parasitoids (and predators) became established. Some believe that they have given appreciable control, so that gypsy moth outbreaks are reduced in range and severity comparable to those occurring in Europe (Clausen 1956). In contrast, others have concluded that biological control of the gypsy moth "has been tried and is hopeless . . ." (DeBach 1974). The question persists if among the remaining species not established, or others not yet discovered, "the ultimate successful solution lies hidden" (DeBach 1974).

The value of biological control is well recognized; a 30:1 benefit to cost ratio is often cited, in addition to the recognized ecological benefits of successful permanent biological control (Huffaker 1971). The established gypsy moth parasitoids should be evaluated in the light of biological control introduction theory as *no* new establishments have occurred within the past 35 years, with the questionable exception of *Brachymeria intermedia* (Nees). Thus, establishment tactics should perhaps be altered, either by altering the species types imported, the colonization methods used, or a combination of both.

Nearly all workers recognize that it is impossible to make reliable predictions about the effectiveness of a given parasitoid, or even if it will establish (Clausen 1956, Sweetman 1936, DeBach 1964b, Huffaker et al. 1971, Stehr 1974, Beirne 1974, Messenger 1971). This paper attempts to evaluate why certain gypsy moth parasitoids became established and why others did not establish, based upon available records of ecological and/or biological information, or based upon establishment tactics used. Assuming that new introductions will be made, it seems that first priority should be given to maximizing the probability that such new introductions lead to establishment.

SPECIES ESTABLISHED AGAINST THE GYPSY MOTH

Ten species of gypsy moth parasitoids attack a sequence of the host life stages in North America (Table 1): two attack eggs, two attack small larvae, four are found in large late larvae, and two attack pupae. Their introduction histories demonstrate several interesting phenomena, including establishment of a facultative hyperparasitoid, delayed establishment, taxonomic confusion, etc. For the purposes of this chapter, information about their establishment history and biology was obtained from reports by Howard and Fiske (1911), Burgess and Crossman (1929), and Dowden (1962), although additional information was obtained from others.

Discrepancies occur with respect to insect numbers and species identifications in a number of the papers. Some errors are probably unavoidable because of the time that has elapsed since the original introductions were made and the unavailability of adequate insect specimens for taxonomic confirmation. Sabrosky and Reardon (in press) review the taxonomy and bionomics of tachinids that attack the gypsy moth; a similar, forthcoming manuscript by P. M. Marsh (pers. comm.) on the braconid species should fill additional gaps.

Egg Parasitoids

Anastatus disparis Ruschka (Eupelmidae), called *A. bifasciatus* Fonscolmbe in older publications, is a solitary egg parasitoid from Europe and Japan. *A.*

disparis attacks unembryonated gypsy moth eggs. It is univoltine, host specific, synchronous with the gypsy moth and overwinters in host eggs. *A. disparis* established easily, apparently at the original colonization site (Table 1). However, it dispersed slowly (about 60 m/year) and had to be extensively colonized to aid its spread, possibly because the females do not fly. In 1911, this species was judged to be the "better" of the two egg parasitoids (Howard and Fiske 1911) as it was the more winter-hardy of the two. Yet, today it is exceedingly spotty in its distribution and incidence is rarely high (Tigner 1974), although between 1919–1927 average parasitism ranged up to 34% (Burgess and Crossman 1929). Reasons suggested for the decline include: high winter mortality, slow dispersal rate, inability to attack eggs in the lower layers of the egg cluster, and competition with *Ooencyrtus kuwanai* Howard, although the latter was discounted by Parker (1933).

Ooencyrtus kuwanai (Encyrtidae) was called *Schedius* in the older literature. This multivoltine internal egg parasitoid also established rapidly (Table 1). *O. kuwanai* arrived from Japan in 1909 and was established in Massachusetts by 1910 (Crossman 1925), after a few adults were bred to produce many progeny. *O. kuwanai* dispersed faster (at least 120 m/year) than *A. disparis*, perhaps because females can fly. It overwinters as adult females in forest litter (Crossman 1925). Burgess and Crossman (1929) predicted that the large overwintering mortality of females would prevent extensive spread, but it has become the dominant egg parasitoid extending over the entire gypsy moth range, and usually attacks most of the reachable eggs in the top layers of the multilayered egg mass (Weseloh 1972a, Tigner 1974).

Thus, early predictions did not hold up, and were in fact reversed with respect to the relative effectiveness of these egg parasitoids (Parker 1933). Both species are limited to the top egg mass layers; thus, parasitism is limited to about 30–40% of the eggs unless the egg masses are unusually small. Additional species of parasitoids, or predators, should be considered for introduction that can break up or get to the bottom layers of larger egg masses.

Parasitoids of Small Larvae

Apanteles melanoscelus Ratzeburg (Braconidae) is a bivoltine, solitary, early larval endoparasitoid, with generation I females attacking first and second stage gypsy moth larvae, and generation II females attacking larger larvae. *A. melanoscelus* overwinters in diapause in cocoons attached to tree trunks, etc. (Burgess and Crossman 1929). It was collected in Sicily in 1911; adults were released at one site in Massachusetts, and establishment occurred the first year (Table 1). Spread was rapid. *A. melanoscelus* may parasitize up to 39% of gypsy moth larvae; thus, it is ranked about fourth in importance among the parasitoid complex in North America (Tigner 1974). Effectiveness may be limited by a huge overwintering mortality (often 95%) due to attack by more than 35 species of native hyperparasitoids (Muesebeck and Dohanian 1927). *A. melanoscelus* is also known to attack the satin moth (*Stilnoptia salicis* (L.)) and the whitemarked tussock moth (*Hemerocampa leucostigma* (J. E. Smith)) in North America (Schaffner 1934). Schaffner believed *A. melanoscelus* could exist in the whitemarked tussock moth independently of the gypsy moth. This may have facilitated establishment on the gypsy moth.

   A. melanoscelus may provide a systematic enigma, as Nixon (1974) recently synonomized *melanoscelus* with *A. solitarius* Ratzeburg, the "satin moth parasitoid", which was established in North America in 1927 (Parker 1935). Unequivocal breeding tests are unpublished, although a cross between *A. solitarius* from satin moth in British Columbia and *A. "melanoscelus"* from gypsy moth in Connecticut yielded fertile female progeny in the backcrosses and in the F_2 generations in 1975 (Hoy, unpublished). There are interesting discrepancies in the phenologies of the parasitoid populations associated with the two host species.

   Phobocampe disparis (Viereck) (*Hyposoter* in older literature) is a univoltine, solitary ichneumonid endoparasitoid that attacks small gypsy moth larvae. It established rapidly (Table 1). Pupae were received from Italy in 1911 and about 12,000 were released in 1912, with establishment certain in four of the five original colonies by 1913. It is not known to develop in insects other than the gypsy moth in the field. Its host specificity and the large numbers released helped achieve establishment, but it dispersed slowly and is now recovered only sporadically and locally (Tigner 1974). Muesebeck and Parker (1933) noted that this species may not be well adapted to the gypsy moth as they observed possible host defense responses. *P. disparis* is also attacked by hyperparasitoids and may not be well adapted to the New England climate (Muesebeck and Parker 1933). It may be more effective in dense woodlands in Europe. Possibly a more cold-hardy and/or host adapted strain of *P. disparis* should be sought and introduced, although it is not thought to be important in Europe. There appears to be room for additional species of univoltine or bivoltine, host specific parasitoids attacking the smaller gypsy moth larvae.

Parasitoids of Larger Larvae

   Blepharipa scutellata (Tachinidae), known as *Crossocosmia, Blepharipoda* or *Sturmia* in the older literature, was recently designated as *B. pratensis* (Meigen) by virtue of priority (Sabrosky and Reardon, in press). It is a large, solitary, univoltine endoparasitoid that overwinters in puparia in the soil. Gypsy moth larvae ingest microtype eggs, but development is arrested until the host reaches the late larval or pupal stadium. *B. pratensis* established rapidly (Table 1) and dispersed well (up to 48 km/season). Initial colonies came from several areas in Europe. It ranks among the better species established against the gypsy moth (Tigner 1974, Clausen 1956). Average parasitism may be as high as 49% (Burgess and Crossman 1929). It is rarely recovered from native hosts (Schaffner 1934), despite its tactic of deposition of many microtype eggs.

Compsilura concinnata (Meigen) (Tachinidae) was called the most important U. S. parasitoid by Clausen (1956), perhaps because it attacks so many hosts besides the gypsy moth. It larviposits one to five larvae/host, which later emerge from large gypsy moth larvae or pupae. *C. concinnata* is multivoltine, (two–four generations/year) and overwinters as a second stage maggot in native lepidopteran hosts. These maggots emerge from their host in the spring, complete development, and pupate in the soil before producing adults that attack the gypsy moth in April and May. *C. concinnata* established quickly (Table 1), and dispersed rapidly (more than 40 km/season). Today it is widespread with a distribution greater than the gypsy moth in the U. S. (Schaffner 1927) because its host range is possibly greater than 200 species (Webber and Schaffner 1926). It is considered "certainly one of the most beneficial introductions that have been made" (Burgess and Crossman 1929), not only against the gypsy and brown-tail moths, but also against the satin moth, particularly in the state of Washington and in British Columbia (Tothill and McLaine 1919). Its extensive host range more than counteracted the disadvantage of an overwintering host requirement, and it established easily.

Exorista larvarum (L.) (Tachinidae), a multivoltine, solitary or gregarious endoparasitoid, attacks large larvae of the gypsy moth. It established more slowly than the preceding species. Releases in the interval 1906–1911 resulted in no establishment (Table 1); between 1925–1927, more were released and recoveries were made in 1940 and 1941. *E. larvarum* is polyphagous and overwinters as immature maggots within alternate hosts. Several parasitoids may develop after macrotype eggs are deposited on the gypsy moth caterpillar. *E. larvarum* is not common. Its effectiveness may be reduced because it may hybridize with the similar native American species, *E. mella* (Wlkr.), which has been reared only rarely from the gypsy moth (Clausen 1956). In Europe, *E. larvarum* has been evaluated as an important tachinid parasitoid of the gypsy moth (Herting 1960). Establishment may have been slow because numbers released were low originally, and also because it requires an overwintering host.

Parasetigena silvestris (Robineau-Desvoidy) (Tachinidae) has been known as *Phorocera* or *Parasetigena agilis* or *Parasetigena segregata* or *Phorocera silvestris*. It is a solitary, univoltine endoparasitoid that deposits large eggs near the head region. Maggots bore into the host and develop; pupation occurs in the soil. It develops in few hosts other than the gypsy moth. In Europe it was ranked as a very important species (Burgess and Crossman 1929). A few were released in North America in 1910 (Table 1). More were released between 1924–1926, with first recoveries in 1927. It is well synchronized with the gypsy moth and requires no alternate host.

Thus, we have four parasitoids affecting large larvae, including two species

TABLE 1 *Gypsy moth parasitoids successfully established in North America*

Host stage(s) in which parasitoid develops	Species	Dates Released Until Establishment	No. Released at Original Establishment Site(s)	No. of Original Colonies	First Recovery Indicating Establishment	Recent Relative Abundance and Importance
Egg	*Anastatus disparis* Ruschka	1908 1909	513 128,180	1 5	1910	patchy distribution, often rare; not thought important
	Ooencyrtus kuwanai (Howard)	1909 1910	46,415 889,120	5 89	1910	common, widespread; "effective" in N. America
Small larvae	*Apanteles melanoscelus* Ratzeburg	1911	23,000(?)	1	1912	widespread; often abundant; limited by hyperparasitism
	Phobocampe disparis (Viereck)	1912	12,000	5	1913	rare; patchy; not thought important
Large larvae	*Blepharipa pratensis* (Meigen)	1907 1908 1909 1910	"a few" 100 1,086 3,962	1?	1910? 1911	common, widespread often a dominant parasitoid
	Compsilura concinnata (Meigen)	1906 1907 1909 1910	" a few" "more" 6,121 749	1?	1907? 1909	common; widespread even beyond gypsy moth distribution; on many hosts
	Exorista larvarum (L.)	1906-1911 1925-1927	3,363 38,789	?	1940	rare; little information available
	Parasetigena silvestris (R-D)	1910 1924	1,183 1,850	1 3	1927	widespread, common; moderately important

Pupae	*Monodontomerus aereus* Walker	1925	8,555	5	1908-1909 winter	rare; does better on brown-tail moth which is now rare
		1926	2,112	2	1941?	widespread; only abundant in defoliated or sunny, dry sites
	Brachymeria intermedia (Nees)	1906	some of 17,000	?	1967(CT)	
		1908	"more"			
		1910	"more"			
		1908-1909	"few"	?		
		1911	15,567			
		1924	307			
		1925	956			
		1927	644			
		1963	10,636	4		

that are fairly host specific and two that are broader in their host range. There may be more effective parasitoids to add to this complex, however.

Pupal Parasitoids

Monodontomerus aereus Walker (Torymidae) attacks gypsy moth and brown-tail moth pupae. Unfortunately, it also attacks braconid cocoons and even prefers tachinid puparia, particularly those of *Compsilura concinnata* (Muesebeck 1931). Burgess and Crossman (1929) note that "little can be said in favor of the establishment of this species", but that is a retrospective judgment. When introduced, this parasitoid appeared to be a primary with only facultative secondary parasitic habits. Some *M. aereus* were released in 1906 and more were liberated between 1908–1910 from Europe and Japan (Table 1). It established and dispersed quickly but it is now rare, perhaps because the brown-tail moth, *Nygmia phaeorrhoea* (Donovan), has also become rare in North America. Thus, while it would have been better not to have released it, it is not clear how much genuine harm has resulted.

Brachymeria intermedia (Nees) (Chalcididae) has an intriguing establishment history with an apparently happy ending. This polyphagous pupal parasitoid was introduced as *Chalcis flavipes* Panzer (Howard and Fiske 1911) beginning with a few specimens from France and Italy in 1908 and 1909 (Table 1). More from Sicily were released in 1911, and between 1924–27 (Dowden 1935), without establishment. More material from Spain was released in Connecticut in 1963. Burks (1960) found one pinned reared specimen in a collection of parasitoid material recovered from a leafroller in 1942. Finally, Leonard (1966, 1967, 1971) reported *B. intermedia* to be well established on the gypsy moth in Connecticut and Maine. No one knows what happened during the interval from 1908–1966. It is possible that some 1963 Connecticut releases "took"; alternatively, it may have been sparsely present the entire time, but unrecovered. Considerable speculation exists about the need for alternate hosts by this bivoltine (uni- or tri-voltine?) species. Leonard (1967) suggested that the presence of abundant leafroller species allowed *B. intermedia* to expand. At any rate, it is now found over the northeastern United States.

B. intermedia overwinters as an adult and it is suspected that its establishment was delayed by winter mortality and/or a need for an alternate host (Dowden 1935). *B. intermedia* appears to prefer bright, open sunny areas. Thus, it may not be effective at low host densities, and a high priority might be the addition of a pupal parasitoid that prefers low host densities.

A potential source of new pupal parasitoids includes "adaptation" of one of the native, polyphagous ichneumonid parasitoids such as *Itoplectis conquisitor* (Say) which attacks gypsy moth pupae but rarely successfully develops in them (Campbell 1963a). Unfortunately, this species may also be most active only at high host densities. *Brachymeria obscurata* (Walker) from Japan (Table 3) should be evaluated as a candidate for introduction; earlier introduction attempts were inadequate.

SPECIES IMPORTED BUT NOT ESTABLISHED

It is difficult to evaluate all the species introduced but not established for a variety of reasons including: (1) their taxonomy is often confused so that names and identifications are lacking or inaccurate; (2) records are confusing or missing; and (3) basic bionomic data are frequently unavailable. Thus, one is rarely able to do more than speculate about reasons for the lack of establishments. However, Tables 2–4 include brief outlines of some of the unestablished species based on available information.

Estimates of the world-wide establishment rate for natural enemies varies, but averages 20–30% (Huffaker 1971, DeBach 1974). Reasons for failure of an exotic species to establish are rarely known with any certainty but may include: (*a*) climatic non-adaption involving latitude, altitude, temperature, and rainfall; (*b*) lack of synchronization with the host, including lack of alternate and/or overwintering hosts; (*c*) host density was too low or too close to the crash phase; (*d*) numbers released were inadequate; (*e*) production of "laboratory" strains unable to survive in the natural environment after inadvertent selection; (*f*) improper parasitoid stage released; (*g*) adequate food, water, etc. missing in the release environment; (*h*) lack of mating prior to release; and (*i*) improper timing of releases.

Ten of about 40 (25%) gypsy moth parasitoids became established. This is about average compared to biological control introduction history. Since additional introductions will be made, however, several questions are relevant: (1) Can other parasitoids be established, or have all the ones capable of establishment been established? (2) Which species are desirable and where are they? (3) How best can they be established? There are no definitive answers, but a few suggestions can be given.

It seems likely that other parasitoids can be established. Historical analysis of many biological control programs suggests that additional effort is warranted (Messenger and van den Bosch 1971), particularly using strains or races that are preadapted climatically (Messenger 1971).

Furthermore, there is some evidence (Pimentel 1963) that parasitoid species from related host species may provide a desirable source of new species for consideration. Rao (1966) reports a survey of *Lymantria obfuscata* Walker (a species very closely related to the gypsy moth) parasitoids in India conducted between 1961 and 1968. Parasitoids of related host species could be useful additions to the North American fauna. During the survey, 5 egg, 33 larval, and 11 pupal parasitoids of *L. obfuscata* were recorded as well as parasitoids from 8 other lymantriid species. Some of these species were known from Europe but a

TABLE 2 *Exotic braconid parasitoids unsuccessfully introduced into North America against the gypsy moth: Possible reasons for non-establishment*

Species	Host Stage(s) Attacked	Colony Source(s)	Host Range	Reasons Suggested for Lack of Establishment			Authority
				Alternate Host Requirement	Numbers	Other	
Apanteles liparidis (Bouché) (released also as *A. fulvipes* and *A. japonicus*)	large larvae preferred; gregarious	Japan and Europe	oligophagous *Dendrolimus pini* L. in Europe and *D. spectabilis* Butl. in Japan are hibernating hosts	absence of overwintering host in North America	adequate; large numbers released many years in many areas	?	Burgess and Crossman 1929, Wilkinson 1945
Apanteles porthetriae Muesebeck	small larvae	Europe	common on gypsy moth; oligophagous	absence of overwintering hosts	probably adequate	?	Burgess and Crossman 1929
Meteorus japonicus Ashmead	larvae	Japan	unknown	unknown; alternate host requirement suspected	too few released; 400 in 1923	?	Burgess and Crossman 1929
Meteorus pulchricornis Wesmael	larvae	Europe	polyphagous; not common on gypsy moth in Europe	unknown but alternate host requirement suspected	probably adequate	?	Burgess and Crossman 1929, Anon. 1973
Meteorus versicolor Wesmael	larvae	Europe	not a gypsy moth parasitoid primarily	this species established on satin and brown-tail moths in North America	adequate	?	Howard and Fiske 1911

Rogas indiscretus Reardon	small larvae	Northern India	oligophagous(?) naturally attacks *Lymantria obfuscata* Walker; does well on gypsy moth in laboratory	alternate host requirement suspected	inadequate?	diapause lost after inadvertent selection?	Hoy (unpubl.), Reardon et al. 1973

TABLE 3 *Exotic ichneumonid and chalcidid parasitoids unsuccessfully introduced into North America against the gypsy moth: Possible reasons for non-establishment*

Species	Host Stage(s) Attacked	Colony Source(s)	Host Range	Reasons Suggested for Lack of Establishment				Authority
				Alternate Host Requirement	Numbers	Other		
Brachymeria obscurata (Walker)	pupae	Japan	unknown	may require alternate host, but overwinters as adult females	inadequate	high winter mortality of adults		Burgess and Crossman 1929, Howard and Fiske 1911
Casinaria spp.	larvae	Europe	polyphagous(?)	?	?	?		Anon. 1973
Coccygomimus instigator Fab. and *C. examinator* Fab.	pupae	Europe	broadly polyphagous	multivoltine; need alternate hosts(?)	perhaps adequate	?		Dowden 1962, Howard and Fiske 1911, Anon., 1973
Coccygomimus turionellae (L.)	pupae	Northern India	broadly polyphagous	alternate host requirement suspected	probably adequate	?		Anon., 1973
Phobocampe spp.	larvae	Europe	unknown	unknown	?	?		Dowden 1962 Anon., 1973

TABLE 4 *Exotic tachinid parasitoids unsuccessfully introduced into North America against the gypsy moth: Possible reasons for non-establishment*

Species	Host Stage(s) Attacked	Colony Source(s)	Reasons Suggested for Lack of Establishment				Authority
			Host Range	Alternate Host Requirement	Numbers	Other	
Blondelia (= *Lydella*) *nigripes* (Fallen)	larvae	Europe	polyphagous; prefers "hairless" larvae	absence of overwintering host; multivoltine	probably inadequate	?	Dowden 1933, 1962
Blondelia piniariae (Hartig)	larvae	Europe	*Bupalus piniarius* pine geometrid, is true host	not common on gypsy moth	1929-30 about 24,612 released	does not mature in gypsy moth larvae	Dowden 1933, 1962
Blepharipa schineri (Mesnil) (= *B. sericariae* ?)	microtype eggs ingested by larvae	Europe and Japan?	oligophagous; also from *Bombyx mori* L.; biology like *B. pratensis*	univoltine; none required	inadequate	"no serious attempt" made to establish	Howard and Fiske 1911, Burgess and Crossman 1929
Carcelia gnava (Meigen)	larvae	Europe	gypsy moth an accidental host	absence of alternate hosts	inadequate	?	Howard and Fiske 1911, Sabrosky and Reardon in press
C. laxifrons Villeneuve (= *C. cheloniae*)	larvae	Europe	primarily a brown-tail moth parasitoid	?	This species established on brown-tail moth in N. America		Sabrosky and Reardon in-press

228

TABLE 4 (cont.)

Species	Host Stage(s) Attacked	Colony Source(s)	Host Range	Reasons Suggested for Lack of Establishment			Authority
				Alternate Host Requirement	Numbers	Other	
C. separata (Rondani) (also introduced as C. gnava and C. excisa)	larvae	Europe	polyphagous; especially Endromis versicolora; rare on gypsy moth	absence of overwintering host; bivoltine	adequate; a total of 17,061 liberated	?	Burgess and Crossman 1929, Dowden 1962, Sabrosky and Reardon in press
Exorista japonica (Townsend)	larvae	Japan	polyphagous	unknown	inadequate; 471 released up to 1927	?	Dowden 1962
E. rossica (Mesnil)	larvae	Northern India	oligophagous; from L. obfuscata; satin moth	absence of overwintering host; multivoltine	?	mating difficult in lab rearing	Reardon et al. 1973
E. segregata (Rondani) (= Tricholyga grandis)	larvae	Europe	broadly polyphagous including gypsy moth	absence of overwintering host; multivoltine	?	?	Burgess and Crossman 1929, Reardon et al. 1973
Masicera sylvatica (Fallen)	larvae	Europe	oligophagous; primarily on Macrothylacia rubi, a lasiocampid	not a gypsy moth parasitoid	inadequate; 23 released before 1927	?	Dowden 1962, Howard and Fiske 1911

Species	Stage	Distribution	Host range	Limiting factors	Status	References
Pales pavida (Meigen)	larvae ingest microeggs	Europe	polyphagous; prefers brown-tail moth (?)	absence of alternate host; multivoltine	582 to 1928 rare on 850 to 1932 gypsy moth	Dowden 1962
Palexorista inconspicua (Meigen) (= *Drino "inconspicuoides"*?)	larvae	Europe Northern India	polyphagous overwinters in Europe in *Dendrolimus pini* and in diprionid sawflies	absence of overwintering host; bivoltine	adequate? ?	Dowden 1962, Webber 1932
Palexorista sp. nr. *solennis* (WK) (= *Drino discreta* "of Rao 1967")	larvae	Northern India	polyphagous (?) from *L. obfuscata*	?	? ?	Sabrosky and Reardon in press
Tachina magnicornis (Zetterstedt)	large larvae	Europe	polyphagous; usually attacks noctuid larvae; also brown-tail moth	?	inadequate? ?	Howard and Fiske 1911
Zenillia libatrix (Panzer)	microtype eggs ingested; development delayed until pupa	Europe	oligophagous (?) primarily a brown-tail moth parasite (?)	absence of overwintering host pupae, 1-3 generations a year	1906-1910 504 released 1927-1933 1,400 released	Dowden 1934, 1962, Burgess and Crossman 1929

number were new. Reardon et al. (1973) reported biologies and release attempts (Tables 2, 4) for only two species.

In addition, perhaps 70–90% of all parasitic Hymenoptera remain to be discovered and named (DeBach 1974). Some of these may be gypsy moth parasitoids suitable for establishment. Thompson (1946) listed 196 species of gypsy moth parasitoids worldwide. Some of these are errors or are strays (see Table 4), but there may be species missing from the list that are adapted to the gypsy moth or to closely related host species. Possible new parasitoid sources include Afghanistan, China, Formosa, Iraq, Israel, Japan, Korea, Lebanon, Persia, Syria, Tibet, Turkey, the U.S.S.R., Algeria, Morocco, and Tunisia. None of these sources have been adequately surveyed.

It appears that little can be done with the unestablished European parasitoids. Most of these species are unlikely to establish because of an alternate host requirement or because they are incidental or stray species (Tables 2–4). Many of these species attack the satin, brown-tail, or nun (*L. monacha* (L.)) moths in Europe, and unless these pest species become abundant or are introduced into North America there seems little hope of establishment or expansion of their parasitoids. The North American species of Lepidoptera that overwinter as larvae do not appear to be sufficiently and reliably abundant (Schaffner and Griswold 1934) to provide adequate overwintering host populations.

The question of how best any newly discovered or collected exotic species can be established is less easy to answer. Data in Tables 1–4, however, allow certain generalizations.

Seven of the 10 established parasitoids were recovered from overwintering sites within 3 years *or less* after release (Table 1). Thus, they established rapidly at their release points. The exceptions involve *B. intermedia, P. silvestris,* and *E. larvarum*. No one knows just where *B. intermedia* and *E. larvarum* were during the period prior to their recovery, but *P. silvestris* may well have established within the 3-year period during the second attempt. In general, the parasitoids capable of establishment did so rapidly, although this did not necessarily indicate their ultimate effectiveness.

Another fact evident from Table 1 is that the numbers of insects released were often in the range of 1,000–20,000, with releases often made at only one to five sites. I suspect that recent releases may be inadequate in terms of numbers, especially with tachinids.

Furthermore, early, successful releases were made at sites with abundant hosts in expanding host populations (Howard and Fiske 1911, Burgess and Crossman 1929). Additionally, most of the parasitoids were collected in Europe and Japan and, after screening for hyperparasitoids, released into the field without *any* laboratory propagation.

Laboratory propagation is known to affect insect quality detrimentally

(Mackauer 1972, House 1967, Boller 1972, Hoy 1975a, Ashley et al. 1973, Young et al. 1975). One reason for laboratory propagation prior to release is that so few insects are received that multiplication is necessary. This could be one reason for recent difficulties in obtaining establishments. Most authors agree with Simmonds (1963) that "there is obviously a wide field for research into and application of genetical principles in connection with biological control work. . . " We have inadequate data to settle a series of genetic questions. Some authors (Remington 1968, Wilson 1965, Price 1972a) have discussed theoretical aspects of these problems, but few experimental tests have been conducted (Ashley et al. 1974, Hoy 1975b).

The practical problems of preventing genetic deterioration during laboratory propagation have thus not been solved. Furthermore, foreign collection is often difficult and expensive. It is usually difficult to ship large numbers of parasitoids. Therefore, some type of host population "seeding" may allow larger numbers to be collected. If trays or containers of gypsy moth larvae were placed into areas where desirable parasitoids were present, parasitized hosts could be harvested and shipped to the quarantine facility. Or, one may "seed" an area with gypsy moth eggs or larvae.

Field cages may be desirable for multiplicative propagation after release from quarantine so that natural conditions can be maintained. The colony could also be observed for its overwintering ability in the new environment prior to release. Knowledge of overwintering sites or need for alternate hosts is nearly obligatory to ensure establishment. If alternate hosts are needed, special efforts could be made to release in areas with suitable hosts. However, the general unavailability of overwintering hosts is a serious problem in North America. Desirable species such as *Apanteles liparidis* (Bouché) and *A. porthetriae* Muesebeck seem unlikely to establish in spite of releases of large numbers over many years (Table 2).

Multiplicative propagation for mass release is difficult with species having an obligatory diapause. For species with a facultative diapause, knowledge of relevant induction mechanisms may be crucial to prevent inadvertent removal of diapause prior to release (Hoy 1975a, b). It is possible that desirable genetic modifications could be made so that strains with a desired critical photophase could be produced for a particular area (Hoy 1975a) but this has not yet been tested practically.

Field cages could also provide other bionomic information, such as host suitability. Incidental species found rarely on the gypsy moth are unlikely to establish, or to be effective subsequent to establishment. Efforts should thus not be wasted on apparently non-adapted parasitoids such as *Blondelia nigripes* (Fallen), *B. piniariae* (Hartig), *Carcelia gnava* (Meigen), *Pales pavida* (Meigen), *Palexorista inconspicua* (Meigen), and *Zenillia libatrix* (Panzer) (Table 4).

Generally, gypsy moth parasitoid establishments will be most likely with host specific, synchronous species. These parasitoids will not be found in Europe. Attention should be given to releases of large numbers, at a few sites, of insects reared under relatively natural conditions in outdoor insectaries. Thus, both the species released and the methods of release ought to be revised to obtain additional establishments of beneficial gypsy moth parasitoids.

ACKNOWLEDGMENTS

R. W. Weseloh, R. C. Reardon, J. R. Coulson, T. M. Odell, D. E. Leonard and P. S. Messenger made helpful comments on the manuscript.

Special appreciation is extended to Curtis Sabrosky and Richard Reardon for allowing me to see their in press manuscript on the tachinid parasitoids of the gypsy moth.

Chapter 16

Egg Parasitoids
of Forest Defoliating Lepidoptera

John F. Anderson

Department of Entomology
The Connecticut Agricultural Experiment Station
New Haven, Connecticut 06504

INTRODUCTION

Few detailed bionomic studies of egg parasitoids of forest defoliating Lepidoptera have been reported. Yet evidence suggests that these parasitoids may be more important in natural control and have more potential in biological control than has been recognized. Space limitations preclude consideration of all aspects of their biology. Systematics, host parasitism, host specificity, dispersal, overwintering and diapause, hyperparasitoids and diseases, rearing, colonization and effect of insecticides will be reviewed. Parasitoid behavior, juvenile developmental types and rates along with other aspects of parasitoid biology have been reviewed elsewhere (Doutt 1959, 1964, Clausen 1962, Hagen 1964, Askew 1971, and Weseloh, Chapter 8).

SYSTEMATICS

The systematics of the most important egg parasitoids of forest defoliating Lepidoptera (*Trichogramma*, Trichogrammatidae; *Telenomus*, Scelionidae; and *Ooencyrtus*, Encyrtidae) are poorly known. Compere (1969) writes: " . . . of the named species, relatively few have been adequately described, . . . The great majority of described chalcidoids cannot be identified with any degree of certainty on the basis of existing descriptions." L. Masner (pers. comm.) has indicated that only a fragment of the collected species of *Telenomus* in North

America have been described. Published articles often refer to the parasitoids only to the generic level; sometimes the parasitoids are misidentified. Major taxonomic revisions of species in North America are needed, but apparently are not underway. The genus *Telenomus* is particularly in need of revision. Little biological information is available for the majority of species, thereby making the validity of species determinations and affinities that much more difficult. Good keys are usually unavailable, though a key to the *Telenomus* of Palearctica (Kozlov 1967) has been published. Nagarkatti and Nagaraja (1971) and Nagaraja and Nagarkatti (1973) reported on the *Trichogramma* species, but difficulties remain with their identification. All of these unfortunate circumstances severely hamper research with egg parasitoids in biological control.

HOST PARASITISM

Reports of egg parasitoids of forest defoliating Lepidoptera are too numerous to list. Hosts of North American species may be found in the catalogs of Thompson (1950), Muesebeck et al. (1951), Krombein (1958), Peck (1963), Krombein and Burks (1967) and Stehr and Cook (1968). More recent listings of egg parasitoids of various host groups may be found in the articles of Ticehurst and Allen (1973), Witter and Kulman (1972), Harman and Kulman (1973), Nagarkatti and Nagaraja (1971) and Nagaraja and Nagarkatti (1973). Nikol'skaya (1963) lists the hosts of chalcids in the USSR, and Kozlov (1967) identifies the hosts of scelionids in Palearctica.

Effects on Host Populations

The effect of egg parasitoids on forest defoliators is incompletely known. Some parasitoids are known to have minor, or at best, moderate effects. Generally, polyphagous species will be dependent upon the abundance of alternate hosts and thus unable to increase in a density dependent manner. Also, parasitization of egg masses which are multi-layered is usually low as is the case with those which are covered with scales or accessory gland material. Other parasitoids have been shown to exert greater pressure on their hosts. These species are often monophagous or oligophagous, and their hosts lay eggs which either are not covered with scales or accessory gland material or are covered lightly. Little is known about the effects of egg parasitoids when their hosts are scarce, though *Telenomus tetratomus* Thomson (= *T. gracilis* Mayr) has been reported to prevent outbreaks of *Dendrolimus sibiricus* Tschtev. (Boldaruyev 1971).

Natural parasitization of eggs is given in Table 1. These data indicate that egg parasitoids may have an important influence on populations of some host species. The role of *Ooencyrtus ennomophagus* Yosh. in the collapse of the elm spanworm, *Ennomos subsignarius* (Hübner), outbreak is one of the better documented studies (Kaya and Anderson 1972, 1974a). This parasitoid decimated host eggs in southwestern Connecticut in 1971 and in central and eastern Connecticut in 1972. No more than 2 years of defoliation by the elm spanworm occurred in any given location in southwestern and central Connecticut (Anderson and Gould 1974). None occurred in eastern Connecticut, even though large numbers of host eggs were deposited.

Another egg parasitoid, *Telenomus* sp. (originally considered *T. alsophilae* Viereck), was important in terminating an outbreak of the elm spanworm in the southern Appalachians (Ciesla 1964b, 1965, Drooz 1964), but was relatively unimportant in the Connecticut outbreak (Anderson and Kaya 1973a, 1974a). Shortage and quality of food also contributed to the collapse in the southern Appalachians (Ciesla 1964b, Drooz 1970, 1971). The major factor in preventing noticeable defoliation in older outbreak populations of another geometrid, *Hydria prunivorata* (Ferguson) was another species of *Telenomus* (Schultz and Allen 1975).

The collapse of the outbreak of *Symmerista canicosta* Franclemont in Connecticut was caused in part by *Telenomus* sp. and to a lesser extent by *Trichogramma* sp. (Anderson and Kaya unpublished data). Parasitization of 64% was recorded in 1974 1 year after severe defoliation and was in excess of 86% in 1975.

Telenomus coelodasidis Ash. is an important parasitoid of the saddled prominent, *Heterocampa guttivitta* (Wlkr.) (Table 1). Collins (1926) indicated that this parasitoid was the single most important factor in its control. Allen (1972) suggested that it was capable of keeping defoliation caused by its host to a tolerable level.

Outbreaks of *D. sibiricus* are prevented and terminated by *T. tetratomus* (Boldaruyev 1971). Outbreaks occur following fire which kills overwintering parasitoid females. In the absence of fire, this egg parasitoid is numerous enough to suppress host populations before an outbreak occurs.

Mortality of the eye-spotted bud moth, *Spilonota ocellana* (D. & S.), by *Trichogramma minutum* Riley was reported to be at a high level, but was not an important "key factor" in predicting the population trend (LeRoux et al. 1963). Parasitization was important, however, in reducing summer larval populations. Likewise in the pine looper, *Bupalus piniarius* L., parasitization by *Trichogramma embryophagum* Htg. may be as high as 69%, but at most it acts as a secondary effect superimposed upon larval mortality, which is the primary cause of population fluctuations (Klomp 1966). In general, parasitization by *Trichogramma* may be quite high but is variable and is dependent upon the density of alternate hosts (Miller 1953, 1963, Neilson 1963a, Harris 1960, Klomp 1966).

There have been several studies which show that egg parasitoids are relatively unimportant in the dynamics of some hosts. *T. minutum* is unimportant in the natural control of the spruce budworm, *Choristoneura fumiferana* (Clem.) (Miller 1963). Egg parasitoids from six families have been

TABLE 1 *Parasitization or Abundance of Parasitoids of Eggs of Forest Defoliating Lepidoptera*

Host	Parasitoid	Parasitization or Abundance	Location	Reference
SATURNIIDAE				
Coloradia pandora Blake	Tetrastichus pandora Burks	17%	N.A.[1]	Patterson 1929
Pseudobunaea irius (F.)	Anastatus sp. Mesocomys pulchriceps Cameron Pediobius	Low	Africa	Van den Berg 1974
Nudaurelia belina (Westw.)	Mesocomys pulchriceps Eupelmus urozonus (Dal.) Anastatus sp. Pediobius	44%	Africa	Van den Berg 1971
Anisota senatoria (J. E. Smith)	Trichogramma pretiosum Riley Tetrastichus sp.	23-74%	N.A.	Hitchcock 1961
ARCTIIDAE				
Hyphantria cunea (Drury)	Trichogramma sp.	Low	N.A.	Tothill 1922, Warren and Tadic 1970
	Trichogramma evanescens Wstw.	Low	Europe	Nagy et al. 1953
NOTODONTIDAE				
Datana integerrima G. & R.	Trichogramma minutum Riley Telenomus sphingis (Ashm.) Tetrastichus sp.	22-93%	N.A.	Leiby 1925
	Trichogramma minutum Telenomus ichthyurae Ashm.	Low to High	N.A.	Haseman 1940, Baerg 1928, Hixson 1941
Symmerista canicosta Francl.	Telenomus sp. Trichogramma pretiosum or Trichogramma sp.	33-86%	N.A.	Hitchcock 1958, Anderson and Kaya, unpublished data, Wallner and Surgeoner, unpublished data

236

Host	Parasite	Percentage	Region	Reference
Heterocampa manteo (Dbldy.)	*Telenomus* sp. ⎫ *Trichogramma* sp. ⎬	up to 80%	N.A.	Kearby, unpublished data, Wallner and Surgeoner, unpublished data
Heterocampa guttivitta (Wlkr.)	*Telenomus coelodasidis* Ashm.	17-100%	N.A.	Fiske and Burgess 1910, Collins 1926, Allen 1972, Ticehurst and Allen 1973
	Trichogramma minutum	1-20%	N.A.	Collins 1926, Allen 1972
Thaumetopoea wilkinsoni Tams.	*Ooencyrtus pityocampae* Mercet ⎫ *Anastatus bifasciatus* Fons. ⎬	17%	Europe	Wilkinson 1926

LYMANTRIIDAE

Host	Parasite	Percentage	Region	Reference
Hemerocampa pseudotsugata McD.	*Trichogramma minutum*	High	N.A.	Keen 1938
Stilpnotia salicis (L.)	*Telenomus californicus* Ashm. ⎫ *Trichogramma minutum* ⎬	Low	N.A.	Burgess and Crossman 1927, Jones et al. 1938
	Telenomus mayri Kief.	Low	Europe	Jones et al. 1938, Brown 1931
Lymantria dispar L.	*Telenomus* sp.	Low	Europe	Howard 1910
	Gryon lymantriae (Masner)	Low	Europe	Masner 1958
	Gryon howardi (Mokr. and Ogl.)	75-85%	Europe	Mokrzecki and Ogloblin 1931
	Anastatus disparis Ruschka	Rarely over 50%, usually lower	N.A.	Howard 1921, Burgess and Crossman 1929
	Anastatus disparis	3%	Asia	Crossman 1925
	Anastatus disparis	up to 25%	Europe	Crossman 1925, Burgess and Crossman 1929, Tadic 1961
	Ooencyrtus kuwanai (Howard)	up to 51%	N.A.	Howard 1924, Doane 1968b, Crossman 1925
	Ooencyrtus kuwanai	up to 33%	Asia	Crossman 1925
	Ooencyrtus kuwanai ⎫ *Telenomus phalaenarum* Nees ⎬ *Anastatus disparis* *Kranophorus extentus* Wlkr. *Gryon lymantriae*	Low, maybe to 50%	Europe	Keremidchiev and Gantschev 1973

TABLE 1 (cont.)

Host	Parasitoid	Parasitization or Abundance	Location	Reference
LYMANTRIIDAE				
Nygmia phaeorrhoea (Donov.)	*Telenomus phalaenarum*	Low	Europe	Howard and Fiske 1911
	Trichogramma pretiosum	Low	N.A.	Howard and Fiske 1911
	Trichogramma sp.	Low	Europe	Howard and Fiske 1911
Orgyia antiqua L.	*Telenomus dalmanni* Rtzb.	up to 70%	Europe	Wellenstein and Fabritius 1973, Kolomiets 1958
	Trichogramma dendrolimi Mats.	Common	Europe	Kolomiets 1958
Dasychira abietis Schif.	*Trichogramma dendrolimi*	Frequent	Europe	Kolomiets 1958
	Telenomus tetratomus Thomson	Frequent	Europe	Kolomiets 1958
Dasychira plagiata (Wlkr.)	*Trichogramma minutum* Riley, *Telenomus bifidus* Riley	2-6%	N.A.	Walgenbach and Benjamin 1963
LASIOCAMPIDAE				
Malacosoma disstria Hübner	*Ablerus clisiocampae* (Ashm.), *Trichogramma evanescens* Wstw., *Ooencyrtus clisiocampae* (Ashm.), *Tetrastichus sylvaticus* Gahan, *Telenomus clisiocampae* Riley	up to 10%	N.A.	Stehr and Cook 1968, McLeod and Ayre 1956, Hodson 1941, Witter and Kulman 1972, Witter et al. 1972, Langston 1957
M. americanum (Fab.)	*Tetrastichus malacosomae* Girault, *Ooencyrtus clisiocampae*, *Telenomus clisiocampae*, *Ablerus clisiocampae*, *Anastatus* sp.	Low	N.A.	Langston 1957, Stehr and Cook 1968

Host	Parasite / Predator	Rate	Region	Reference
M. californicum (Pack.)	*Tetrastichus malacosomae*	Low	N.A.	Langston 1957, Stehr and Cook 1968, McLeod and Ayre 1956
	Tetrastichus sylvaticus			
	Ooencyrtus clisiocampae			
	Ooencyrtus sp.			
	Telenomus clisiocampae			
	Telenomus sp.			
	Anastatus sp.			
	Microdontomerus fumipennis Cfd.			
	Trichogramma minutum			
M. incurvum (Neu.)	*Tetrastichus malacosomae*	Low	N.A.	Stehr and Cook 1968
	Ooencyrtus clisiocampae			
M. constrictum (Henry Edwards)	*Tetrastichus malacosomae*	Low	N.A.	Stehr and Cook 1968
	Dirhicnus sp.			
	Ooencyrtus clisiocampae			
M. tigris (Dyar)	*Ooencyrtus clisiocampae*	Low	N.A.	Stehr and Cook 1968,
	Ablerus clisiocampae		N.A.	Stehr and Cook 1968
M. neustrium L.	*Telenomus laeviusculus* Ratz.	>40%	Europe	Romanova and Lozinskij 1958
	Ooencyrtus neustriae (Mercet)			
	Ooencyrtus tardus Ratz.			
	Trichogramma pallida (Meyer)			
Dendrolimus sibiricus Tschetv.	*Telenomus tetratomus*	Common	Europe	Kolomiets 1957, 1958,
		up to 95%		Boldaruyev 1971
	Ooencyrtus pinicola Mats.	Rare	Europe	Kolomiets 1958
	Trichogramma dendrolimi Mats.	Common	Europe	Kolomiets 1958
D.s. albolineatus Mats.	*Ooencyrtus pinicola*	up to 94%	Asia	Tabata and Tamanuki 1940
	Telenomus dendrolimusi Chu			
	Trichogramma dendrolimi			

TABLE 1 (cont.)

Host	Parasitoid	Parasitization or Abundance	Location	Reference
LASIOCAMPIDAE				
D. pini L.	*Telenomus tetratomus*	up to 56%	Europe	Kolomiets 1958, Ryvkin 1959
	Trichogramma dendrolimi	Frequent	Europe	Kolomiets 1958
	Ooencyrtus sp.	Rare	Europe	Kolomiets 1958
D. spectabilis Butler	*Trichogramma dendrolimi*	up to 62%	Asia	Kim et al. 1965
	Telenomus dendrolimi Mats.	up to 9%	Asia	Kim et al. 1965
	Anastatus sp.	up to 3%	Asia	Kim et al. 1965
GEOMETRIDAE				
Alsophila pometaria (Harris)	*Telenomus alsophilae* Vier. *Trichogramma minutum* }	up to 62%	N.A.	Rauschenberger and Talerico 1967, Fedde et al. 1973
	Telenomus alsophilae *Euplectrus mellipes* Prov. }	up to 90%	N.A.	Neilson and Cuming 1958
Lambdina fiscellaria (Guenée)	*Telenomus* sp.	3%	N.A.	Otvos and Bryant 1972
Ellopia somniaria Hlst.	*Telenomus* sp.	Very high	N.A.	Fletcher 1893
Ennomos subsignarius (Hübner)	*Telenomus* sp.	up to 87%	N.A.	Ciesla 1964b, 1965, Drooz 1964, Anderson and Kaya 1973a, 1974a
	Ooencyrtus ennomophagus Yosh.	up to 99%	N.A.	Kaya and Anderson 1972, 1974a
Bupalus piniarius L.	*Trichogramma embryophagum* Htg. *Trichogramma evanescens* }	up to 69%	Europe	Ryvkin 1959, Klomp 1966
	Telenomus sp.	49%	Europe	Steiner 1931
Erannis jacobsoni Djak	*Telenomus mayri* Kieff.	53%	Europe	Boldaruyev 1972

Host	Parasitoid	Parasitism	Origin	Reference
Hydria prunivorata (Ferguson)	*Telenomus* sp.	57-100%	N.A.	Schultz and Allen 1975
	Trichogramma minutum	1%	N.A.	Schultz and Allen 1975
OLETHREUTIDAE				
Rhyacionia buoliana (Schiff.)	*Trichogramma evanescens*	up to 17%	Europe	Harris 1960, Thorpe 1930, Arthur and Juillet 1961, W.E. Miller 1959, 1967, Haynes and Butcher 1962, Kulman 1965
	Trichogramma minutum	up to 84%	N.A.	
R. frustrana (Comst.)	*Trichogramma minutum*	High	N.A.	Underhill 1943
R. zozana (Kearfott)	*Trichogramma* sp.	Rare	N.A.	Stevens 1966
Rhyacionia sp.	*Trichogramma minutum*	64%	N.A.	Yates III 1966
Spilonota ocellana (D. and S.)	*Trichogramma minutum*	up to 77%	N.A.	Lochhead 1915, DuPorte 1917, Gilliatt 1932, LeRoux et al. 1963
Epinotia aceriella (Clemens)	*Trichogramma minutum*	up to 36%	N.A.	Côté and Allen 1973
TORTRICIDAE				
Archips cerasivoranus (Fitch)	*Trichogrammatomyis tortricis* Gir.	75-80%	N.A.	Baird 1918
A. argyrospilus (Wlkr.)	*Trichogrammatomyis tortricis*	High	N.A.	Thatcher 1926, Garman and Townsend 1952
A. rosaceana (Harr.)	*Trichogramma minutum*	3 to 5%	N.A.	Schuh and Mote 1948
Argyrotaenia velutinana (Wlkr.)	*Trichogramma pretiosum*	Low	N.A.	Townsend 1943
	Trichogramma minutum	Very high	N.A.	Glass 1963
A. mariana (Fernald)	*Trichogramma minutum*	up to 6%	N.A.	Gilliatt 1937
Acleris variana (Fernald)	*Trichogramma* sp.	Very high	N.A.	Graham 1945
A. gloverana (Wals.)	*Trichogramma minutum*	up to 22%	N.A.	Torgersen 1970

TABLE 1 (cont.)

Host	Parasitoid	Parasitization or Abundance	Location	Reference
TORTRICIDAE				
Choristoneura fumiferana (Clem.)	Trichogramma minutum	up to 77%, usually below 15%	N.A.	Hewitt 1912, Miller 1963, MacDonald 1963, Jaynes and Drooz 1952, Dowden et al. 1948, Wilkes et al. 1948, Dowden et al. 1950, Miller 1953, Carolin and Coulter 1959, Thomas 1966
C. pinus Freeman	Trichogramma minutum	up to 63%	N.A.	Benjamin and Drooz 1954, Dixon and Benjamin 1963
COLEOPHORIDAE				
Coleophora serratella (L.)	Trichogramma minutum	.2%	N.A.	LeRoux et al. 1963
NYMPHALIDAE				
Caligo eurilochus (Cramer)	Xenufens sp.	up to 100%	S.A.[2]	Malo 1961

[1] North America
[2] South America

recorded from various species of *Malacosoma* (Witter and Kulman 1972), yet the combined incidence of parasitism from all species for any given host has been below 10% (Table 1). Egg parasitism in the Lymantriidae has likewise been relatively low. The one exception is the 75–85% rate of parasitism of the gypsy moth, *Lymantria dispar* L., by the scelionid, *Gryon howardi* (Mokr. and Ogl.) (Mokrzecki and Ogloblin 1931). This report has not been verified and L. Masner (pers. comm.) doubts its validity because species of *Gryon* usually attack Hemiptera.

Parasitization is affected by the size of the egg mass. The rate of parasitism by *T. minutum* in eggs of the European pine shoot moth, *Rhyacionia buoliana* (Schiff.), was highest in egg masses with four eggs and showed a decline in both larger and smaller egg masses (Kulman 1965). Smaller egg masses of the gypsy moth are more heavily parasitized than the larger ones because of the multilayering of the eggs (Crossman 1925, Burgess and Crossman 1929, Dowden 1961a, Weseloh 1972a). Percent parasitism of the elm spanworm eggs by *O. ennomophagus* was either not correlated with egg mass size or was correlated negatively (Anderson and Kaya 1973a). Thomas (1966) reported that egg mass size of the spruce budworm did not affect parasitization by *T. minutum*.

Microhabitat and Spatial Distribution

Parasitization also is affected by the tree species upon which host eggs are laid. European pine shoot moth eggs laid on Scotch pines, *Pinus sylvestris* L., were more heavily parasitized by *T. minutum* than were eggs deposited on jack pines, *P. banksiana* Lamb., (Haynes and Butcher 1962). Allen (1972) reported that the rate of parasitism of saddled prominent eggs on beech, *Fagus grandifolia* Ehrh., was twice that on sugar maple, *Acer saccharum* Marsh. Likewise, the composition of the forest stand may affect parasitization (Steiner 1931, Kim et al. 1965). Parasitization of pine looper eggs by *T. embryophagum* in pure pine stands was lower than in pine stands mixed with spruce, *Picea*, or beech. Similarly, parasitization of *D. spectabilis* Butler by *Trichogramma dendrolimi* Matsumura was lower in pure pine stands than in mixed forest stands. Possibly, mixed stands are more favorable for polyphagous parasitoids because of the occurrence of a greater variety of hosts.

Parasitization also varies with the height at which eggs are deposited within the forest. Allen (1972) reported that parasitism of saddled prominent eggs by *Telenomus coelodasidis* and *Trichogramma minutum* was higher in the upper crown, but Ticehurst and Allen (1973) reported no differences. Incidence of parasitism of elm spanworm eggs by *O. ennomophagus* was greater in the upper portions of the forest (Anderson and Kaya 1973a). In contrast, parasitization by *Telenomus* sp. was similar at all levels. Parasitization of spruce budworm eggs by *T. minutum* tends to be higher in the upper crown (Miller 1953, Thomas 1966).

Trichogramma embryophagum also tends to concentrate in the upper parts of trees (Scepetil'nikova 1970, Ryvkin 1959). Gypsy moth eggs are parasitized similarly by *Ooencyrtus kuwanai* (Howard) and *Anastatus disparis* Ruschka at all levels of the forest (Crossman 1925, Burgess and Crossman 1929, Weseloh 1972c). Thus, with some parasitoids, at least, sampling at various crown levels may be necessary to acquire a more accurate assessment of the impact of the parasitoid on the host.

HOST SPECIFICITY

Host specificity ranges from the polyphagous *Trichogramma* to the more specific encyrtids. The seasonal host sequence for polyphagous species has not been determined. For example, the sequence of alternate hosts of the only egg parasitoid, *T. minutum*, of the well-studied spruce budworm is unknown (Neilson 1963a). Exceptions are *T. embryophagum* which was reported to parasitize six hosts in Holland and 13 hosts in the USSR during its six annual generations (Ryvkin 1959, Klomp 1956), and *T. dendrolimi* which was reared from eight hosts in Korea (Kim et al. 1965). The hosts parasitized during each generation were identified, including the overwintering hosts.

The encyrtid parasitoids appear fairly host specific. For example, *O. kuwanai* has been reared on nine species of Lepidoptera in the laboratory (Crossman 1925, Burgess and Crossman 1929), but in the field it essentially parasitizes only the gypsy moth, though occasional hyperparasitism of *Apanteles melanoscelus* (Ratz.) has been reported (Muesebeck and Dohanian 1927). *O. ennomophagus*, in addition to parasitizing the elm spanworm, also has been infrequently recovered from *Malacosoma americanum* (Fab.) and possibly *Alsophila pometaria* (Harris) (Kaya and Anderson 1976, Fedde et al. 1973). *O. clisiocampae* (Ashm.) has been recovered from six species of *Malacosoma* (Stehr and Cook 1968).

A. disparis mainly parasitizes eggs of the gypsy moth. It has been reared from *Palomena prasina* L. eggs (Moravskaya 1973) and from cocoons of *A. melanoscelus* (Burgess and Crossman 1929). *A. semiflavidus* Gah. is a common parasitoid of *Hemileuca oliviae* Ckll. and also has been taken from *H. nevadensis* Stretch (Caffrey 1921). The latter host may be a reservoir for the parasitoid when the former species is not abundant. *A. bifasciatus* Fonscolombe was recovered from three hosts in Asia (Kim et al. 1965).

The gaps in the taxonomy of the genus *Telenomus* make it difficult to evaluate host specificity. It appears that species are monophagous or oligophagous. Most have been recorded from a single host; a few have been recorded from several hosts. *T. alsophilae*, which parasitizes the fall cankerworm, has been reared from at least 10 species of Lepidoptera in the laboratory (Fedde 1975) and parasitized *Oxydia trychiata* (Guenée) in the field (Drooz, in press). *T. californicus* Ashm., a native parasitoid of *Hemerocampa pseudotsugata* (McD.), also parasitizes the introduced satin moth, *Stilpnotia salicis* (L.) (Burgess and Crossman 1927). *T. tetratomus* has been reared from eggs of five host species in Europe (Kozlov 1967); *T. dendrolimi* Matsumura was recovered from four host species in Asia (Kim et al. 1965).

DISPERSAL

Dispersal of a few species has been studied. The flightless females of *A. disparis* have limited dispersal capabilities (Burgess 1916), but are capable of jumping and are wind blown 91–122m. Crossman (1925) reported that the annual spread of well established colonies was greater than recently established ones. This parasitoid dispersed only 61 m in the year that it was liberated, but had an average spread of 1,417 m from its point of release 5 years later.

O. kuwanai spread more rapidly (Crossman 1925), dispersing 366 m from the point of release in a single generation, and more than 0.8 km in 1 year. Colonies had spread nearly 3.2 km by the end of the second year. Its flight activities were reported to be maximal in the subcrown levels of the forest (Weseloh 1972c) which is consistent with its responses to abiotic environmental factors in the laboratory (Weseloh 1971).

O. ennomophagus may disperse several kilometers within 1 year (Kaya and Anderson 1974a), tends to move to the upper parts of the forest (Anderson and Kaya 1973b), and disperses laterally at or above the canopy (Kaya and Anderson 1974b). Parasitoids were caught most frequently on clear plastic panels at 1530 to 2030 hrs.

Trichogramma minutum dispersed over an area of 3,010 sq m within 3 days in an orchard when released from a single point (Schread and Garman 1933); *T. embryophagum* dispersed 120–130 m within 4 weeks after release in a forest (Ryvkin 1959).

Phoresy is a method of dispersal for some species of *Telenomus*, *Trichogramma* and *Xenufens* (Tabata and Tamanuki 1940, Kolomiets 1957, Malo 1961, Zinov'yev 1962 and Boldaruyev 1971).

OVERWINTERING AND DIAPAUSE

Egg parasitoids overwinter as adults or as juveniles within host eggs. *T. embryophagum* diapauses in eggs of hosts which have fallen from trees to the ground litter (Klomp 1956, Ryvkin 1959). Experimentally, various species of *Trichogramma* survive within host eggs at low temperatures for several months (Howard and Fiske 1911, Flanders 1930, Peterson 1931, Mokrzecki and Bragina 1916, Schread and Garman 1933). Some species of *Ooencyrtus* and *Telenomus* overwinter as adults in the litter or under loose bark, e.g., *O. kuwanai* (Crossman 1925), *Telenomus* sp. parasitizing *Heterocampa manteo* (Dbldy.) and *T. tetratomus* (Kearby unpublished data, Boldaruyev 1971). Others overwinter as larvae in host eggs, e.g., *O. ennomophagus* and *O. clisiocampae* (Anderson and Kaya 1974b, Hodson 1939), and *T. clisiocampae* (Hodson 1939). *A. disparis* overwinters as a larva within its host egg.

Factors responsible for induction and termination of larval diapause have been studied in but few species. Diapause in *O. ennomophagus* is facultative and is a response to short-day photophases in the maternal generation or to low temperatures (18°C) during larval development (Anderson and Kaya 1974b). It has a long-day/short-day diapause induction curve with a critical photophase between 14 to 15 hrs. Termination of diapause was hastened by chilling at 5°C, which also reduced variation of adult emergence (Anderson and Kaya 1975). Diapause in *Tetrastichus sylvaticus* Gahan, *O. clisiocampae* and *Telenomus clisiocampae* is terminated by 6 months exposure to 2°C (Hodson 1939).

Trichogramma cacoeciae Marchal enters diapause as a larva within diapausing eggs of its host, *Archips rosana* L., in July. It is conjecture if diapause is induced because its host is in diapause as Marchal (1936) explained, or if a seasonal factor such as the length of day induced diapause (Lees 1955).

Danilevskii (1965) reported that larval diapause in *Trichogramma evanescens* Wstw. was photoperiodically controlled. Maslennikova (1959) showed that 95–97% of *T. evanescens* entered diapause at 10°C regardless of the photophase whereas none diapaused at 25°C. However, the duration of the photophase at 15°C did influence the incidence of diapause. Bonnemaison (1972) reported that low temperature, and not varying photophases during juvenile development, induced diapause. Neither of the latter two authors investigated the possible effect of photoperiod on the maternal generation, the critical period of photoperiodic induction of diapause in *O. ennomophagus*.

Larval diapause in *O. clisiocampae, Telenomus clisiocampae, Tetrasticus sylvaticus* and *A. disparis* may be obligatory, though the latter two species on occasion produce two generations of adults per year (Hodson 1939, Burgess and Crossman 1929, Moravskaya 1973).

HYPERPARASITOIDS AND DISEASES

Egg parasitoids seem to have few hyperparasitoids or diseases. Howard (1910) and Howard and Fiske (1911) listed three species of hyperparasitoids of the principal egg parasitoids of the gypsy moth. *Telenomus* sp. is parasitized by *Pachyneuron solitarius* Rtzb., Miscogasteridae (Kolomiets 1958). No primary pathogens have been reported.

REARING

Much has been written about culturing insect parasitoids, but information pertaining specifically to egg parasitoids of forest defoliators is limited.

Large-scale rearing of *Trichogramma* has been reported by several authors as reviewed by Finney and Fisher (1964). These species are often reared in factitious hosts. Probably the most sophisticated approach to mass production has been described by the USSR (Anon. 1975). Inasmuch as there are many biotypes of *Trichogramma*, one should be certain to use the appropriate one for the host that is being controlled (DeBach 1974).

Mass rearing of *O. kuwanai* has been described by Crossman (1917). Field-collected eggs of the gypsy moth were used as the host. *A. disparis* also has been reared in large numbers, though consecutive generations were not usually produced in the laboratory (Crossman 1925, Burgess and Crossman 1929). The usual procedure was to collect gypsy moth eggs in the field where the parasitoid was abundant, separate the parasitized eggs in the laboratory by mechanical means, and then redistribute the juvenile parasitoids in the field via the host eggs.

Rearing procedures also have been described for *Telenomus phalaenarum* Nees on live and dead browntail moth eggs, *O. ennomophagus* on elm spanworm eggs and *T. alsophilae* on fall cankerworm eggs (Howard and Fiske 1911, Anderson and Kaya 1974b, 1975, Drooz et al. ms. submitted). The latter two species have been reared on alternate hosts as well (Kaya and Anderson 1976, Fedde, unpublished data).

COLONIZATION

Colonization of Exotics

There have been a few attempts to establish imported species of egg parasitoids on forest defoliators. *O. kuwanai* from Asia and *A. disparis* from Europe and Asia were successfully introduced into North America (Crossman 1925) and were subsequently distributed as the gypsy moth spread. *O. kuwanai* also was successfully introduced into Europe (Burgess and Crossman 1929). *Telenomus alsophilae* from North America recently has been introduced and probably recovered for the control of *Oxydia trychiata* in Colombia, South America (Drooz in press). *Telenomus phalaenarum* was released unsuccessfully against the browntail moth in North America (Burgess and Crossman 1929, Dowden 1962). Two *Trichogramma* species from Europe were released in North America, one against the browntail moth, the other against the European pine shoot moth. Neither has been recovered (Dowden 1962).

Periodic Colonization

The largest number of periodic colonization releases has been made with *Trichogramma*. These usually have been carried out against pests of orchards (DeBach and Hagen 1964). Results often have been inconclusive, though promising results have been reported in Russia and Poland (Scepetil'nikova 1970, Wiackowska 1965, Wiackowski and Wiackowska 1966). Schütte and Franz (1961) developed a method of spraying parasitized host eggs onto trees, which increased the effectiveness of the release. Ryvkin (1959) reported that releases of *Trichogramma embryophagum* increased parasitism of eggs of *Dendrolimus pini* L., significantly, but large numbers of host eggs remained unparasitized. Similar results were reported by Kim et al. (1965) with releases of *T. dendrolimi* against *D. spectabilis.*

Periodic colonizations of *Anastatus, Telenomus* and *Ooencyrtus* spp. also have been reported. *A. disparis* was redistributed in Europe for control of gypsy moth (Burgess and Crossman 1929). *Telenomus tetratomus* was released successfully against *Dendrolimus sibiricus* in the USSR (Boldaruyev 1969, 1971). Parasitization following one of the releases was 99%. Releases of *T. dalmanni* Rtzv. were reported to control *Orgyia antiqua* L. (Boldaruyev 1969). Romanova and Lozinskij (1958) experimentally distributed eggs of *M. neustrium* L. which were parasitized by *T. laeviusculus* Ratz., *O. neustriae* (Mercet), *O. tardus* Ratz. and *Trichogramma pallida* (Meyer) and increased parasitism of *M. neustrium* 2- to 3-fold compared to nearby untreated areas. Parasitization was as high as 60–70%. *O. ennomophagus* was introduced against the elm spanworm and recovered in two forests in Connecticut (Anderson and Kaya 1973b) and in Pennsylvania (Fusco, Drooz and Quimby, unpublished data). These data suggest that periodic colonization of parasitoids may be useful in biological or integrated control schemes of some hosts.

EFFECT OF INSECTICIDES

Forest insect spraying programs may reduce parasitoids through direct mortality or more probably through loss of hosts upon which they depend for food and propagation (Dowden 1961b). Effects of aerial application of insecticides on parasitization of gypsy moth eggs have been minimal, if at all (Dowden 1961b, Karpel 1973, McGuire and Mulhern 1974), though Doane (1968b) reported a greater incidence of parasitism in untreated areas. Morris et al. (1974) reported that parasitization of spruce budworm by *Trichogramma* was no less in chemical treated plots than in non-chemical treated plots in the year of application. In the following year, however, parasitization was lower in the plots treated with chemical insecticide. The reduction may have resulted from the effect of the insecticide on alternate hosts or on the parasitoid during development in alternate hosts. Insignificant effects of aerial spraying with DDT on parasitization of spruce budworm eggs by *T. minutum* were reported by MacDonald (1963). In contrast, DDT reduced the number of egg parasitoids of *Dendrolimus sibiricus* 10-12 fold, though parasitoid populations were restored within 1 year when the insecticide was used locally (Kolomiets 1957). Kaya and

Dunbar (1972) reported that immature stages of *Telenomus* sp. attacking the elm spanworm were unaffected by ground application of *Bacillus thuringiensis* Berliner and carbaryl.

Applications of insecticides, dormant oils and fungicides to orchards have been shown to be detrimental to *Trichogramma*. The effect may be a direct one on the juvenile or adult stages, or it may be through the reduction of alternate hosts (Schread and Garman 1933, Chapman et al. 1941, Stultz 1955, Stein 1960, Glass 1963, Besemer 1964).

CONCLUDING REMARKS

With few exceptions, egg parasitoids of forest defoliating Lepidoptera have been neglected. In general, they are easy to rear, have few hyperparasitoids or diseases, are capable of parasitizing a large percentage of some host eggs, have been shown to cause collapses of outbreaks of pest populations and have been successfully released, recovered and established. The recent apparent establishment of a North American species of *Telenomus* on a South American host suggests that further biological control attempts be made to use enemies of allied species as reviewed by Pimentel (1963.) However, an appreciation of the importance of egg parasitoids in natural control and their potential in biological and integrated control will continue to remain obscure until our knowledge of their systematics and biology improves.

ACKNOWLEDGMENT

I thank Carol Lemmon and Elizabeth Wehrli for their assistance with the literature review. A. T. Drooz of the U. S. Forest Service, Research Triangle Park, NC, and Gordon Gordh, USDA, ARS, Washington, D.C., critically read the manuscript.

Chapter 17

Insect Pathogens
in Natural and Microbial Control
of Forest Defoliators

Harry K. Kaya

Department of Entomology
The Connecticut Agricultural Experiment Station
New Haven, Connecticut 06504

INTRODUCTION

Insect pathogens play an important role in the natural control of many defoliators in the forest ecosystem. In outbreaks of forest defoliators, pathogens are frequently the primary mortality factors in causing a population to collapse. In order to hasten the collapse of outbreak populations, pathogens may be colonized into such populations in which they may or may not occur. Pathogens offer an alternative to chemical pesticides, especially because they are often compatible with the other biotic factors in the forest ecosystem. They can be applied in integrated control programs with pesticides, silvicultural practices, and other biotic factors. Microbial control, therefore, is a promising method for reducing forest defoliator populations.

Interest in microbial control of insects is reflected by the recent publication of numerous review articles and texts (see Krieg 1971b). Since Krieg's compilation of key publications, the following have appeared: microbial control and related subjects by Burges and Hussey (1971), Hurpin (1971), Bulla (1973), Tinsley and Entwistle (1974), and Ignoffo (1975); viruses by Tanada (1971a), Gibbs (1973), Krieg (1973), Ignoffo (1973), and David (1975); viruses, protozoa, and fungi by Roberts and Yendol (1973); bacteria by Aizawa (1973); nematodes by Benham and Poinar (1973) and Gordon and Webster (1974);

251

ecology of viruses by Tanada (1971b, Chapter 18) and integrated control by Falcon (1971). Specific reviews on forest insects have been published by Katagiri (1969a, b, 1975), Franz (1970–71, Chapter 20), Gukasyan (1970), Stairs (1972), Wellenstein (1973a), Harper (1974) and Doane (Chapter 19). Inasmuch as detailed information on microbial control and various aspects of insect pathology are available in these reviews, this paper is restricted to the natural occurrence of pathogens in forest defoliator populations and the evaluation of microbial control against such defoliators.

NATURAL OCCURRENCE OF PATHOGENS

Enzootic State

Enzootic diseases, that is, diseases which are continually present in a population but at a low incidence, occur in most insect populations (Burges 1973). The numerous isolations of pathogens from forest insects indicate that many of them exist at the enzootic level. However, only long-term studies such as those pertaining to the population dynamics of the spruce budworm, *Choristoneura fumiferana* (Clemens), the European spruce sawfly, *Diprion (Gilpinia) hercyniae* (Hartig), and the winter moth, *Operophtera brumata* (L.), show the existence of pathogens at the enzootic level.

Three viruses, a nuclear-polyhedrosis (NPV), a cytoplasmic-polyhedrosis (CPV), and a granulosis virus (GV), occur at enzootic levels in *C. fumiferana* populations regardless of host density (Neilson 1963b). In *D. hercyniae*, a NPV is present at enzootic levels when the host density is low (Balch and Bird 1944, Bird and Elgee 1957, Neilson and Morris 1964). A microsporidan occurs at enzootic levels in both dense and sparse *O. brumata* populations in England (Varley and Gradwell 1968). The gypsy moth, *Lymantria dispar* L., has a number of bacterial pathogens which occur in the enzootic state in both dense and sparse populations (Podgwaite and Campbell 1972).

Epizootic State

Epizootic refers to an outbreak of disease which occurs in a large number of individuals in a population and is usually associated with high host densities. Collapses of outbreak populations of the Douglas-fir tussock moth, *Hemerocampa pseudotsugata* McDunnough (O.N. Morris 1963, Dahlsten and Thomas 1969, Mason and Thompson 1971), the tent caterpillar complex, *Malacosoma* spp. (Clark 1955, Benz 1961, Stairs 1972), *L. dispar* (Doane 1970) and the red belly tussock moth, *Lymantria fumida* Butler (Koyama and Katagiri 1959) were caused primarily by epizootics of NPVs of the respective defoliators. The NPV of *D. hercyniae* is a density-dependent mortality factor remaining in the enzootic state at low host densities and reaching epizootic proportions at high host densities (Balch and Bird 1944, Bird and Elgee 1957, Neilson and Morris 1964). A GV of the grey larch budmoth, *Zeiraphera diniana* (Gn.) (= *griseana*), caused the collapse of an outbreak population in Switzerland (Martignoni 1957). Although these viruses brought about the reduction of defoliator outbreaks, the population collapse usually did not occur until the second, third or subsequent generations after the initiation of the outbreak.

Epizootics of bacterial diseases in forest defoliator populations have not been common. Talalayeva (1967) reported an epizootic of *Bacillus thuringiensis* Berliner in a larval population of *Selenephera lunigera* Esp. However, the epizootic was confined to a single tree. *Streptococcus faecalis* Andrewes and Horder occurs naturally in *L. dispar* populations (Cosenza and Lewis 1965, Doane and Redys 1970, Podgwaite and Campbell 1972), and may kill 50% of larvae collected from dense populations (Doane 1970).

Epizootics of protozoan diseases in forest defoliator populations are not uncommon. Epizootics of *Nosema fumiferanae* (Thomson) (Thomson 1958), *N. disstriae* (Thomson) (Smirnoff 1968) and *Nosema* sp. (Kaya, unpublished data) have been documented in spruce budworm, forest tent caterpillar, *Malacosoma disstria* Hübner and fall cankerworm, *Alsophila pometaria* (Harris) populations, respectively. A high incidence of infection by *N. cerasivoranae* (Thomson) and a *Pleistophora* sp. was found in the ugly-nest caterpillar, *Archips cerasivoranus* (Fitch) (Smirnoff 1965). In Germany, *N. tortricis* Weiser was responsible for the collapse of an outbreak of the green tortrix, *Tortrix viridana* L. (Franz and Huger 1971).

Epizootics of fungal diseases have been reported in a number of forest defoliators. Stairs (1972) observed a high mortality of last stage larvae of *M. disstria* by an *Entomophthora* sp. in wet sites of an oak-maple stand. In Connecticut, two *Entomophthora* spp. infected up to 25% of the late instar larvae of the notodontid, *Symmerista canicosta* Franclemont, while *Paecilomyces farinosus* (Dickson et Fries) Brown and Smith infected 33% of the overwintering pupae (Kaya and Anderson, unpublished data). In Japan, Aoki (1974) reported that 99% of the Japanese strain of the gypsy moth died from fungal infections; 79% died from *E. aulicae* (Reich.) Sorok. and 20% died from a mixed infection of *E. aulicae* and *P. canadensis* (Vuill.) Brown and Smith. An epizootic by *E. egressa* MacLeod and Tyrrell and *E. sphaerosperma* Fres. was important in the population reduction of eastern hemlock looper, *Lambdina fiscellaria fiscellaria* (Guenée) in Newfoundland, Canada (Otvos et al. 1973).

MICROBIAL CONTROL OF FOREST DEFOLIATORS

Insect pathogens have been used in three ways to suppress insect pests: 1) short-term (temporary or inundative) control where the pathogen is used

TABLE 1 *Artificial field dissemination of viruses against some North American forest defoliators*

Host	Instar treated	Dose (VIB)[a]/unit	Application method[b]	Results	Reference
Lepidoptera			Nuclear-Polyhedrosis Virus		
Choristoneura fumiferana (Clemens) (Spruce budworm)	2	3x10[11]/acre[c]	A	80% population reduction	Bird et al. 1972
	3-4	3x10[11]/acre[c]	A	69% population reduction	Bird et al. 1972
	2	0.1g/12 ft tree	G	40% infection 32 days after spray	Bird and McPhee 1970
	3-4	0.1g/12 ft tree	G	75% reduction 9 days after spray	Bird and McPhee 1970
	3-4	3x10[9]/10 ft tree	G	28% infection 14-20 days after spray	Stairs and Bird 1962
	4	1x10[11]/acre	A	54-76% population reduction Little foliage protection	Morris et al. 1974
Hemerocampa pseudotsugata McDunnough (Douglas-fir tussock moth)	2-3	1x10[11]/acre	A	96-99.8% population reduction Foliage protection	Stelzer et al. 1975
	3-4	10[7]/ml 8 ft trees heavily sprayed	G	90% mortality 24 days after spray	O. N. Morris 1963

Species	Instar	Dosage	G/A	Effect	Reference
Malacosoma disstria Hübner (forest tent caterpillar)	1	1.5×10^{9}/tree	G	92% mortality 17-24 days after spray	Stairs 1964
	1	1.5×10^{8}/tree	G	28% mortality 17-24 days after spray	Stairs 1964
	3	7.5×10^{8}/tree	G	14% mortality 17-24 days after spray	Stairs 1964
	3-4	2.5×10^{10}/acre	A	no control	Abrahamson and Harper 1973
Malacosoma fragile (Stretch) (Great Basin tent caterpillar)	2	2.2×10^{11}/acre	A	70% population reduction	Clark and Reiner 1956
	1-3	1.8×10^{10}-5×10^{11}/acre	G	Some population reduction	Clark and Thompson 1954
	3-4	5.6×10^{10}-2.2×10^{11}/acre	G	Population reduction	Clark and Thompson 1954
Lymantria dispar L. (gypsy moth)	2-3	4×10^{12}/acre	G	Foliage protection Egg mass reduction	Rollinson et al. 1965
	1-3	1×10^{13}/.405 ha	G	No foliage protection	Yendol 1975
	1-3	1×10^{13}/.405 ha	G	Slight foliage protection Egg mass reduction	Yendol 1975

TABLE 1 (cont.)

Host	Instar treated	Dose (VIB)[a]/unit	Application method[b]	Results	Reference
Nuclear-Polyhedrosis Virus					
Hymenoptera					
Neodiprion sertifer (Geoffroy) (European pine sawfly)	early instars	6×10^{10}/20 trees	G	100% mortality 15 days after spray	Bird 1953b
	early instars	1.5×10^{10}/5 acres	G	Heavy mortality 18 days after spray	Bird 1953b
	early instars	8.3×10^{9}/acre	A	94% mortality 21 days after spray	Bird 1953b
	1	5×10^{10}/acre	A	100% mortality	Dowden and Girth 1953
N. abietis (Harris) (Balsam fir sawfly)	1	3.6×10^{7}/2.5m tree	G	96% mortality	Olofsson 1973
	3	3.6×10^{9}/2.5m tree	G	100% mortality	Olofsson 1973
N. pratti pratti (Dyar) (pine sawfly)	early instars	5×10^{9} - 2×10^{10}/acre	A	88% mortality	McIntyre and Dutky 1961
N. taedae linearis Ross (Loblolly pine sawfly)	1-2	3.8×10^{10} - 3.8×10^{11}/acre	A	69-99% population reduction Foliage protection	Yearian et al. 1973

Species	Instar	Dosage	Application[b]	Result	Reference
N. swainei (Middleton) (Swaine's jack pine sawfly)	1-2	1×10^6/ml trees heavily sprayed	G	89-96% mortality	Smirnoff 1961
	1-2	3×10^4/ml trees heavily sprayed	G	80% mortality	Smirnoff 1961
	early instars	3.8×10^9/acre	A	100% mortality	Smirnoff et al. 1962

Granulosis Virus

Lepidoptera

Species	Instar	Dosage	Application[b]	Result	Reference
C. fumiferana	3-4	high rate	G	61% infection	Stairs and Bird 1962

Entomopox Virus

Species	Instar	Dosage	Application[b]	Result	Reference
C. fumiferana	2	1.2×10^{10} - 1.2×10^{11}/acre[d]	A	40-61% population reduction	Bird et al. 1972
C. fumiferana	3-4	1.2×10^{10} 1.2×10^{11}/acre[d]	A	57-79% population reduction No foliage protection	Bird et al. 1972
	4	2.2×10^{10}/acre	A	22% population reduction Little foliage protection	Morris et al. 1974

[a]VIB is Viral Inclusion Bodies.

[b]"G" refers to application with ground equipment and "A" refers to application from the air by airplane or helicopter.

[c]Contaminated with CPV.

[d]Contaminated with CPV and NPV.

in a manner similar to chemical pesticides; 2) long-term (permanent or inoculative) control where the pathogen is introduced into an area or into the pest population for colonization; or 3) integrated control where the pathogen is used in conjunction with chemical and biotic agents and other control practices.

Short-term Control

Use of Viruses. Table 1 summarizes the use of viruses against some forest defoliators in North America. A number of NPVs have been applied against their respective forest defoliator host and have shown great potential for microbial control.

It is difficult to compare results obtained from one defoliator with another or with the same defoliator under different conditions because of differences in application rates, equipment, evaluation methods, virulence of the virus, forest ecosystem, etc. However, a greater degree of control appears to have been obtained with hymenopteran than with lepidopteran defoliators. In particular, the European pine sawfly, *Neodiprion sertifer* (Geoffroy), has been successfully controlled with a NPV in North America and Eurasia (Bird 1953b, Dowden and Girth 1953, Franz 1961a, Zarin et al. 1974, Glowacka-Pilot 1973, Nuorteva 1972, Donaubauer and Schönherr 1972, Donaubauer 1974).

Franz (1961a) summarized the use of pathogens against forest defoliators in Europe. Recently, a GV was successfully applied from the air at the rate of 8×10^{11} granules/acre against the European fir budworm, *Choristoneura murinana* (Hübner), in Germany (Schönherr 1969). About 57% of the larvae were infected 21 days after spray application and 100% were infected at 31 days.

Magnoler (1974b) used a NPV at 2.5×10^{13} viral inclusion bodies (VIB)/ha against the gypsy moth in an evergreen oak forest in Sardinia. The virus was introduced into a disease-free gypsy moth population, and 85% larval mortality was obtained 35 days after treatment. Foliage protection, however, was not achieved because the mortality occurred after the heavy larval feeding period.

In Japan, a NPV-CPV combination was applied against *L. fumida* and a CPV against the pine moth, *Dendrolimus spectabilis* Butler. The NPV caused 59% mortality and the CPV 24% when applied from the air at 3×10^{10} VIB/ha against young larvae of *L. fumida* (Koyama and Katagiri 1967, Katagiri 1969a, b). Against *D. spectabilis*, the CPV was applied at the rate of 1.5×10^{11} VIB/ha against 7th instar larvae and a reduction in survival rates was obtained (Koyama and Katagiri 1968). Katagiri (1975) reported a rapid reduction of gypsy moth density when CPV from *L. dispar* or *D. spectabilis* was applied from the air.

Use of Bacteria. Bacillus thuringiensis (Bt) has received considerable attention as a microbial control agent of many lepidopterous species, and the literature on this subject is extensive (see Burges and Hussey 1971). The techniques developed for *Bt* have been useful with other insect pathogens. No attempt has been made to cover the vast information available on this bacterium.

Bt has been used in short-term control of many lepidopteran forest defoliators in North America (Harper 1974) and Europe (Franz and Krieg 1967). Some defoliators such as the tent caterpillar and cankerworms are easily controlled with low rates of *Bt*. Others, such as the gypsy moth and spruce budworm, are more difficult to control and require higher rates of *Bt*. In all cases, good foliage coverage and proper timing of application are paramount for effective control. Although other pathogenic bacteria have been isolated from forest defoliators in North America, only *S. faecalis* isolated from *L. dispar* has been field tested (Doane 1971a). The bacterium was applied against 2nd-4th stage larvae with ground spray equipment and foliage protection obtained.

Use of Protozoa. The use of protozoa in the forest has been limited even though many insect species are infected with microsporidans (see McLaughlin 1973). Kaya (1975) used *Pleistophora schubergi* Zwölfer against *S. canicosta* and the orange-striped oakworm, *Anisota senatoria* (J. E. Smith), at the rate of 2×10^8 and 2×10^7 spores/ml. He reported 96 and 72%, respectively, of the *A. senatoria* and 100 and 100%, respectively, of the *S. canicosta* larvae were infected 14 days after spray application. Smirnoff (1971a) adapted the microsporidan, *Thelohania pristiphorae* Smirnoff, to the birch sawfly, *Arge pectoralis* (Leach), and under field conditions applied a spore suspension containing 5×10^6 spores/ml. Infection was observed 20 days after application, and there were some indications that spread of the microsporidan could occur through infected larvae. In Europe, Weiser (1957) and Weiser and Verber (1957) reported a high incidence of infection when *T. hyphantriae* Weiser was applied against the fall webworm, *Hyphantria cunea* (Drury) and the browntail moth, *Nygmia phaeorrhoea* (Donovan).

Use of Fungi. The use of fungi against defoliators in North American forests has been limited. Very early, Speare and Colley (1912) controlled *N. phaeorrhoea* by introducing larvae infected with *E. aulicae* into colonies. Otvos et al. (1973) also artifically infected larvae of *L. fiscellaria fiscellaria* with *E. egressa* and then placed them into field cages with uninfected larvae. About 15% of the uninfected larvae became infected with the fungus. MacLeod (1954) applied *Beauveria bassiana* (Balsamo) Vuill. against larvae of the larch sawfly, *Pristiphora erichsonii* (Hartig) under field conditions and increased the mortality due to the fungus from 1.5 to 9.5% in larvae and from 13.1 to 30.8% in pupae. On the other hand, Abrahamson and Harper (1973) failed to increase the incidence of *E. megasperma* Cohn in the forest tent caterpillar when resting spores were applied from the air.

Use of Nematodes. Field use of nematodes against forest defoliators in North America also has been very limited, Jaques et al. (1968) evaluated soil application of *Neoaplectana carpocapsae* Weiser against pupae of the winter moth and reduced pupal survival to 12%, but a high mortality also occurred in the check plots.

Long-term Control

There are only a few examples of long-term control of forest defoliators with pathogens. In the case of *D. hercyniae*, which was accidentally introduced into North America during the 1900s, a NPV, which was apparently introduced with its parasitoids, appeared in the sawfly population (Balch and Bird 1944). The sawfly was rapidly brought under natural control by the virus. In 1947, a disease-free population was found in Ontario, Canada, and the NPV at a low concentration was introduced into this population in 1950 (Bird and Burk 1961). The virus became established from this small inoculum and spread throughout the infested area. Virus epizootics recurred for 10 consecutive years and maintained the population below levels that cause economic damage. This virus also has been used successfully in Europe (Franz 1961a). With another saw-fly, Bird (1955), using a very dilute aqueous suspension of NPV, introduced the virus into a *N. sertifer* population. The infestation which extended over 100 acres of Scots pine, *Pinus sylvestris* L., was controlled by this one viral application in the subsequent 3 years by epizootics developing each year. When a NPV of the Swaine jack pine sawfly, *N. swainei* Middleton, was introduced into populations by spraying or by dissemination of infected cocoons, it persisted from year to year by transovum transmission (Smirnoff 1962, 1972). Artificial disseminations of the NPV of the forest tent caterpillar (Stairs 1965a) and of the gypsy moth (Magnoler 1974b) have resulted in persistence of these viruses from one year into the next.

Long-term control of forest defoliators with bacteria is unusual, but in Russia, Talalaev (1958) obtained permanent control of the Siberian silkworm moth, *Dendrolimus sibiricus* Tschtv., with *B. thuringiensis* var. *dendrolimus* Talalaev. There appears to be no successful long-term control of forest defoliators with fungi, microsporidans or nematodes.

Integrated Control

Insecticides. Benz (1971) reviewed the interaction of pathogens with chemical pesticides, and Angus and Luthy (1971) the formulations of microbial pesticides. Müller-Kögler (1965) reviewed the literature on the use of fungi with chemical pesticides. Since these reviews, several studies have been published on the combined use of chemical pesticides and pathogens. Morris et al. (1974) showed that a low dose of fenitrothion and a NPV was highly effective in population reduction and foliage protection when applied from the air against the spruce budworm. Fenitrothion plus an entomopox virus also protected the foliage and apparently altered the surviving female:male ratio from 1:1 to 1:2.

In laboratory studies, Morris (1972, 1975) demonstrated that low dosages of some insecticides had no effect on commercial *Bt* preparations. Some forest defoliators fed less on leaves treated with the insecticide-*Bt* mixture than on those with *Bt* alone or on untreated leaves. In Russia, Sikura et al. (1971) obtained 85.3% mortality of *H. cunea* in the field with a 0.2% *Bt*-.002% trichlorphon mixture.

Enhancers. Many additives have been used to enhance the life of pathogens and to improve formulations of microbial insecticides (see Angus and Luthy 1971). Certain substances have reacted synergistically with pathogens. Yadava (1971) showed that 1% boric acid solution enhanced the effective lethality of a NPV of *L. dispar.* According to Lühl (1974), $FeSO_4$ and $CuSO_4$ were synergistic with the NPVs of *L. dispar, Lymantria monacha* L. and *N. sertifer.* Recently, an enzyme was isolated from a GV of the armyworm, *Pseudaletia unipuncta* (Haworth), which enhanced the infectivity of several NPVs of different insect species (Tanada and Hara 1975). The use of this GV enzyme in combination with viruses of forest insects should be explored further.

Smirnoff (1971b) showed that a *Bt*-chitinase preparation was effective against the spruce budworm. In a large field test, spruce budworm mortality between 83–93% was observed in the *Bt*-chitinase plots as compared with the unsprayed plots which had 39–53% mortality (Smirnoff et al. 1973, Smirnoff 1974). Foliage protection was attained in the sprayed plots. Dimond (1972) also obtained greater foliage protection with the *Bt*-chitinase preparation than with *Bt* alone. However, the cost of chitinase as a regular additive to *Bt* preparations is prohibitive. Other alternatives which enhance *Bt* preparations should be studied. Other additives which have shown promise are the boric acid-*Bt* combination (Doane and Wallis 1964) and the β-exotoxin-*Bt* combination (Burgerjon and Biache 1964).

Feeding Stimulus. Yendol et al. (1975) demonstrated that molasses added to commercial *Bt* preparations increased feeding by gypsy moth larvae on molasses-*Bt*-treated leaves as compared to leaves with *Bt* alone. Molasses acted as a feeding stimulus.

Biological Agents. The use of two biological agents has increased their effectiveness in the field. The interactions between pathogens have been reviewed by Krieg (1971a). Stelzer (1967) applied a mixture of *Bt* and NPV from the air against 2nd and 3rd stage Great Basin tent caterpillar, *M. fragile* (Stretch). The impact of *Bt* was not assessed because the larvae fell off the host plant within a few hours after ingesting the spore. However, the NPV infection was assessed and 31–93% of the colonies contained virus-killed larvae 16–24 days after spraying as compared to only 3% in unsprayed colonies. The following year, the populations in sprayed plots were 95% lower than in unsprayed plots.

A combination of NPV and *Bt*, NPV alone and *Bt* alone were tested against 2nd and 3rd stage larvae of Douglas-fir tussock moth by Stelzer et al. (1975). All treatments resulted in effective control with a mean population reduction of 96–99% 35 days after spray application. Foliage protection was also achieved. As mentioned earlier, Koyama and Katagiri (1967) used a NPV-CPV combination to obtain effective control of *L. fumida*. The NPV killed the majority of larvae and pupae. Although the CPV did not kill as many hosts, 31% of the surviving females were infected, which reduced fecundity. A CPV-*Bt* combination was effective against the gypsy moth when applied from the air (Katagiri 1975). In sprayed plots, 0.4% of the initial population became adults while in unsprayed plots 2% reached adulthood.

Generally, microbial pesticides have no direct effect on macrobial agents (i.e. parasitoids and predators). Use of *Bt* and NPV against the satin moth, *Stilpnotia salicis* (L.), had little or no effect on its parasitoid complex (Nef 1971). Similarly, *Bt* had no apparent deleterious effect against *L. dispar* parasitoids (Dunbar et al. 1973, Kaya et al. 1974).

APPRAISAL

Microbial control shows promise against forest defoliators and has been effective especially with *Bt* and the NPVs on sawflies and some lepidopteran species. Although problems such as persistence, safety of the virus to other animals, cost and method of production, storage, and method of application are still to be solved, the viruses next to *Bt* show the greatest potential, especially in long-term control of many forest defoliators.

The fungi and protozoans, in general, have not been studied in depth. Fungi and microsporidans have potential in microbial control of some forest defoliators, but basic ecological studies are necessary prior to field tests. Although epizootics caused by microsporidans occur in natural populations, the effects are usually debilitating rather than quick-killing. This effect, however, should not deter the researcher from using these microorganisms in microbial control. Transovarial transmission occurs with many microsporidans, which enhances their attractiveness as microbial control agents. Moreover, chronically infected insects may be more susceptible to stress factors, such as adverse climate and predation.

At present, nematodes offer little promise against forest defoliators. However, the use of nematodes has not been investigated in depth and may have unrealized potential.

The method of introducing pathogens into the forest ecosystem should be carefully evaluated. Should pathogens be introduced in the manner conventional to chemical pesticides? This technique has been successful with *Bt* and some viruses, but the cost may be prohibitive for use in the forest, especially for short-term control. The technique, however, is useful for small-scale operations or for long-term control. Other techniques that may be considered are: artificially contaminating egg masses with the pathogen (Elgee 1971, Cardinal and Smirnoff 1973); introducing naturally contaminated eggs into uncontaminated areas (Doane 1971b); placing contaminated or infected pupae in the field to enable the emerging adults to contaminate the wild population (Smirnoff 1972); contaminating adult genitalia (Neilson and Elgee 1968); contaminating wild adult populations (Gard 1975); contaminating parasitoids and predators (Stairs 1966, Capinera and Barbosa 1975); and placing infected larvae into disease-free populations (Otvos et al. 1973, Speare and Colley 1912).

A thorough knowledge of the ecology of pathogen and host is needed. In addition, the interactions between pathogens, macrobial agents, and chemicals including pesticides and enhancers, should be investigated so that they can be manipulated to accomplish an effective pest management program.

The forest represents a relatively undisturbed and long-lasting environment in which a complex of biotic factors operate. Usually a very high pest population can be tolerated which in turn provides natural enemies with a sufficient food supply for survival. Insect pathogens by themselves usually cannot regulate populations of forest defoliators, but may play a vital role with other biotic factors in the overall regulation regardless of whether they occur naturally or have been artificially introduced.

Chapter 18

Ecology of Insect Viruses

Y. Tanada

Division of Entomology and Parasitology
University of California
Berkeley, California 94720

INTRODUCTION

Progress in ecological studies of insect pathogens has been most rapid with insect viruses, primarily because of their promise in microbial control of insect pests, and because of the fascination that man has for viruses. A wide variety of viruses have been discovered in insects (David 1975), and in some of them, the physical and biochemical properties have been studied in detail. The mechanism of virus invasion and replication in insects is beginning to be clarified, but we still lack the knowledge that has been assembled for vertebrate and plant viruses. This information is of value in the study of insect virus ecology.

Numerous reviews have touched upon insect virus ecology, especially those dealing with microbial control and epizootiology (Steinhaus 1954, 1957, 1963, 1964, Bergold 1958, Franz 1961b, Tanada 1963, 1971b, 1973, 1975, Aizawa 1963, Huger 1963, Cameron 1963, Hall 1963, 1964, Vago 1963, 1968, Bird 1964, Smith 1967, 1971, 1973, Ignoffo 1968b, Stairs 1968, 1971, 1973, Vago and Bergoin 1968, Aruga and Tanada 1971, Falcon 1971, Tinsley and Harrap 1972, Bailey 1973, Harrap 1973, Krieg 1973, Yendol and Hamlen 1973, Harshbarger and Faust 1973, Jaques 1973a, Tinsley and Entwistle 1974, David 1975). I shall attempt to restrict duplication and emphasize mainly the recent studies.

Insect virus ecology will be treated under two broad categories: (1) biotic and (2) physical (abiotic) environments.

BIOTIC ENVIRONMENT

Mode of Invasion

Insect viruses generally gain entrance into their hosts by way of the mouth and midgut, and transovarially within the egg. They also gain entrance through wounds, such as those made by ovipositors of insect parasitoids and bites of predators. Unlike some vertebrate viruses which infect through the respiratory system, there appears to be no record of an insect virus infecting through the tracheal system.

Midgut

In the midgut, pH and digestive enzymes may or may not favor virus invasion. In the occluded viruses, alkaline pH dissolves the occlusion bodies (polyhedra and capsules) and liberates the virions. However, other mechanisms besides pH may be involved in the dissolution of occlusion bodies (Summers 1972, David 1975).

Antivirus substances effective against several viruses have been reported in insect gut juices (Watanabe 1971). The silkworm, *Bombyx mori* (L.), was more susceptible to a nuclear polyhedrosis virus (NPV) when exposed at 5°C for 24 hr than at room temperatures; the increased susceptibility appeared to be associated with the antivirus activity of gut juices (Ayuzawa and Furuta 1966). Aruga and Watanabe (1964) found no relationship between larval resistance of silkworm strains to peroral infection with a cytoplasmic polyhedrosis virus (CPV) and the antivirus activity of gut juice. On the other hand, Aratake et al. (1974) obtained some correlation among 14 silkworm strains. Hayashiya et al. (1971) isolated from the silkworm gut juice an antivirus substance which appeared to be a conjugated protein. Since certain virus particles are degraded by the gut juice and may be inactivated (Stoltz and Summers 1971, Summers 1972), antivirus activity may be associated with such degradation.

The question arises whether the antivirus factor is synthesized by the plant, the host larva or the microbial flora in the insect's gut. Certain plants have antibacterial and antiprotozoan substances (Kushner and Harvey 1962, Smirnoff and Hutchison 1965, Smirnoff 1967a, Maksymiuk 1970), but the presence of an antivirus substance has not been definitely demonstrated. The antivirus factor in the silkworm midgut was at first thought to be derived from mulberry leaves, but Hayashiya et al. (1971) obtained evidence that it was synthesized *de novo* by the midgut tissue.

Within the capsule of a granulosis virus (GV) of the armyworm, *Pseudaletia unipuncta* (Haworth), there is an enzyme that enhances the infection of a NPV (Tanada et al. 1973, Tanada and Hara 1975). This synergistic enzyme appears to act on the plasma membrane of the midgut cells (Tanada et al. 1975).

Insect viruses are generally able to penetrate the peritrophic membrane, but the degree of penetration varies with the insect host and the virus. Watanabe (1971) observed *in vitro* CPV particles absorbed by the silkworm peritrophic membrane. He suggested that the membrane formed a chemical and physical barrier to the virus particles. In the mosquito larva, the iridescent virus particles were too large to penetrate the peritrophic membrane (Stolz and Summers 1971, Summers 1972).

Nutrition

There is ample evidence that insect host nutrition plays a role in virus infections (Aruga 1968, Watanabe 1971). Unfavorable foliage of poor quality or freshness acts as stressors and increases the susceptibility of the insect to virus. High nitrogen and high carbohydrate may be involved in some cases (Shvetsova 1950, Pimentel and Shapiro 1962).

At present, many insects are reared mainly on artificial diets which may or may not contain host plant material. Such diets may increase the incidence of virus infections. Schmid (1974a) reared the larch bud moth, *Zeiraphera diniana* (Gn.), on a semi-artificial medium and observed an increase in the incidence of GV infection. Silkworm larvae reared on artificial diet containing mulberry leaf powder were more susceptible to NPV than those reared on fresh leaves (Matsubara and Hayashiya 1969). But according to Kunimi and Aruga (1974), even dried leaf powder was beneficial because it reduced the susceptibility of the larvae to NPV and CPV. David et al. (1972) noticed that a reduction in either the sucrose or casein content increased the incidence of deaths by the GV in the European cabbageworm, *Pieris brassicae* (L.). These studies indicated that nutritional stressors altered the physiological or biochemical conditions of the host and favored virus multiplication. This corroborates the findings of Goodwin et al. (1973) that the nutritional state of insect cell lines is a major factor in virus propagation in these cells.

Site of Infection

The insect organs that are infected vary with the type of virus and the intensity of the infection. For mass production of viruses, a systemic infection is most advantageous. However, for virus dissemination, infection in the hypodermis and midgut epithelium is most effective. When the hypodermis is infected, it becomes highly fragile and is easily ruptured, even prior to death of the host. Wilted virus-infected larvae dangling from the plant with their liquified body contents dripping down from the foliage play an important role in rapid virus dissemination, especially under high host densities.

The dissemination of virus appears much more effective when the infection is confined mainly to the midgut epithelium. Such infected insects tend to live longer than those infected systemically, and their midgut cells proliferate excessively and produce enormous quantities of virus which are liberated into the gut lumen and excreted. Thus, the infected insect becomes a motile virus factory. Laboratories that mass produce lepidopterous larvae are well acquainted with the ease and rapidity with which the CPV, which infects the midgut, spreads throughout their insect colonies. In Japan, the most important virus disease of the silkworm at present is infectious flacherie caused by one or more nonoccluded viruses which infect the midgut. The effectiveness of the sawfly NPV results to some extent from the midgut infection. This aspect, however, has not been emphasized by researchers studying sawflies. Recently, a *Baculovirus* has effectively controlled the rhinoceros beetle, *Oryctes rhinoceros* (L.), in islands of the South Pacific (Marschall 1970, Young 1974). The larval and adult midgut cells proliferate excessively because of virus replication (Huger 1973, Monty 1974). There is a continuous defecation of the virus. Since the adult visits the breeding and feeding sites several times (Zelazny 1973a, b), it is an efficient vector in rapid virus distribution (Young 1974). The adult infection plays a more important role in suppressing the beetle population than the larval infection.

When the citrus red mite, *Panonychus citri* (McGregor), was inoculated with a nonoccluded virus, it transmitted the virus to healthy mites within 24 to 48 hrs (Gilmore and Tashiro 1966). The rapid transmission apparently resulted from the replication of the virus in cells of the midgut (Reed and Hall 1972) and the hindgut (Reed et al. 1975). Reed et al. (1975) observed that the virus particles were surrounded by a protein matrix, and when deposited with the feces, appeared to persist longer than the virus applied as a spray.

Mathur (1971) reported that an *Entomopoxvirus* (EPV) which infected mainly the fat body of the lepidopteran, *Amsacta moorei* Butler, was discharged in regurgitations and defecations. Whether other viruses which only lightly, if any, infect the midgut, e.g., *Baculovirus*, are discharged through the digestive tract has not been fully investigated.

Host Resistance

Innate resistance to virus infections occurs in insects. Resistant strains have been reported especially in the domesticated insects, the silkworm (Watanabe 1971) and honey bee, *Apis mellifera* L., (Bailey 1963). There are increasing numbers of reports of resistant strains in other insects (Bergold 1958, Ossowski 1960, Martignoni and Schmid 1961, David and Gardiner 1965). In the laboratory, resistant strains have been selected for *P. brassicae* against the GV (Sidor 1959, Rivers 1959, David and Gardiner 1960), *P. brassicae* with the CPV (Sidor 1959), and *B. mori* (Aizawa and Furuta 1964) and *Plodia interpunctella* (Hübner) (Hunter and Hoffman 1973) against NPV's. The silkworm exhibits interstrain differences in its susceptibility to NPV, CPV, and flacherie virus (Watanabe 1968, 1971). The resistance to CPV is of the polygenic type, but in the highly resistant strain, Daizo, it appears to be a dominant major gene (Watanabe 1971). Although silkworm resistance to flacherie virus is also genetically controlled, it appears to be independent from that of CPV (Watanabe et al. 1974). Inoue (1974a) concluded that the resistance to flacherie virus was due mainly to the regenerative ability of midgut cells to prevent lethal infections.

Recently, stocks of honey bee have been selected which are resistant to a virus producing a hairless black syndrome (Kulinčević and Rothenbuhler 1975, Rinderer et al. 1975). Among different strains of the fall armyworm, *Spodoptera frugiperda* (J. E. Smith), Reichelderfer and Benton (1974) found a greater than 5-fold difference in the LD_{50} to a NPV. The resistance was not sex-linked, but appeared to be associated with a single gene or genes that lacked dominance. According to Kurstak et al. (1975), strains of the wax moth, *Galleria mellonella* (L.), which are resistant to a NPV, could be made susceptible by a second super-infecting virus, such as the *Tipula* iridescent virus.

Attempts have been made to determine whether an insect acquires resistance after continuous exposure to the virus. Watanabe (1967) exposed two highly susceptible silkworm strains to a CPV selection pressure of 30 and 92% mortalities, and obtained after eight generations a 16-fold increase in resistance. On the other hand, Ignoffo and Allen (1972) were not able to detect resistance to a NPV in *Heliothis zea* (Boddie) which had been placed under a selection pressure of LD_{50} 20-70 for 20-25 generations.

Some insects exhibit maturation immunity, i.e., the younger larval instars are more susceptible than the older instars. The susceptibility to NPV decreased as the *Heliothis* larvae matured; but the apparent increase in resistance was partially explained by a normal increase in body weight (Ignoffo 1966). Magnoler (1974a) noticed also a 2-fold increase in the resistance of the gypsy moth, *Lymantria dispar* L., to a NPV with a 4-fold increase in body weight.

The embryonic midgut cells of sawfly prepupae (Bird 1953a), and of *G. mellonella* and *Choristoneura fumiferana* (Clem.) (Stairs 1965b) are immune to infection, but become susceptible when they differentiate. Moreover, when the prepupae or pupae undergo diapause, they are less susceptible to NPV's than nondiapausing individuals (Stairs 1970, Watanabe and Aruga 1970). Since sawfly prepupae may remain in diapause for as long as six winters, the virus persists in such insects for a long period (Tinsley and Entwistle 1974). When the silkworm larva is molting, the development of the CPV polyhedra is almost suppressed but the virus RNA synthesis continues uninhibited (Watanabe 1971). Plant ecdysone analogues produce in the molting larvae a similar suppression of polyhedra production. Accordingly, Watanabe (1971) concluded that virus development was dependent on the physiological host condition which was controlled by hormone. This is also indicated in certain virus infections which develop a syndrome resembling that produced by hormone.

Retnakaran and Bird (1972) noticed that the pathology caused by an EPV in the spruce budworm was similar to that of a juvenile hormone. They suggested that infection resulted in a continuous secretion of juvenile hormone.

On the other hand, in some virus infections, precocious adult characteristics (prothetely) developed in larvae infected with NPV's (Vago 1956, Morris 1970). Morris (1970) observed, in such larvae, injuries in corpora allata and the brain, which appeared to be incapable of producing sufficient juvenile hormone to maintain the larval state. Teratological effects, especially to the elytra, were observed in virus-infected adults of rhinoceros beetle (Monty 1974), and of Lepidoptera (Atger 1962, Neilson 1965, Vail et al. 1969, Vail and Gough 1970, Maleki-Milani 1970). When the silkworm was infected with the *Chilo* iridescent virus, certain parts of the larval integument were not molted, and persisted in the pupal and even in the adult integuments (Ono and Fukaya 1969, Ono et al. 1972). Such larval integuments contained cells infected with virus. The application of phytoecdysone or alletectomy did not affect the appearance of the larval region on the virus-infected pupa (Ono et al. 1972). In *Spodoptera littoralis* (Boisd.), allectectomy performed on the larvae doubled the percentage of overt NPV-infected larvae as compared to untreated larvae (El-Ibrashy and Sadek 1973). Keeley and Vinson (1975) treated *Heliothis* larvae with β-ecdysone 4 to 9 days after the inoculation of a NPV and found that mortality was significantly lower than that of larvae treated with Ringer's solution. They concluded that the hormone stimulated host cell metabolism, particularly protein and RNA synthesis, and interacted with the virus infection.

In the honey bee, the sacbrood virus, which was considered for many years as being infectious only for the brood, was found infectious for the adult (Lee and Furgala 1967). Infected adult bees displayed abnormal behavior (Bailey and Fernando 1972).

Cellular and humoral immunities occur in insects. Insect hemocytes are capable of phagocytizing virus particles, but their importance in preventing virus infection has not been evaluated. In some cases, the virus particles gain entrance into the cell through phagocytosis or pinocytosis (Leutenegger 1964, Younghusband and Lee 1969, Vaughn et al. 1972). Humoral factors are important in bacterial infections in insects, but their role in virus infection has not been thoroughly investigated. Kawarabata and Aizawa (1968) detected a virus inhibitory factor in the hemolymph of silkworm larvae infected with NPV. The factor was isolated by column chromatography. It was inactivated by acid treatment (pH 2) but not by trypsin, pronase, nagarse, and lysozyme. Odier and Vago (1973) immunized the wax moth larva against the densonucleosis virus (DNV) with heat-inactivated virus. Since immunity was obtained with various substances, and even by simple injury, Odier and Vago (1973) suggested that the immune response was induced by trauma, and that the progressive reaction indicated an accumulation of a protective substrate.

Insect viruses which occur in occlusion bodies are able to withstand relatively high temperatures that are lethal to their insect hosts. However, when virus-infected insects are reared at high temperatures (approximately 30–37°C), they survive infection and emerge as adults (Tanada 1967). Although the basis for this resistance has not been established, there is increasing evidence that it is caused mainly by the inability of the virus to replicate and infect the cell, and that humoral host immunity may not play a major role. Day and Dudzinski (1966) speculated that the decrease in the numbers of *Seriscesthis* iridescent virus in larvae held at 32°C was caused by an inhibition to the assembly and synthesis of the virus precursors. This was indicated by the production of virus particles in larvae held at 30°C and fed a high protein diet, but no virus production occurred in larvae fed the usual diet of beeswax. Inoue et al. (1972) noted, in their fluorescent antibody studies, that the silkworm infected with flacherie virus and reared at 37° ± 1°C, had fewer numbers of fluorescent cells in the midgut, and that the fluorescent intensity decreased with time at the high temperature. Inoue and Tanada (unpublished data) applied thermal therapy to fifth-instar silkworm larvae which had been exposed to the flacherie virus in their fourth instar, and obtained normal cocoons. Watanabe and Tanada (1972) conducted autoradiography on armyworm larvae with nuclear polyhedrosis which were reared at a high temperature (37°C). Viral DNA synthesis occurred only in a few cells, but the polyhedron-protein synthesis did not occur. This suggested that high temperatures reduced the adsorption and/or penetration of the virus into cells, and also suppressed the development of polyhedra.

Occult Virus

There is evidence that insect virus may occur in an occult form or as a latent infection. It should be emphasized that the action of stress, which results in an acute or virulent infection, and the transovarial transmission of the virus are not conclusive evidence of a latent state. In the former, the stressor may have acted on a chronic but active infection, and in the latter, an active virus may have been transmitted to the egg.

Transovarial Transmission

Vertical virus transmission from adult to offspring occurs commonly, but such transmission is usually by virus contamination on the egg surface (transovum transmission) or in the vicinity of the egg or larva. Concrete evidence of virus transmission within the egg (transovarial) is still limited. There are a few direct observations of virus particles in adult reproductive organs or within the eggs. Particles resembling GV capsules were observed in insect eggs (Smith et al. 1956, Sager 1960). According to Devauchelle and Durchon (1973), an iridescent virus developed in the cytoplasm of spermatocysts of *Nereis diversicolor* (O. F. Müller) and was transmitted to the offspring. Monsarrat et al. (1973, 1974) detected in *Oryctes rhinoceros* adults, *Baculovirus* particles in the nuclei and cytoplasm of spermatids, in the cells and lumen of accessory glands and in the ejaculatory canal, but not in the spermatozoa. In females, the virions occurred in the somatic cell nuclei, especially the follicular cells in the oviduct.

Iridescent virus is transmitted transovarially in the mosquito (Linley and Nielsen 1968a, b, Wagner et al. 1974). However, the reports of transovarial transmission of NPV's and CPV's should be reevaluated. Thorough sterilization of egg surfaces may indicate that the virus is transmitted on the surface rather than within the egg (Sikorowski et al. 1973, Mery and Dulmage 1975). Bird (1961) suggested that the sawfly NPV was transmitted within the egg, but Neilson and Elgee (1968) found that vertical transmission was mainly through ingestion of foliage contaminated by diseased and/or externally contaminated adults. They concluded that transovum and transovarial transmission occurred rarely, if ever. Etzel and Falcon (1976) extensively investigated the transmission of the codling moth, *Laspeyresia pomonella* (L.), GV through the egg by means of bioassay, serology, fluorescent antibody technique, and the use of stressors, but they failed to demonstrate transovarial transmission.

Adults artifically contaminated with virus have disseminated the virus in their environment (Martignoni and Milstead 1962, Elmore and Howland 1964, Gard 1975). Elmore and Howland (1964) distributed the virus by contaminated adults, but obtained limited distribution as compared to a virus spray application. Gard (1975) was more successful in distributing the *Heliothis* NPV by attracting winged adults to black-light traps baited with virus. He reported that contaminated adults disseminated the virus at least 250 m. A flagellate, *Herpetomonas swainei* Smirnoff and Lipa, was used by Smirnoff (1972) as a marker to detect the transovum transmission of a NPV of the sawfly, *Neodiprion swainei* Middleton, and to positively identify the introduced virus.

Host Density

There is considerable evidence that the incidence of virus infections is density dependent, and that epizootics occur at both high and low host densities. The early belief that high host densities spontaneously activated an occult virus, which produces an epizootic, appears to be unfounded. Recent studies on the gypsy moth (Doane 1970), the citrus red mite (Gilmore and Munger 1965, Shaw et al. 1968), and several insects of alfalfa (Tanada and Omi 1974a) showed that virus infection was initiated at low host density, and as the host density increased, the virus spread, creating an epizootic. But epizootics did not invariably develop at high host density. Doane (1970) observed that the virus epizootics in gypsy moth populations were density dependent, and the rapid spread of pathogens was enhanced by the behavior of early instar larvae. The movement of infected larvae made the host density more dense and increased virus transmission.

Alternate Hosts

Numerous studies have shown that some viruses infect only one or a few insect species, whereas others have a wide host range (Ignoffo 1968a, Tanaka

1971). There is little information regarding the basis for host specificity. In some cases, maturation immunity is involved because infectivity tests fail when conducted with older larvae, but are successful with younger larvae (Aruga et al. 1963a). The iridescent viruses infect a large number of species when inoculated into the hemocoel, but not when fed to insects (Smith 1967). As pointed out previously, the midgut may act as a barrier. In general, the *Baculovirus*, especially GV appears to be host specific. Recently, the NPV's of *Autographa californica* (Speyer) (Vail et al. 1971, Vail and Jay 1973, Vail et al. 1973), and *B. mori* (Aratake and Kayamura 1973) and the GV of *P. unipuncta* (Tanada and Omi 1974b) were found to infect several species. In the GV of *P. unipuncta*, the synergistic (Hawaiian) strain infected several lepidopterous species but not the nonsynergistic (Oregonian) strain (Tanada, unpublished data). Successive passages in alternate hosts may increase the virulence of the virus for this host, as the NPV of *Yponomeuta malinella* Zell. adapted to *G. mellonella* (Simonova and Fufaeva 1974), as the *Chilo* iridescent virus adapted to *B. mori* (Ohba 1975a), and as the *Galleria*-adapted NPV of *B. mori* adapted to the rice stem borer, *Chilo suppressalis* (Wlkr.) (Aizawa 1975). In the rice stem borer, Aizawa (1975) reported an increase of 4.0–5.0 times in the infectivity titre after the virus was passed through 18 generations of the borer.

Insect virus, when propagated in alternate hosts or in insect cell lines (Ignoffo et al. 1974), generally retains its infectivity and virulence for the original host. But this may not always be the case. Aizawa (1975) cautioned strongly of the possibility of a loss in virulence in mass virus production in an alternate host. The NPV of *B. mori*, after passage through more than 80 *Galleria* generations, lost some of its virulence for silkworm (Aizawa 1975). Abnormal virus replication has been reported in alternate hosts. Hunter and Hoffman (1972) transmitted the GV of almond moth, *Cadra cautella* (Wlkr.) to the Indian meal moth, *Plodia interpunctella*, and observed abnormal capsules which contained up to 18 virions. When returned to *C. cautella*, the virus developed normally and each capsule contained one virion. Watanabe et al. (1975) transmitted *B. mori* NPV to the rice stem borer and observed a replacement of the icosahedral by cuboidal polyhedra after successive passages in the alternate host. There was a difference not only in the formation of cuboidal polyhedra, but also in the occlusion of only a few virions.

Alternate hosts are of value in mass culture of viruses, but they are of little significance in virus epizootiology unless such hosts occur in the same ecosystem. In this case, the alternate hosts may serve as reservoirs and vectors in virus transmission and dispersal. *Tetranychus cinnabarinus* (Boisd.) is susceptible to the nonoccluded virus of citrus red mite. Beavers and Reed (1972) showed that it served as a vector and transmitted the virus to citrus red mite. A lepidopteran, *Wiseana cervinata* (Wlkr.), and a scarabaeid occur in the same habitat, and the iridescent viruses, types 9 and 18, isolated from them are serologically identical and completely homologous in their DNA nucleotide sequence (Kelly and Avery 1974). The *Baculovirus* of the rhinoceros beetle infects *Scapanes australis* (Boisd.), a pest of palms which is also attacked by the rhinoceros beetle (Bedford 1973). In several lepidopterous species on alfalfa, the GV's and CPV's persist in alternate hosts (Tanada and Omi 1974b). According to Cunningham (1968), the NPV isolated from four nymphalid species, which occurred in the same ecosystem, appeared to be morphologically and serologically identical. There is need for caution in the interpretation of serological results because antigens derived from different hosts may result in differences that are not due to the virus itself. Cunningham and Tinsley (1968) reported that the *Tipula* iridescent virus isolated from *P. brassicae, L. dispar,* and *G. mellonella* behaved serologically identically and was related to, but distinct from, the virus isolated from its original host, *Tipula paludosa* Meigen. They believed that host antigens were incorporated with the virus particles.

Interaction with Other Biotic Agents

A virus may infect an insect simultaneously with other viruses or pathogens, such as rickettsiae, bacteria, protozoa, fungi, and nematodes (Vago 1963, Krieg 1971a). In general, a multiple infection causes the host to die earlier than with only the virus infection, especially when a bacterium or a fungus is involved. Most of the interactions of viruses with other pathogens have not been studied in detail.

The interaction of virus complexes in the same insect may result in: (1) interference or antagonism, (2) independent coexistence, and (3) complementation or synergism (Tanada 1971c). A fourth category, phenotypical mixing, was proposed by Kurstak et al. (1975). There are numerous examples of multiple virus infections, especially when the viruses infect different tissues or organs. In some cases, two different viruses occupied the same cell but in different regions, such as the nucleus and cytoplasm. A NPV or a DNV developed in the nucleus and an iridescent virus or an EPV in the cytoplasm of *Galleria* cells (Garzon and Kurstak 1972, Vago 1975); a NPV in the nuclei and *Chilo* iridescent virus in the cytoplasm of *B. mori* hemocytes (Ohba 1975b); a small flacherie virus developed in the nucleus and the typical flacherie virus in the cytoplasm of columnar midgut cells of silkworm (Matsui and Watanabe 1974). It is rare to find two different viruses in the same cell area, but Amargier et al. (1968) observed a NPV and a DNV in the same nucleus of a *Galleria* fat cell. Also rare was the triple infection of a *Galleria* cell with a NPV and a DNV in the nucleus, and an iridescent virus in the cytoplasm (Vago 1975). Federici et al. (1974) reported small virus-like particles in the occlusion bodies of an EPV that infected a chironomid, *Goeldichironomus holoprasinus* (Goeldi).

When two different viruses occur in the same cell, there is a possibility of a mixing or interchange of nucleic acids and proteins which can result in virus hybridization. Whether this takes place has not been established for insect viruses. However, Aruga et al. (1961a) observed a small number of intermediately shaped polyhedra in silkworm larvae fed a mixture of hexagonal and tetragonal polyhedra strains of CPV. This suggested a phenotypic mixing between the two strains. In the case of a NPV and the *Tipula* iridescent virus infection in *Galleria,* Kurstak et al. (1975) reported that, depending on the invasion of the cytoplasm by the iridescent virus, the NPV polyhedra and virion might be modified. Vago (1975) also reported abnormal occlusion body formation and virus replication in mixed virus infections in the same cell.

In a mixed infection, the nature of the disease may vary with the effect of temperature on the pathogenesis of each pathogen. In *Melolontha melolontha* L. exposed to a virus and a rickettsia, Hurpin and Robert (1968) observed that the percentage of virosis was higher than that of rickettsiosis at high temperatures, and that it was lower at low temperatures.

Complementation (Synergism). There are only a few reports of synergistic interaction between viruses (Table 1), but there are more observations between viruses and other pathogens. The synergism is based on either an enhanced infection in one or both partners or in an increase in host mortality. In evaluating a synergistic response, care should be taken to differentiate it from an additive effect of the two pathogens.

A synergistic effect was suggested by Clark and Fukuda (1971) in the mosquito, *Aedes sollicitans* (Wlkr.), in which the presence of a nonfatal CPV predisposed the larva to a NPV and resulted invariably in a lethal infection. As reported earlier, the Hawaiian GV strain enhanced the infection of a NPV (Tanada 1959), but the Oregonian GV strain did not (Tanada and Hukuhara 1968). The Hawaiian strain also enhanced its own GV, the hypertrophy NPV strain of the armyworm, and the GV's and NPV's of the cabbage looper (*Trichoplusia ni* (Hübner)) and the beet armyworm (*Spodoptera exigua* (Hübner)) (Tanada, unpublished data). A synergistic factor that had enzymatic properties was isolated from the capsule (occlusion body) protein surrounding the GV particle (Tanada and Hara 1975). The site of action of the enzyme appeared to be the plasma membrane of the midgut cell (Tanada et al. 1975). In the mosquito, *Aedes taeniorhynchus* (Wiedemann), Wagner et al. (1974) reported that the infection by the mosquito iridescent virus appeared to depend on a small *Picornavirus*. They speculated that the iridescent virus acted as a helper virus to the *Picornavirus*.

Interference (Antagonism). Antagonistic interactions among viruses (Table 2), and between viruses and other pathogens occur in insects. When both pathogens develop in the same tissue, there is often an antagonistic interaction especially if one of the pathogens is more virulent and invasive than the other. However, this is not to be ascribed only to the live virus, because virus

TABLE 1 *Synergism (complementation) between viruses in insect hosts*

Synergist	Recipient	Host	Reference
Granulosis virus	NPV	*Pseudaletia unipuncta* (Haworth)	Tanada 1959
CPV-*B. mori*	CPV-*C. eurytheme*	*Bombyx mori* (L.)	Tanada & Chang 1964
CPV	NPV	*Aedes sollicitans* (Wlkr.)	Clark & Fukuda 1971
CPV	Flacherie virus	*Bombyx mori*	Inoue 1974b
Sacbrood virus	Bee virus X	*Apis mellifera* L.	Bailey & Woods 1974
Mosquito iridescent virus	Picornavirus	*Aedes taeniorhynchus* (Wiedemann)	Wagner et al. 1974

CPV = cytoplasmic polyhedrosis virus; NPV = nuclear polyhedrosis virus.

TABLE 2 *Interference (Antagonism) between viruses in insect hosts*

Antagonist	Recipient	Host	Reference
NPV-Triangular	NPV-Tetragonal	*Hyphantria cunea* (Drury)	Aruga et al. 1961b
NPV-Tetragonal	NPV-Hexagonal	*Hyphantria cunea*	Hukuhara 1968
NPV-Typical	NPV-Hypertrophy	*Pseudaletia unipuncta* (Haworth)	Tanada et al. 1969
NPV	Granulosis virus	*Choristoneura fumiferana* (Clem.)	Bird 1959
NPV	Entomopoxvirus	*Choristoneura fumiferana*	Bird et al. 1972
CPV-Hexagonal	CPV-Tetragonal	*Bombyx mori* (L.)	Aruga et al. 1961a
CPV	CPV-Nuclear	*Bombyx mori*	Aruga 1968
CPV-*D. spectabilis*	CPV	*Bombyx mori*	Aruga et al. 1963a
CPV	CPV-*B. mori*	*Colias eurytheme* Boisd.	Tanada & Chang 1964
CPV	NPV	*Choristoneura fumiferana*	Bird 1969
CPV	NPV	*Malacosoma disstria* Hübner	Bird 1969
Densonucleosis virus	NPV	*Galleria mellonella* (L.)	Amargier et al. 1968
Flacherie virus	CPV	*Bombyx mori*	Aruga et al. 1965

CPV = cytoplasmic polyhedrosis virus; NPV = nuclear polyhedrosis virus inactivated by heat or UV also inhibited the infection of a second virus (Aruga et al. 1963b, c, Aruga and Hashimoto 1965).

In general, when a facultative bacterium or a fungus invades the host with the virus, the host is usually killed so rapidly that there is little or no development of the virus. On the other hand, Sicker et al. (1965) made a surprising observation in the tent caterpillar, *Malacosoma disstria* Hübner. When larvae already infected with a NPV were fed *Bacillus thuringiensis* Berliner, they lived longer than those infected only with the virus. The delayed mortality was not the result of a feeding stop caused by the bacillus; apparently the development of the virus in its final stage was retarded. When larvae of fall webworm, *Hyphantria cunea* (Drury), were fed a mixture of a NPV and a *Nosema* sp., there was less mortality (70%) than when fed the virus alone (97%); invasion of the midgut by the microsporidan apparently affected virus invasion (Nordin and Maddox 1972).

Aruga (1968) pointed out that virus interference occurred at the cellular and organismal (individual) levels. At the organismal level, the first invading virus inhibited a second virus from provoking a disease. At the cellular level, there was no simultaneous infection in the same cell. Kurstak et al. (1975) reported that a NPV interfered with a DNV at the cellular level. The interference was due to competition for the nucleolus because the DNV replication depended on the nucleolus, which was rapidly destroyed during NPV replication.

The mechanism of interference, which is unknown in most cases, may involve humoral responses. The extent of interference depends on the larval instar; the virulence of the virus; the degree of virus multiplication, which is usually associated with the dosage; the advantage given one virus in time of infection; and the environmental conditions. In the silkworm, the CPV which had been inactivated by heat or UV interfered with other CPV's, but the degree of interference was masked by a very high dosage of the challenge virus (Aruga 1968). This was also the case when the time of inoculation of the challenge virus was delayed after the inoculation of the inactivated virus. An interference occurred between the tetragonal polyhedron strain of CPV and the hexagonal polyhedron strain when the silkworm larvae were reared at 25°C for 20–24 hr, but no interference occurred at 36°C (Aruga and Watanabe 1965). Schwenson (unpublished data) made an interesting observation at the organismal level of interference. When the typical virulent NPV was fed together with the less virulent hypertrophy NPV, even at a low dosage of the former and a very high dosage of the latter, the armyworm appeared to be infected by either, but not by both virus strains. A mixed infection was obtained only when the hypertrophy strain was fed to the larva before the typical strain.

Parasitoids and Predators. Viruses generally complement and augment the action of parasitoids and predators in insect pest control. Viruses are usually more effective at high host densities, whereas parasitoids are effective at low densities. Thus far, there is no record of a virus of a lepidopterous insect being infectious for an insect parasitoid or predator. However, the survival of a parasitoid within a virus-infected host may be jeopardized, especially if the host dies before the parasitoid has attained adequate maturity (Steinhaus 1948, Bird, 1961, Laigo and Tamashiro 1966, Laigo and Paschke 1968, Elsey and Rabb 1970, Irabagon and Brooks 1974, Beegle and Oatman 1975). This suggests a diminution of favorable nutrients for the parasitoid. On the other hand, a very interesting observation was made by Kaya (Kaya 1970, Kaya and Tanada 1972a, b, 1973) that the synergistic Hawaiian GV and the hypertrophy NPV strains produced a proteinaceous substance toxic to the braconid parasitoid larva, *Apanteles militaris* (Walsh), but nontoxic to the host armyworm larva. Its effect appeared to be confined to the braconid.

An insect parasitoid may not favor a virus. Beegle and Oatman (1974) observed that nonparasitized second-instar larvae of *T. ni* were twice as susceptible (LD_{50} level) to a NPV as those parasitized by the ichneumonid, *Hyposoter exiguae* (Viereck).

There are numerous reports of insect parasitoids and predators disseminating viruses. Hymenopterous parasitoids serve as vectors in transmitting the virus by means of the ovipositor which has been contaminated after stinging a virus-infected host (Laigo and Tamashiro 1966, Kurstak and Vago 1967, Laigo and Paschke 1968, Irabagon and Brooks 1974). The feces, especially of predators, may disperse active virus. Capinera and Barbosa (1975) reported that the insect predator, *Calosoma sycophanta* (L.), eliminated feces containing virus polyhedra after feeding on gypsy moth larvae infected with NPV. The adult parasitoid, *Sarcophaga aldrichi* Parker, fed on the virus-killed larvae of the tent caterpillar and contaminated the foliage with its mouthparts and feet (Stairs 1966). From field studies, Stairs (1966) concluded that an epizootic developed most rapidly when both a relatively high population of the parasitoid flies and the virus occurred together.

Recently bird predators have received some attention for their part in virus ecology especially because of their large numbers in certain insect populations (Reed 1971, Polson and Gitay 1972, Matthiessen and Springett 1973). Earlier reports had indicated that viruses within occlusion bodies were not affected by passage through the digestive tracts of bird predators. Polson and Gitay (1972) detected GV particles in feces of the cattle egret (*Ardeola ibis* (L.)), but not the NPV.

Host Plant. The host plant plays a part in virus ecology as a source of nutrition and virus inoculum. This review has already discussed the effect of inadequate or unfavorable nutrition as a stressor in activating latent or chronic virus infection, and also the possibility of antivirus substances occurring in plants. The occurrence of viruses as contaminants on plants will be discussed under the section of physical environment.

Over two decades ago, Thompson and Steinhaus (1950) reported that the NPV of alfalfa caterpillar, *Colias eurytheme* Boisd., was not able to enter through the roots and be transported throughout the alfalfa plant. More recently, Reed (1971) used the scanning electron microscope to observe the GV capsules of potato tuber moth, *Phthorimaea operculella* (Zell.), which had penetrated through the stomata and into the leaflet. He believed that the virus persisted for long periods in this manner and might have brought about the unexpected effective control of the tuber moth. This observation suggests that more studies should be made on the penetration of viruses through openings in plants, in addition to the stomata, such as lenticels and hydathodes.

Some viruses persist for long periods especially on tree limbs and trunks (Clark 1958, Bird et al. 1972). In gypsy moth, Doane (1975) noted on trees the debris mats, which were composed of exuviae, larval and pupal cadavers, and shed pupal cases. The mats were heavily contaminated with NPV. They did not occur in sparse to moderately low populations, but occurred in dense populations which would favor virus transmission. As debris mats also served as oviposition sites, young larvae developing in such areas might become infected.

PHYSICAL (ABIOTIC) ENVIRONMENT

Sunlight

The most important virus-inactivating factor in the physical or abiotic environment is sunlight, especially UV which may reduce the viability of the virus to one or a few days. Many substances have been combined with the virus to serve as solar protectants, but none is effective for long periods (Yendol and Hamlen 1973). The more promising protectants are activated carbon (Hostetter et al. 1973, Ignoffo et al. 1973), 2% dried skimmed milk powder (Keller 1973, Schmid 1974b), 1% milk and 1% India ink or 2% sucrose (Schmid 1974b), 1% charcoal added to 1% milk powder, egg albumin or brewer's yeast (Jaques 1972), 25% molasses (Stelzer et al. 1975), and Shade and lignin sulfate (Young and Yearian 1974).

According to Ramoska et al. (1975), short exposure to UV radiation activated the *A. californica* virus produced *in vitro*. This is the first account of UV-induced activity of an insect virus and differs from the photoreactivation of UV-inactivated virus. David and Magnus (1967) inactivated the European cabbageworm GV with UV (250 or 260 nm); when immediately exposed to strong visible light, it regained most of its activity.

The structure, texture and volatile substances emitted by leaves have influenced the denaturing effect of sunlight. When the NPV of *M. disstria* was exposed to sunlight on a glass surface and on leaves of *Liquidamber styriciflura* (L.), it was inactivated faster on glass than on leaves (Broome et al. 1974). When the *Heliothis* NPV was applied to leaves of cotton, soybean, and tomato, it was inactivated most rapidly on cotton, with little activity remaining after 24 hrs (Young and Yearian 1974). Young and Yearian (1974) reported that the virus persisted better on hirsute than on smooth leaf varieties.

Temperature

Next to sunlight, temperature appears to be an important inactivator of viruses (David et al. 1971, Morris 1971, Keller 1973). The effect of temperature on the period of lethal infection of the host has already been touched upon. Failures in the control of certain insect pests with viruses have been attributed to the prolonged period of infection and the low mortality obtained in insects exposed to low temperatures (Smirnoff 1967b, Reed 1974).

Relative Humidity and Rain

The general consensus is that relative humidity has little effect on the inactivation of viruses. However, it may affect the resistance and behavior of the insect to virus infections. This aspect needs further investigation. When the citrus red mite was infected with the nonoccluded virus and reared at a high humidity, the birefringent crystalline bodies, which were used as a diagnostic character for virus infection (Reed et al. 1974), were absent. Since the crystals were merely a symptom and not involved directly with the virus, the effect of high humidity appeared to be a physiological host reaction.

Heavy simulated rain on cabbage leaves which had been sprayed with a GV suspension did not completely wash off the virus (David and Gardiner 1966). Although rain may not completely remove the virus from leaves, it nonetheless disperses the virus from the upper to the lower parts of plants (Bird 1961). Rain also disperses the virus by splashing virus-containing soil onto low-growing plants (Jaques 1964).

Wind

There is little information on the effect of air current or wind on outbreaks of virus in insects. Wind would be expected to disperse virus contained in soil particles or in the liquefied remains of virus-killed larvae which drip from treetops. It is also important in the movement of virus-infected insects, noninfected carriers, and airborne vectors. Gard (1975) detected most of the virus, distributed by contaminated insects, downwind from the light trap. According to Magnoler (1974b), wind and the predator, *Calosoma sycophanta,* played important roles in the widespread epizootic of NPV in a gypsy moth population.

pH

Virus survival may be limited when occlusion bodies are dissolved under alkaline and acid conditions (Ignoffo and Garcia 1966). Thus the pH of the microenvironment is important. Not much attention has been paid to the pH of rain which may be far from neutral under certain environmental conditions. Some plants, such as cotton, have sufficient alkali on their leaf surfaces to reduce virus persistence (Falcon 1971, Andrews and Sikorowski 1973). Falcon (1971) used buffered solutions to prolong the activity of the *Heliothis* NPV on cotton. Andrews and Sikorowski (1973), after testing the dews on cotton leaves, concluded that the loss of virus activity was associated with concentrations of salts and other chemicals in addition to pH.

Soil pH affects the virus. Jaques and Harcourt (1971) found that a soil pH as low as 5.6 had no effect on the concentration of *T. ni* viruses, but the GV of *P. rapae* (L.) was found more frequently in soils of pH 5.6—6.0 than in more alkaline soils. On the other hand, Thomas et al. (1973) reported that the *T. ni* NPV was inactivated more rapidly in loamy sand with pH 4.83—7.17. They believed that the practice of liming the soil enhanced virus persistence.

Soil

Recent studies have shown that soil is a major site of prolonged virus persistence (Jaques 1964, 1967b, 1969, 1970a, 1974a, b, David and Gardiner 1967, Harcourt and Cass 1968, Hukuhara and Namura 1971, 1972, Hurpin and Robert 1972, Thomas et al. 1972, 1973, Hukuhara 1973, 1975, Tanada and Omi 1974b). Certain viruses, especially the *Baculovirus*, persisted in the soil for several years, even during the winter months when there was no host plant (Jaques 1974a, b, Thomas et al. 1972, Tanada and Omi 1974b). Hukuhara and Namura (1971) observed in thin sections of soil profile, virus polyhedra absorbed to the soil particles. Most of the polyhedra were near the soil surface (Jaques 1969, Hukuhara and Namura 1971, 1972, Thomas et al. 1972).

According to Jaques and Harcourt (1971), the concentrations of viruses of *T. ni* and *P. rapae* in the soil were influenced by host density, crop protection, soil pH, and the month of sampling. Under high host densities, especially when virus epizootics developed, there were greater concentrations of virus in the soil (Jaques 1974a, b). Repeated cropping also increased the virus in the soil, apparently because the plants became infested with virus-infected insects. A correlation between host plant and virus concentration in the soil had also been shown for the NPV of fall webworm and its favorable host plants (Hukuhara and Namura 1972, Hukuhara 1973). Since the virus in soil was effective for long periods, Jaques (1967b, 1970b) suggested that better control of the cabbage looper might be obtained by applying the NPV to soil than to foliage.

Adjuvants, Chemical Insecticides, and Fungicides

Viruses are compatible with most chemical insecticides, fungicides, and adjuvants. A chemical insecticide may be combined with the virus to kill insect pests not controlled by virus. The combination is also used against a single target insect in order to reduce the quantity of insecticides needed for control, thereby reducing pollution and protecting other biological control agents from the insecticide. However, this aspect needs careful evaluation as to whether the reduced chemical insecticides will still destroy the major parasitoids. Recently, the following combinations resulted in better control of insect pests: NPV and EPV with fenitrothion for spruce budworm (Morris et al. 1974), NPV of *T. ni* and GV of *P. rapae* with endosulfan or methonyl (Jaques 1973b); NPV and rotenone for *G. mellonella* (Hsieh et al. 1974); NPV and boric acid for the gypsy moth (Yadava 1971).

The GV of the codling moth was not inactivated by the fungicides: sulfur, Folpet, Dinocarp, Zineb, and Captan (Keller 1973). The fumigant, methyl bromide, inactivated the GV of the Indian meal moth, *Plodia interpunctella*, but phosphine, CCl_4-carbon bisulfide and ethylene dichloride-CCl_4 had no effect (McGaughey 1975).

Viruses have been incorporated into baits which have increased their effectiveness, such as the NPV's of the pink bollworm (Bell and Kanavel 1975) and *Heliothis* spp. (Andrews et al. 1975).

The viruses are generally compatible with the adjuvants used in dust and spray formulations. The use of UV protectants to increase the persistence of the virus has already been discussed. Some materials enhanced virus infection, such as peanut oil for *G. mellonella* NPV (Hsieh et al. 1974), silica powder for CPV of the pine caterpillar, *Dendrolimus spectabilis* (Butler) (Katagiri 1975), and the chemical mutagen, 3-methylcholanthrene, for NPV of *Spodoptera frugiperda* (Reichelderfer and Benton 1973). The inorganic compounds, $CuSO_4$, $FeSO_4$, and $ZnSO_4$, reduced the period of lethal infection of the NPV in *Lymantria monacha* (L.) (Wellenstein and Lühl 1972), and a sodium silicate (Na_2SiO_3) and plant ash did likewise in the NPV infection of gypsy moth larvae (Yadava 1971).

CONCLUSION

In order to obtain effective use of viruses in microbial control and to predict and manipulate epizootics, we must have a sound knowledge of virus ecology. Recently, rapid progress has been made on the biochemistry and other physical properties of insect viruses, especially in their characterization. These studies are of value in virus ecology, but there is also a need for greater emphasis on field studies. This is still an area, relatively untouched, that should yield abundant interesting findings to investigators.

Chapter 19

Ecology of Pathogens of the Gypsy Moth

Charles C. Doane

Department of Entomology
The Connecticut Agricultural Experiment Station
New Haven, Connecticut 06504

INTRODUCTION

The gypsy moth, *Lymantria dispar* L., was first brought into North America to Medford, Massachusetts in 1869 and, following its release, soon spread to many areas in New England (Forbush and Fernald 1896). It appears to have been introduced without the nuclear polyhedrosis virus (NPV) which is the causal agent of wilt disease or polyhedrosis. There is no record of disease prior to about 1900, but in 1907 Howard and Fiske (1911) noted outbreaks of disease in several localities. The destructive nature of the gypsy moth stimulated early workers to begin research on the causal agent of these epizootics (Jones 1910, Reiff 1911, Glaser and Chapman 1912, 1913, Glaser 1915). Glaser (1915) believed that the disease organism was brought into North America when large numbers of parasites were introduced from Eurasia for control of the gypsy moth.

Progress in the ecology of insect pathogens, especially in epizootiology, has developed largely during the past two decades. A number of excellent reviews discuss the intricate relationships existing between the host population, the pathogen, and the environment (Steinhaus 1954, Franz 1961a, 1964, Krieg 1961, Aruga 1963, Tanada 1963, 1964, 1971b, 1973, Vago 1963, Stairs 1972). As with most insects, these relationships are only partially investigated in the gypsy moth. Until they are more thoroughly understood, it is likely that attempts to use NPV for control of the gypsy moth will fail. In this chapter, the major emphasis will be on NPV since relatively little is known of the ecology of other pathogens.

NPV IN GYPSY MOTH POPULATIONS

Gypsy moth populations, both in Eurasia and North America, character-istically fluctuate from innocuous levels to high densities (Schedl 1936, Friend 1945, Vasiljević 1957, 1961, Bess 1961, Campbell 1967, 1973a, b). Some populations increase to high levels and remain so for several successive generations, while others may remain high for only 1 year. In New England, some populations remain at the sparse level for many generations while others fluctuate frequently. The unpredictable nature of these gradations, that is, the time interval between one lowest point of the animal population and the next, thus including one full wave of numerical fluctuation of the population, indicates that the factors regulating change may not be the same for the Eurasian and North American populations, or even for populations in the same geographical area (Campbell and Podgwaite 1971).

NPV is considered the most important pathogen of the gypsy moth in both Eurasia and North America (Steinhaus 1949); many have commented on the dramatic effects of the epizootics (Glaser 1915, Schedl 1936, Steinhaus 1949, Doane 1970, Stairs 1972, Leonard 1974). The apparently sudden outbreak of NPV disease, usually during the latter part of larval life, has led to consideration of divergent hypotheses regarding the mechanisms governing development of epizootics (Bergold 1958, Steinhaus 1958a, b, 1960a, b, Aruga 1963, Tanada 1971b, 1973). One hypothesis is that most larvae are latently infected and that some external stress factor activates the occult virus, bringing on acute infection. Apparent induction of NPV in *Lymantria monacha* L. by solar radiation and moist, warm weather was noted by Wellenstein (1942a). Steinhaus (1960a, b) noted sudden, apparently spontaneous, outbreaks of virus disease in the alfalfa caterpillar, *Colias eurytheme* Boisduval, and speculated on latent infection of the population. Steinhaus (1958b) also considered that stress factors may be related to crowding. Wellington (1962) attributed certain apparently spontaneous outbreaks of NPV in *Malacosoma pluviale* (Dyar) to latent infection. Wallis (1957, 1962) observed a direct correlation between high humidity and the appearance of epizootic outbreak of disease in *L. dispar.* He suggested that in high humidity larvae were unable to eliminate excess water ingested with leaves and that this physiological stress activated subacute infection.

The hypothesis that dense larval populations may carry occult NPV and that epizootics may develop spontaneously under certain conditions of stress have been considered a general occurrence (Steinhaus 1949, 1958a, b, Krieg 1957, Aruga 1963, Gershenzon 1964, Orlovskaya 1964). Although occult virus and latent infection may eventually prove to be important factors, evidence supporting this hypothesis for field populations has been slow to accumulate. In fact, careful studies of the epizootiology of NPV of a number of insect species provide evidence for an alternate hypothesis. That is, virus epizootics of the gypsy moth and a number of other insects do not arise spontaneously, but instead act in a density-dependent manner. Virus present at low levels in the beginning of the host outbreak increases as the density of the host increases. This pattern of infection and spread occurs with viruses of the European spruce sawfly, *Diprion hercyniae* (Htg.) (Bird and Elgee 1957, Bird and Burk 1961), the armyworm *Pseudaletia unipuncta* (Haworth) (Tanada 1961), the eye-spotted bud moth, *Spilonota ocellana* (Denis and Schiffermüller) (Jaques and Stultz 1966), the spruce budworm, *Choristoneura fumiferana* (Clemens) (Bird et al. 1972) and of a number of other insect and mite species (Tanada 1971b). The density of the population of susceptible insects affects the rate of development of the epizootic (Clark 1956, Steinhaus 1958b, Jaques 1962).

DEVELOPMENT OF AN EPIZOOTIC

Transstadial Transmission

The accumulated evidence supports the hypothesis that the NPV spreads, at least in part, in a density-dependent manner. There are two interrelated aspects in the development of disease outbreaks. The first is horizontal spread of NPV within the population during a single larval generation, and secondly, vertical transmission of NPV during several generations, especially during one gradation.

The major source of infection for the hatching larva appears to be the egg surface and hair of the egg mass (Doane 1969, 1970, 1971b, 1975), which may become contaminated with NPV from the mucilagenous material produced by the female to cement the mass. The hatching larva ingests parts of the egg shell and hair in reaching the surface of the egg mass. It often remains on the surface of the mass until the following morning before ascending the tree (McManus 1973); in cool weather it may remain for several days. The longer the time spent on the mass, the more likely that larvae will become infected (Doane 1975). Larvae that acquire a lethal infection die in the first instar and constitute the primary inoculum for horizontal transmission (Doane 1969, 1970, 1971b). Laboratory studies show that most larvae able to molt to the second instar developed into adults.

Tanada (1963) emphasized that the spatial arrangement of the host, rather than the total number of individuals present, may be of greater importance in the spread and development of the epizootic, which may also be true for the gypsy moth. Larvae, whether infected or not, tend to concentrate in the tops of trees both for food and shelter until about the fourth instar. McManus (1973) reported that 75% or more of hatching first instar larvae moved to the tops of trees. Doane and Schaefer (1971) found three times as many third and fourth instar larvae on terminals in the upper half of the tree compared with the number on terminals in the lower half. If infected, these early instar larvae usually die on, and adhere firmly to, the upper surfaces of the leaves, especially on the upper terminals (Doane 1970). The dark cadavers which may be attractive to healthy feeding larvae (Magnoler 1968) contain masses of polyhedra. The upper terminals where larvae concentrate become heavily contaminated during most of the larval feeding period.

Behavioral changes may also influence the likelihood of infection. Wellington (1962) found in inactive colonies of *Malacosoma pluviale* that the cadavers of infected larvae remained on the surface of the single tent and that the other larvae spent long periods on the tent, thereby increasing chances of infection. In active colonies, larvae spent less time on the tents and built several new tents during the same period, leaving dying larvae behind.

The characteristic concentration of dead and living larvae in the tree top has long been noted in *L. monacha* and has been termed "Wipfelkrankheit" or tree-top disease (Růžička 1924, Komárek and Breindl 1924, Steinhaus 1949). It was thought that the disease altered the behavior of nun moth larvae resulting in their upward migration. Růžička (1924) explained that if the weather was damp and cold when polyhedrosis occurred, the larvae climbed to escape to drier air. If the larvae were infected when the weather was hot, they descended to seek a cooler location. An alternate explanation, at least with the gypsy moth, is that they follow the same pattern of ascending or descending, whether infected or not. As earlier discussed, first stage larvae tend to go to the tops of trees regardless of temperature; but they may be responding to cool temperatures when they gather on the tops of leaves. Normally these larvae seek shelter during the day on the undersides of branches or leaves a short distance from feeding sites.

As they spend more time on the leaf surface, they would also be more likely to die in these same locations during cool weather (Doane 1970). Later larval instars establish daily sheltering sites on the main scaffold branches, the trunk or the surface litter, many yards from feeding sites (Forbush and Fernald 1896, Bess et al. 1947, Wallis 1959). They may seek other resting sites if these become exposed to the sun during defoliation. Many larvae may die of NPV in these resting sites.

Environmental Contamination

The egg surface and hair of the gypsy moth egg mass are probably the most important sources of NPV, but there are others as well. Fifth instar larvae, which congregate in protected locations on the scaffold branches and on the trunks of trees, deposit silken matting which is augmented later as larvae spin up for pupation. This debris mat eventually consists of several layers of silk webbing, larval exuviae, pupal cases and dried cadavers of larvae, prepupae and pupae. During the epizootic phase, larvae and pupae wilt on the mat and contaminate the debris. In dense populations, new larvae continually come to pupate on the mat. Females that emerge on the mat often lay their eggs in the same location.

Newly-hatched larvae exposed to the debris suffered very high mortality in laboratory tests (Doane 1975). The body contents and dark cadavers probably protect the NPV from decomposition by sunlight as has been demonstrated for *Trichoplusia ni* (Hübner) (Jaques 1971, 1972).

Although NPV on the debris mats is highly infective to larvae in the laboratory, the role these mats play in the infection process in the field is unknown. First-instar larvae emerging on the mat would likely acquire infection but we do not know how late-instar larvae would be affected when using these natural resting sites for shelter during the following year. Debris mats, which are characteristic of dense populations, may remain in place for 1 or 2 years after the epizootic occurs. Larvae of the next generation, even in a sparse population, would tend to use the same sites for shelter and be exposed to NPV.

Leaf litter under the trees may also be heavily contaminated and may contribute to the infection of larvae in the next year (Steinhaus 1949). Komárek and Breindl (1924) and Růžička (1924) transported forest litter contaminated with the nun moth NPV to start new epizootics.

Parasites and predators, which may also become contaminated, contribute to the spread of NPV (Stairs 1966, Capinera and Barbosa 1975, Tanada Chapter 18).

Thus, much of the environment of the gypsy moth becomes contaminated during the first epizootic. Larvae of succeeding generations would be likely to acquire infection even if they escaped infection from the egg surface during hatch. The importance of an environment contaminated with virus to the development of disease in a population has been shown with *T. ni*. NPV of *T. ni* persists in soil for many years (Jaques 1967b, 1969, 1970b, 1974a), while weathering of NPV occurs quickly on foliage (Jaques 1967a). The amount of virus naturally occurring in soil was related qualitatively and quantitatively to the residues on leaves and to the incidence of NPV mortality in the host. As the epizootic progressed, the level of virus in the soil increased (Jaques 1970a, 1974a, Jaques and Harcourt 1971).

QUANTITATIVE ESTIMATION OF NPV IN POPULATIONS

Factors governing the incidence of polyhedrosis in gypsy moth populations during the course of one gradation are not well known. Especially of interest is how NPV persists in collapsed and sparse populations. Quantitative estimates of the amount of mortality by NPV in samples of overwintering egg masses have been used to measure the amount of virus in the population, to predict the likelihood of disease outbreak, and the amount of defoliation caused by larval populations (Doane 1971b). Egg masses were collected singly in the field, incubated in the laboratory, and larvae were reared individually on artificial food (Leonard and Doane 1966). First-instar larvae dying from NPV infection thus provide an estimate of the amount of primary inoculum that would be present in the field. While the test does not include an estimate of the infection from other sources, it does indicate whether the major sources of infection for hatching larvae, the egg surface and the hair of the egg mass, are contaminated. New outbreak populations have a very low incidence of NPV (Doane 1971b), while egg masses from populations in the second and third years of heavy infestation are heavily contaminated. Average larval mortality was higher from mixed egg masses than from single egg masses. Although this point has not been clarified, it would appear that some egg masses are able to contaminate all in the mix. In any event, mixing egg masses increases the chances of finding virus in a sample when the incidence in a population is very low, but it would distort the first instar mortality in samples from populations which have a high level of NPV.

If there is high mortality of larvae hatching from single egg masses, one may predict that the population will collapse in that generation and that little defoliation will occur. In one population studied with a density of over 5,000 egg masses per acre, there was commonly over 90% mortality in larvae hatched from single egg masses. In the field, the predicted epizootic occurred early in larval life and defoliation was less than 10% at the end of the larval feeding period. Conversely, if mortality from mixed egg masses is about 1% or less, then no epizootic is likely, and heavy defoliation may be expected. Such low incidence of virus is indicative of an uncontaminated environment. The method seems to work well with the gypsy moth if the NPV incidence is either very high or low. With intermediate levels, an epizootic may occur in a dense population, but one would be unable to predict the time of the epizootic wave and thus the amount of defoliation that would occur. Bird (1961) found that epizootics in sawfly populations resulted from less than 10% infection of the eggs. Interestingly, Bergold (1943) suggested the possibility of predicting the extent of epizootics in the nun moth by estimations based on larval mortality from eggs hatched in the laboratory.

A MODIFICATION OF DENSITY-DEPENDENCE HYPOTHESIS

The hypothesis of density-dependent regulation of gypsy moth populations by NPV should now be modified to accommodate present knowledge. When NPV is newly-introduced into a healthy gypsy moth population, or is present at a very low level in the progressive part of the gradation, then it increases in a density-dependent manner. Polyhedrosis will increase as the virus spreads through the host population until the epizootic wave brings on collapse and the regressive phase of the gradation. This may occur in one or two generations since both the gypsy moth and the virus have a high capacity for increase in numbers. Collapse over a wide geographical area is usually involved (Glaser 1915, Campbell 1973a, b, Anderson and Gould 1974). Once the epizootic occurs, the environment of the gypsy moth becomes heavily contaminated with NPV and the disease will not necessarily act in a density-dependent manner from that point on. Larvae emerging in later generations at the end of the gradation will be exposed to contaminated surfaces other than the egg masses. For the same reason, healthy larvae blowing into a contaminated area would be unlikely to start an outbreak. The population would become successively sparse, not from larva-to-larva spread of NPV, but because healthy larvae would likely contact contaminated surfaces before they reached the pupal stage. After a number of years, the NPV on contaminated surfaces weathers and disappears or is covered by vegetation; the stage is then set for another gradation.

This modification appears to fit well with the zone density effect elaborated by Campbell (1973a, b). In part, he found that local populations, whether of high or low density, tended to be affected by the area around them and to follow the course of the surrounding populations. For example, a localized outbreak of the gypsy moth within a larger area where the population has collapsed will also tend to collapse. Conversely, a low population surrounded by an area where the populations are already rapidly increasing will tend to increase.

There appear to be other NPV diseases where density-dependent action may not always occur after the environment becomes contaminated. Tanada and Omi (1974a, b) found that virus epizootics of the beet armyworm, *Spodoptera exigua* (Hübner) and the alfalfa looper, *Autographa californica* (Speyer) occurred at very low host densities. However, they noted that the viruses of both species acted in a density-dependent manner, with marked increases in virus infection occurring with an increase in host densities. They suggested that observed epizootics at low densities occurred because the viruses were present in the soil and contaminated the environment of both species. Rain and wind were found important in disseminating the viruses onto plants (Tanada 1973).

Whenever soil, bark, or leaf litter become contaminated there is an opportunity for these areas to play a role in infection of sparse populations. Virus of the tent caterpillar, *Malacosoma fragile* (Stretch), in addition to trans-ovum transmission, appears to survive on plant surfaces and remain infectious after passing the winter (Clark 1955, 1956). Epizootics of *L. monacha* probably have many characteristics in common with those of *L. dispar*. The environment becomes contaminated with NPV and larvae may become infected when exposed to these surfaces (Komárek and Breindl 1924, Růžička 1924, Wellenstein 1942a, Steinhaus 1949).

SEX RATIO AND NPV

One of the more interesting implications of virus infection in populations is the effect of survivors on the next generation. The change in sex ratio, the ability of the insect to escape attack by parasites and predators, and altered physiology of the surviving individual are all worthy of consideration.

Reiff (1911) was probably one of the first to note that there were many more males than females present after an epizootic in populations of the gypsy moth. Campbell (1963a, b) found that NPV epizootics occurring during the late instars were strongly selective against the female larvae. Differential mortality caused a change in the female pupal sex ratio from about 70% where no disease occurred, to less than 25% following an epizootic. Mortality was further compounded by attack from ichneumonids. These parasites normally kill more male pupae; but with reduction in size of the female pupae resulting from disease and competition, their attacks further reduced the females to about 2% in the adult population. Burgess and Crossman (1929) and Dowden (1962) also noted that parasitism in dense populations was considerably higher among females. Thus, the forces exerted by parasites and pathogens cooperated in suppression of the population.

Magnoler (1974b) reduced the ratio of female to male gypsy moths by treating plots with NPV. Bird (1961) observed that females of the European pine sawfly, *Neodiprion sertifer* (Geoffroy), also suffered higher mortality than males because they require about a week longer to complete their development. Following aerial application of virus for control of the Virginia pine sawfly, *Neodiprion pratti pratti* (Dyar), the sex ratio was altered 9:1 in favor of males (McIntyre and Dutky 1961). Morris et al. (1974) reported that after application of an entomopox virus to populations of the spruce budworm, *Choristoneura fumiferana* (Clem.), the ratio of males to females changed from 1:1 to 2:1. Schönherr (1969) found that granulosis virus infection of *Choristoneura muriana* (Hübner) caused a marked reduction in the female population. Generally, altered sex ratio appears to result from viral infection (Franz 1970/71) in species where the female larva requires more time or extra instars before reaching the pupal stage (Campbell 1963c, Bird 1961, McIntyre and Dutky 1961). In nature, altered sex ratio may be associated mainly with late virus infection. Interestingly, while early larval stages are susceptible to virus infection, the later stages are resistant (Stairs 1972, Doane 1967); pupal tissues may be immune (Bird 1953a). Population quality changes operating in dense populations may place the female gypsy moth at even greater risk of virus infection. Leonard (1968, 1970, 1971b, 1974) has shown that crowding, common to dense populations, increases the percentage of extra instars in both sexes.

Disease and competition in larval life may also decrease the ability of the female to produce normal amounts of pheromone; thus, further limiting the reproductive capabilities of survivors. Bobb (1964, 1972) found that in dense populations of the Virginia pine sawfly, *N. pratti pratti*, the loss of ability of females to produce pheromone resulted in rapid decline of the population. If inability to release pheromone is the result of disease, we may speculate that a similar alteration may also occur in the gypsy moth.

OTHER PATHOGENS

There are other pathogens beside NPV, but these will not be reviewed in any detail. Motile strains of *Streptococcus faecalis* also have been implicated in epizootics of the gypsy moth (Doane 1970). Laboratory (Doane and Redys 1970) and field tests (Doane 1971a) show that the strains are very pathogenic. The disease may have been noted by Glaser (1918) but little is known of its importance in controlling the gypsy moth. Many streptococci have doubtful status as pathogens (Bucher 1963, Vago 1963). Serological studies of the motile isolates show that they are different from non-insect *S. faecalis* (Doane and Redys 1970). While there can be no doubt that these strains can be highly pathogenic, they may be effective only at certain densities of the gypsy moth or only in certain localities. More should be known about wild streptococci. *S. faecalis* may be isolated from plants (Mundt 1963) and occurs naturally in wild populations of insects without apparent harm to the host (Eaves and Mundt 1960). Pathogenicity may be peculiar only to certain antigenic types of *S. faecalis*, such as those associated with disease in the gypsy moth (Doane and Redys 1970).

Weiser (1961) discusses five species of Microsporida and their effects on the gypsy moth. While not dramatic in their external pathology or ability to produce disease, he noted that many have promise in reducing natural infestations of the gypsy moth. In general, the Microsporida have not been intensively studied; more should be learned of their ecology, especially relationships with the environment and with alternate hosts.

CONCLUSION

Study of the ethology of the gypsy moth in relation to its pathogens should be pursued. Elucidation of host-pathogen relationships in a variety of insects will enhance the successful use of virus in nature.

Chapter 20

Towards Integrated Control of Forest Pests in Europe

J. M. Franz

Biologische Bundesanstalt für Land–und Forstwirtschaft,
Institut für biologische Schädlingsbekämpfung, Darmstadt

INTRODUCTION

In this paper, I shall report on some European trends in integrated control of forest pests. Subjects were selected which best characterize the situation in Europe. Strategies and tactics reported upon fit into a simplified definition of integrated control which states, "The control of pests employing all methods consistent with economic, ecological, and toxicological requirements while giving priority to natural limiting factors and threshold values." Most of my European colleagues will agree with the order of entities and terms as they have been developed in North America: Management of resources as the all comprising frame, integrated management of forest pests as that part of it which is concerned with the decision-making process, and integrated control as the approach to actual regulation of pest populations (Stark 1971). It might become clearer by a diagram of a model structure of the integrated pest management system, which shows the basic components of the system, their linkages, and the information flows and feedbacks to the forest management decision and planning process (Fig. 1) (Franz et al. 1975). This review will be limited to some subjectively selected examples of the inner square, mainly pest population dynamics, monitoring techniques, and treatment strategies and tactics. The selection was made to summarize some typical European activities and to go into some detail in such cases which may be new or otherwise of particular interest to American colleagues. The time covered will be limited in most examples to the last 5 years because extensive review articles appeared in 1970 (Franz 1970/71,

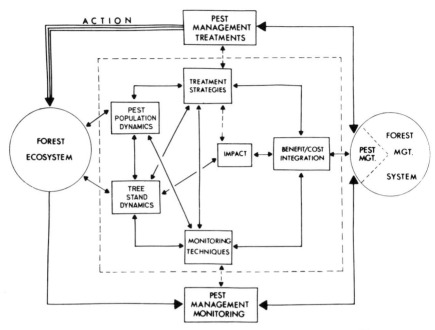

FIGURE 1. *Model structure of Integrated Pest Management System (Mgt. = management). - From Franz et al. 1975 (adapted from D.L. Wood - NSF GB 34718).*

Grison 1970). The area considered includes eastern European countries, but rarely the European part of the Soviet Union.

Discussions of terminology and the differentiation between integrated control and integrated management of pests are not important in Europe. Perhaps our forests or our pest problems or both are not large enough. The pattern of national borderlines and the use of at least 14 different languages may also discourage the development of approaches to analyse the management of complex ecosystems such as the forests of a whole continent. Consideration of socio-economic problems in decisions dealing primarily with problems of integrated forest pest control is perhaps self-evident in Europe because of its generally high population density, its structure of interwoven forests, villages and roads, and the closeness of the industrialized centres to recreational forests. Systematic research has been initiated on the quantification of sociological and recreational functions of the forests (Jacsman 1974).

With the exception of Scandinavia, areas and distances of potential control operations are usually small in comparison to those of the North American or Asiatic continent. The limited size and easy accessibility of most European forests allow intense silvicultural measures. Artificial fertilization and particularly modification of the structure of endangered parts of the forest—for instance by raising a hardwood undergrowth in coniferous stands—are contributions to forest pest management typical for Europe. In Scandinavia, requisite-governed pest insects (Eidmann 1976) like weevils or bark beetles are of particular importance after some catastrophic event like storm or snow-break in the huge forest areas. Here again, silvicultural control, assisted by proper handling of timber and pulpwood, is almost the only available control.

Conditions for the perfection of integrated control in central European forests are not always favourable. In northern Germany, for instance, felled stems are rarely barked by the workers on the spot as in the past, but remain in the forest until stationary debarking equipment is available. This might be in late summer, so bark beetles (mainly *Ips typographus* L. and *Trypodendron lineatum* (Olivier)) more often have to be controlled with insecticides. In addition, in Germany about 1 million ha. of former agricultural land will soon come under forest management. It is well known that new forests on old agricultural land are particularly subject to damage by forest insects and diseases. This again favours use of pesticides (Schindler 1971).

HISTORICAL PERSPECTIVES

The concept of silvicultural control, utilization of available natural enemies, and particularly the importance of sustained yield is deeply rooted in European forestry. The temptation of cheap and easy solutions to some insect problems by application of broad-spectrum and persistent insecticides had a relatively short life; the concept of "harmonious control" (Voûte 1964) was born from a store of fundamental knowledge built up over the centuries.

The almost 100-year-old tradition to follow closely the pattern of gradations of defoliating Lepidoptera in the pine forest of northern Germany stemmed from the man-caused transformation of mixed forests into pure pine stands early in the 19th century. The results of 60 successive census counts, taken after 1881, of hibernating instars in the forest litter, show the frequency and the range of changes (Schwerdtfeger 1935). In his treatise on forest insects of central Europe, Escherich (1914) described in detail the sampling techniques as well as the methods of evaluating the degree of natural mortality of hibernating insects due to parasites and diseases. This prognostication system weighed carefully all available data and made it possible to reduce or cancel planned control operations when natural limiting factors, mainly enemies, were recognized as likely to be effective. This tradition continues. Recent examples are natural terminations of incipient gradations by parasites of the lymantriid *Orgyia antiqua* L. and the spruce bark tortricid *Laspeyresia pactolana* (Zeller) (Bogenschütz 1975).

Insect pathology is a rather young branch of entomology, but during the 1930's in Germany, the diagnosis of some diseases was used to plan future control operations against the nun moth (*Lymantria monacha* L.). Wellenstein (1942b) used diagnosis of disease around 1935 in conjunction with the phase of the gradation of the pest, i.e. with some qualities of the host population. Janisch (1958) examined the incidence of disease in prematurely activated larvae of the nun moth to forecast the necessity of artificial control. More recently, chemical control of the green oak tortrix (*Tortrix viridana* L.) was cancelled in Germany because monitoring of the health of young larvae had allowed a forecast of a general collapse of the population due to a microsporidan (Franz and Huger 1971). The last historical example of activities in Europe which paved the way for the present day concept of forest pest management is the first presentation of a life table study of a forest insect (the pine noctuid *Panolis flammea* Schiffermüller) by Schwerdtfeger in 1932. More examples are in a recent review on the history of forest entomology (Schwerdtfeger 1973). Thus, because of the structure of the forests and the traditions of foresters, most if not all elements of integrated control of forest pests have been used in Europe for a considerable time.

The latest holistic approach to insect control, developed in the United States, is characterized by the construction of models, application of system analysis and simulation with the aid of computers (Stark and Smith 1971). In Europe, this approach is just beginning to draw some interest. It may even yield some information which is able to influence practical measurements in forestry, mainly in silviculture, but I doubt if it will find an important place during this century. I shall restrict myself to pest insects and to the following four topics: population dynamics, biological control, biotechnical control, and some remarks on the selectivity of pesticides.

POPULATION DYNAMICS

Studies of dynamics of forest insects are generally acknowledged to contribute to a better understanding of population fluctuations in time and space. That is, they contribute to the understanding of the causes of appearance, duration, and consequences of what we call gradations. The zone of high probability for gradations leading to the destruction of forests can be approximately defined. A scheme of the distribution of natural forest formations on an idealized continent is a useful tool to recognize two points: the basic limitation of most mortal outbreaks to the centre of natural coniferous forests, and the risk connected with the artificial shift of coniferous (endangered) stands into the natural hardwood zone (Franz 1948). A transfer of this very general observation to the Eurasian continent helps in understanding why high risk zones of gradations, mainly by defoliators, consist of coniferous forests planted in natural hardwood or mixed forest zones, particularly in the more continental climate as in Poland (Koehler 1974) or in lower altitudes of the Central European Hills. In the Soviet Union, four distinct geographic zones of pine forests and accordingly developed four variants of integrated pine stand protection have been discerned (Vorontsov 1975).

To my knowledge, only four long term studies of population dynamics of typical defoliators (Lepidoptera) have been made in Europe. The first involves the pine looper caterpillar (*Bupalus piniarius* L.) in Dutch pine forests. Klomp (1966) published life tables covering the years 1950-65, and discovered a temporal change of the key factors. Larval mortality dominated during the first 14 years, and pupal mortality during the subsequent 8 years. The recent disappearance of the ichneumonid parasite causing pupal mortality, has allowed the host population to recover so that in 1974 density proved to be higher than in any of the previous years (Klomp 1973 and 1975, unpublished data). This parasite needed alternate hosts which occur only on distant birch trees. Here, the problem of duration and of extension of the range of such population studies appears. The extension beyond the activity range of any important natural enemy is a problem which often requires a team of scientists. Local studies frequently will have limited general value. For example, the critical threshold figures, empirically worked out for the same looper in central Europe, are invalid in England (Bevan 1974).

The second long-term population study deals with the winter moth (*Operophthera brumata* (L.)) in England. Varley and co-workers identified the main causes of year-to-year population change (life tables), and also studied the effect of key factors, many of which act in a density-dependent manner. Population models emerged and were improved continuously; they helped to forecast the effect of interaction of the various components and stimulated general studies on population ecology (Varley et al. 1974). Although former predictions on the effect of the parasitic tachinid, *Cyzenis albicans* (Fallén), on the host population after its introduction into Canada could not be confirmed, the success of this biological control assisted in further improvements to a predictive model.

The third extensively studied insect is the Mediterranean pine processionary caterpillar *(Thaumetopoea pityocampa* (Denis & Schiffermüller)) in southern France, Corsica, and Spain. A forest area of 12,000 ha. (Mora de Rubielos) was set aside in Spain for a joint French-Spanish team to establish life tables, to investigate population dynamics and to construct predictive models (Demolin 1970, Montoya 1970). One of the first achievements was the determination of actual and potential outbreak zones, which were mainly governed in France by the availability of sunshine ($> 2,000$ hours per year) and mild winter temperatures (above $-2°C$) (Huchon and Demolin 1970). Such data are helpful in forecasting outbreaks and in making decisions concerning integrated control.

This species is capable of causing heavy and extensive damage in the study area; therefore, practical consequences of this work are to be expected.

The fourth insect, the palaearctic grey larch bud moth (*Zeiraphera diniana* (Hübner)) has been studied mainly in the Alps, beginning in the Engadine Valley in Switzerland. A team from the Entomology Department at the Technical University at Zürich, set up originally by P. Bovey, has quantitatively observed the remarkably regular outbreaks within rather narrow limits of altitude. There is a cyclic sequence of gradations, which is known to have occurred every 8 to 10 years since 1854.

This tortricid has proven ideal for population studies. It allows comparison of the conditions which generate various types of fluctuations in close proximity (Baltensweiler 1968). This study grew into an international team work covering the Alps from France to Austria. The present opinion as to the causes of cycles is that in the optimum zone density independent environmental factors favour permanent population growth (determination). Regulation is achieved by various complementing and compensating processes of which intraspecific competition for food is decisive. The cyclic numeric fluctuation may thus be regarded as the manifestation of an autoregulating life-system. The larch bud moth multiplies for 4-5 generations under favourable conditions until it exceeds the carrying capacity of the ecosystem and thereby changes the nutritional base in such a manner that the subsequent four generations suffer from high environmental resistance (Benz 1974). The collapse is accelerated by parasites, predators, occasionally by virus epizootics, and heavy emigration flights.

These four examples of long-term population studies have contributed and still are contributing to our general knowledge of the causation of fluctuations. Thus, they can be considered as preparatory steps for the development of control strategies and predictive models, even if their immediate assistance in actual control operations is negligible. I think that the larch bud moth is an excellent example to demonstrate the advantage of having available a model species which performs one gradation after the other in a predictable shape and sequence, in well separated populations and on host trees which are capable of tolerating cyclic defoliation.

BIOLOGICAL CONTROL

Biological control is usually defined in Europe as utilization by man of natural enemies, i.e. parasites, predators and pathogens, for the reduction of pest populations. Along with silvicultural control, biological control is extremely compatible with other control measures and is therefore a most useful element in any program for integrated control. Without discussing general points, I will review some recent progress in Europe.

Development of microbial control usually goes through several phases: first, the pilot test to examine how well a certain pathogen performs; second, the government-financed, large-scale trials plus demonstration of efficacy; and third, the routine incorporation into the planning of control. Phases 2 and 3 will depend on the availability of commercial preparations, and phase 3 on some sort of registration.

In the case of *Bacillus thuringiensis* Berliner (*Bt*), one French and three American brands are available and are used in phases 2 and 3 in western and central Europe. Permission for use depends in many countries on numerical proof of efficacy for each target species. The guidelines, developed for official tests of *Bt* preparations on forest defoliators in Germany, are adjusted so that special advantages are offered this selective agent; that is, the rate of mortality of target pests, which is normally >90% for chemical preparations has been reduced to 70% for bacterial preparations (Franz et al. 1970).

Examples of Lepidoptera that are susceptible to and controlled sometimes by *Bt* in western Europe are: *Tortrix viridana* L., *Thaumetopoea pityocampa, Operophthera brumata, Euproctis chrysorrhoea* L. (= *Nygmia phaeorrhoea* (Donovan)) and *Stilpnotia salicis* (L.) (Nef 1975). The gypsy moth, of particular importance in Mediterranean and southeastern countries, proved to be less susceptible (Magnoler 1974c), whereas the fall webworm (*Hyphantria cunea* (Drury)) could be effectively controlled by *Bt* preparations in eastern Europe (e.g. Andriescu et al. 1972/73). Here, we observe a strange zonation of use of *Bt* preparations. Decisions seem to be governed mainly by the immediate economic effect. The acreage treated remains relatively small, probably due to cost. Some local industrial production of *Bt* preparations begins.

In some countries like Rumania where an excellent prognostic service exists, efforts to reduce the dosages of conventional insecticides to control oak defoliators have reached a high degree of perfection (Fratian 1975). In the Soviet Union, however, tremendous forest areas are treated regularly. Several bio-preparations, based on different strains and serotypes of *Bt*, have been developed and are applied against Lepidoptera such as *Dendrolimus sibiricus* (Tschetverikov). The trend, not to say the fashion toward inrecasing the efficacy of *Bt* preparations by addition of so-called "sublethal" dosages of normal chemical insecticides originated in Kiev in use against agricultural pests. It spread to Europe and North America. Opinions of synergism are controversial. The reviews by Benz (1971) and Krieg (1971a) facilitate systematic examination of various types of mixed preparations.

I suppose there will be agreement that no mixture of a pathogen and an insecticide should be labelled "integrated control". When dosages of broad-spectrum insecticides are reduced so that target insects do not die (sublethal doses), chances still remain that residues eliminate beneficial species which usually are more susceptible than the pests. Thus, the addition of conventional insecticides to microbial control preparations usually results in the sacrifice of one of the most valuable qualities of a pathogen—its selective effect on certain pest insects. Bearing this in mind, the gradual disappearance of recommendations for these types of mixtures even in eastern Europe becomes understandable. The minimum requirement, therefore, should be the quantitative measurement of side-effects on entomophagous arthropods prior to large-scale application of such mixtures. Reservations are reinforced by the additional fact that supplemental and potentiating synergism is relatively rare in such cases.

On the other hand, the importance of faster and higher mortality of pests has to be acknowledged as a prerequisite, even for the protection of forest trees in some cases. Let us briefly return to the larch bud moth and its predictable, cyclic outbreaks. In the years of culmination, killing of up to 80% of the larvae with a *Bt* preparation does not prevent visible damage because the remaining larvae kill most needles. Incidentally, economic damage in the optimum zone for the larch and the larch bud tortricid is not so much caused by death or reduced growth of the trees, but by discoloration of needles in mid-summer near St. Moritz and other tourist centres. Benz (1975) reports on experiments to enhance the effect of a commercial *Bt* preparation by additon of a reduced dose of DDT or of the heat-stable β-exotoxin that is released into the culture medium by some serotypes of the *Bacillus*. In a field test, both combinations increased the final mortality satisfactorily, i.e. to 92%. Only the exotoxin, however, produced supplemental synergism without unduly reducing the selectivity of the bacterial preparation. Since toxicological difficulties are not insurmountable and such combinations of *Bt* and exotoxin also are used in the USSR, a trial in the New World might be worthwhile.

It is extremely difficult to alter the course of a gradation of the larch bud moth. Experiments by Auer (1974), carried out in 1963 in the Wallis Valley, showed that neither 97% mortality by a DDT treatment nor 92% by a Phosphamidon treatment could do more than postpone for one year the peak and subsequent decline. There has been another approach to cut off the peak or to damp the course of cyclic larch bud moth outbreaks. The treatment with *Bt* of larch forests of a whole valley near Briançon, France, carried out during the early ascending part of the gradation, succeeded in keeping the rate of population increase lower than in the untreated neighbouring valleys, but only for 2 years (Grison et al. 1971). The culmination later occurred simultaneously in treated and untreated valleys. These experiments offer very instructive examples of the powerful forces built into outbreak populations, a pattern regularity in fluctuations which, as Watt (1970) suggests, may depend on the importance of two-and-more-year lag effects. Such experiences will be valuable for the construction of predictive models.

Viruses have been used against many forest insects. Trials to initiate an epizootic in the larch bud moth by artificial dissemination of a granulosis virus were not successful partially because of its low persistence (Schmid 1974b). However, many other experiments using virus preparations for control of forest Lepidoptera and sawflies were successful in Europe, beginning in 1954 (Franz and Niklas 1954) with the use of the nuclear polyhedral virus (NPV) of the European pine sawfly (*Neodiprion sertifer* (Geoffroy)). It is still the most widely used virus, and about 300 ha were treated recently in Sweden (Eidmann 1976) and Norway (Bakke unpublished data). Smaller plots were treated in Austria (Donaubauer 1973), Finland (Nuorteva 1972) and other countries. A special colloquium of the relevant Working Group of the West Palaearctic Regional Section (WPRS) of the International Organization of Biological Control (IOBC) was devoted in 1971 to the discussion of the use of viruses and bacteria against the gypsy moth, particularly the differential virulence of various geographical virus sources (Vasiljević 1973). For the control of satin moth larvae, *Bt* acted quicker and, therefore, was better than NPV (Nef 1975).

The epizootiology of the NPV diseases of the European spruce sawfly (*Diprion hercyniae* (Hartig)) has been studied in Great Britain since 1971 (Entwistle 1974). The spatio-temporal form of the spread of infection reflects the passage of a spatial infection wave developing through time. The primary epizootic module grew in a continuous manner, about 2,000 m in diameter in 5 years, and additionally by a process of discontinuous spread to fresh disease epicentres. The speed of such epizootic waves depends on the persistence of the virus, its dispersal, and its innate infection rate. Results of these studies will not only increase our understanding of the basic elements of insect epizootics, but they will also help in the artificial manipulation of the disease, e.g. for the implantation of inocula instead of large areal spray operations. According to Entwistle (unpublished data) at least 16 species of birds are involved in the carry-over and spread of NPV of the sawfly, partially by passing faeces contaminated with infectious NPV. Such observations will help us understand better and utilize intentionally the after-effect of epizootic waves as observed sometimes one generation after the artificial application, e.g. with the gypsy moth (*L. dispar*) in Sardinia (Magnoler 1974b) or with the nun moth (*L. monacha*) in Sweden (Wellenstein 1973a, Eidmann 1976), and probably also in Denmark (Bejer-Petersen 1974 and unpublished data).

The next example selected from the vast field of biological control is the augmentation of native parasites of the gypsy moth by the artificial increase of the host population in Yugoslavia (Maksimović et al. 1970). After introduction of egg masses into a forest during 4 years of the ascending slope of the gradation, the population at culmination remained below the economic density threshold.

Simultaneously, the rate of parasitization by the larval parasite, *Apanteles porthetriae* Muesebeck, increased considerably so that a causal relation was very probable between the increase of natural enemies and the low level of the peak population. This was compared with a similar site without artificial augmentation of the host. Perhaps, this example will stimulate repetition in America.

Intra-areal transfer of natural enemies is the implantation of beneficial organisms into sites where they do not occur, but which they could reach, theoretically, by natural dispersion because they belong .to the same faunal region. Opportunities to apply this rather neglected technique always appear when forests have a patchy distribution and when the pest reaches distant and rather isolated sites earlier than its enemies. An example is the distribution pattern of fir trees (*Abies alba* Miller) in Europe where the sites in Scandinavia are about 800 km from the nearest natural fir stand in southern Germany. Massive occurrence of fir-tree chermesids of the genus *Dreyfusia* in southern Sweden initiated the transfer of the coccinellid, *Pullus impexus* Mulsant, specialist on those woolly aphids, from the Black Forest to Sweden and led to its establishment (Eidmann and Ehnström 1975).

Intra-areal transfer of the predatory red forest ant of the *Formica rufa*-group was in full swing about 10 to 15 years ago, when barrels full of nest material, including the ants, were transported to ant-free forests, for instance, in Germany, Italy and Spain, for establishment of new colonies and, hopefully, permanent protection of various forest types (for Italy: Pavan and Ronchetti 1971/72). The low rates of successful colonizations taught us to study more carefully the conditions of the new habitat before new transfers would be tried and to realize the limitation of red forest ants in their capabilities to suppress pests. One interesting side effect is worth noting: *Formica* ants stimulate honey-dew production of relatively harmless aphids (Lachnidae) on coniferous trees thereby enabling bee-keepers to harvest, on an average, at least twice as much valuable forest-type honey (aphid honey-dew) than if ants were absent (Wellenstein 1973b). A general review on the present status of biological control in Europe is given by Greathead (1976).

BIOTECHNICAL CONTROL

I should like to strike a balance and demonstrate with the help of Fig. 2 how little my report has covered and how much remains to be said. The scheme shows the multitude of control techniques available. As the methods to the left are usually summarized as technical, and those to the right as biological methods, the designation of the central group as "biotechnical controls" will be understandable. This term summarizes the effects of artificially applied chemical or physical key stimuli (attraction, repulsion or similar disturbances of normal behaviour) which release intensive reactions in pest organisms. Because of their

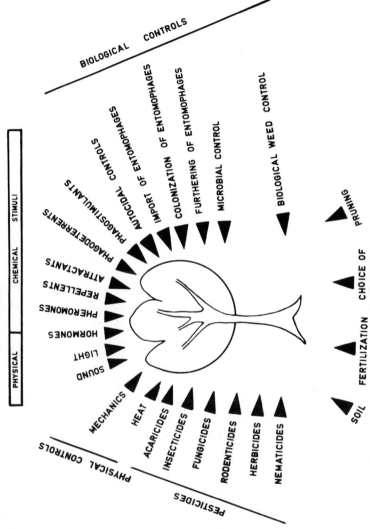

FIGURE 2. *Synopsis of important elements and procedures available for an integration of different measures in forest pest control (from Franz 1973).*

more or less selective effect, biotechnical methods are particularly suitable for integrated control programs (Franz 1973).

I can only summarize some examples of biotechnical control by showing that there are many research activities in the use of growth regulators, pheromones, repellents and other biogenic materials. The general direction is almost identical with that in North America; progress, with a few exceptions, lags behind that in the New World. One reason might be that forerunners of some of these techniques have been used in Europe for a long time, so the need to develop additonal methods was not so pressing. Examples are the use of trap trees in monitoring bark beetles and the use of virgin female nun moths, first developed in the ČSR in 1933. It was shown conclusively by Mors (1938) that the number of males attracted to unmated females of the nun moth had no relation to the size of the population. Now, the availability of synthetic pheromones and hormones offers some refinement, increase of efficiency, and new approaches.

Research on synthetic sex pheromone as an aid in monitoring forest Lepidoptera is actively underway, especially on the gypsy moth. Disparlure is presently used to monitor populations of the gypsy moth (Boness et al. 1974, Maksimović et al. 1974, Skuhravý et al. 1974) and the nun moth (Schneider et al. 1974, Schönherr 1972a, Schröter and Lange 1975, Skuhravý and Hochmut 1975). The first field experience with the confusion technique was gained here. The study of population aggregation pheromones of bark beetles in Europe is predominantly concerned with biological and/or chemical characterization. This has been at least partially established for the following species: *Ips typographus* L. (Bakke 1970, Rudinsky et al. 1971); *Ips acuminatus* Gyllenhal (Bakke 1967); *Ips sexdentatus* (Boerner) (Vité et al. 1974); *Ips duplicatus* (Stahlberg) (Bakke 1975); *Pityokteines curvidens* (Germar) (Harring et al. 1975); *Myelophilus piniperda* L. (Schönherr 1972b); *Leperisinus fraxini* Panzer (Schönherr 1970); and *Xyloterus domesticus* L. (Francke 1973). The work in Europe is summarized by Bakke (1973). The pheromone "Multilure" which was synthesized in the United States also proved to be attractive to *Scolytus multistriatus* (Marsham) in Europe (Vité et al. 1976). There is much similarity or even identity between pheromones of bark beetles from Europe and North America. The trend to use them for control is in the direction of strengthening the effect of trap trees.

Juvenile hormone analogs (JHA) and moulting inhibitors have recently been tried in the field. Skuhravy and Hochmut (1975) applied JHA from Zoecon ("Altozar") against the green oak tortricid (*T. viridana*) on 3 ha in 1972. This pioneering experiment caused approximately 65% reduction of larvae and pupae of the treated generation as well as of eggs and larvae of the subsequent generation, and resulted in very little leaf damage on the treated plot 1 year after the application. Such a time lag seems to be typical and will probably limit the applicability of JHA to forest pests causing permanent types of outbreaks. A small field test on the larch casebearer (*Coleophora laricella* (Hübner)) had preceded this experiment and yielded similar results (Skuhravý 1973). A moulting inhibitor (diflubenzuron) was successfully tested against the nun moth, gypsy moth, European pine sawfly, winter moth (*Boarmia bistortata* Goeze) and other defoliating Lepidoptera in Germany (Skatulla 1975). Although detailed results are not yet reported on the side-effects on entomophagous arthropods, the limitation to peroral uptake will probably help to protect parasitic and predatory arthropods.

SELECTIVITY OF PESTICIDES

Before closing this report, I should like to discuss briefly some diverging opinions on the selectivity of pesticides. Selectivity of fungicides or fungistatica is understood by some plant pathologists as an indication that not all, but only some fungi are affected. In entomology, selectivity means that only target organisms are killed and others remain undamaged. Unfortunately, so-called selective fungicides behave differently. For example, some benzimidazole compounds like "Benomyl" are notorious for their unwanted side-effects on other organisms (Frahm 1973). It was also supposed that this so-called selectivity of fungicides could have caused the quick appearance of resistant strains (biotypes) of fungi. Two suggestions are offered to understand this point: (1) quick appearance of resistance in the field after use of benzimidazoles might be related to the mutagenic action of this chemical group of fungicides; (2) biotic limiting factors of plant pathogenic fungi are probably less important than natural enemies of (say) pest insects. Therefore, selective action of pesticides may not contribute so much to the regulation of fungi as it does to the regulation of arthropods.

The ecological basis for the desirability of selective material and selective action in the control of most pest organisms stems, thus, from the following observation: the protection of a complex of biotic antagonists, if it occurs, increases the capability of self-regulation in the ecosystem. In addition, it saves energy and avoids unilateral selection for biotypes resistant to one constantly applied chemical mortality factor. Therefore, selectivity of pesticides as defined in entomology is being considered as one of the tools to reduce the danger of resistance of pests and to avoid unnecessary contamination of the environment.

A Working Group called "Pesticides and Beneficial Arthropods" has been set up by the WPRS of IOBC. The aim of the Group is to develop standardized test methods for evaluation of the side-effects of pesticides on beneficial entomophagous arthropods. These tests are sensitive enough to indicate damages which appear slowly and accumulate; they will yield comparable results (Franz 1974). Laboratory tests and field tests will complement each other. Guidelines for each parasite or predator to be tested are being drafted—some are already in use. Twenty-four colleagues from nine countries have agreed to draft guidelines for tests of 31 entomophagous arthropods. The meaningful combination of reproducible laboratory tests and special field tests should be acceptable to authorities responsible for pesticide registration or recommendations in countries in which member institutions of WPRS operate. Actually, the first four guidelines have been officially accepted by the Biologische Bundesanstalt in the Federal Republic of Germany. Tests on side-effects of pesticides on beneficial arthropods have been incorporated on a voluntary basis into the protocol for registration (Herfs 1975). Other European countries are expected to follow this example soon. Results of tests made according to internationally coordinated guidelines will be mutually acceptable to other countries. In essence, the aim of these activities is to initiate a stronger influence of consideration of the ecological consequences of pesticide application for their overall evaluation. In other words, and coming back to our starting point, selectivity of pesticides will get a chance to be officially acknowledged (Franz 1975).

Space does not permit analysis of the technical details of test methods. The first relevant experiment for evaluation of laboratory tests was made at The Connecticut Agricultural Experiment Station and was published in the Bulletin No. 353 by Schread and Garman in 1933. The authors were the first to show the influence of a pesticide—in this case sulfur—on the behaviour and total parasitism of *Trichogramma*. Following this lead we have based the evaluation of this type of side-effect on the reduction of the beneficial capability instead of on mortality. The reduction of parasitization or, with predators, of prey consumption plus fertility, is a more sensitive and a more relevant measurement than any other method. We think this approach will stimulate the development of selective pesticides, not only insecticides, but also fungicides and herbicides, because damage to entomophagous arthropods is caused by many, but not by all of them. For those who develop integrated control programmes, the task will be facilitated when they know in advance what side-effects could be caused in case pesticides have to be applied in forestry.

ACKNOWLEDGMENT

Thanks are due to many European colleagues for permission to quote from unpublished material and for mailing special information, like A. Bakke (Ås, Norway), B. Bejer-Petersen (Copenhagen), G. Benz (Zürich), H.H. Eidmann (Stockholm), P.F. Entwistle (Oxford), P. Grison (La Minière par Versailles), H. Klomp (Arnheim), A. Magnoler (Tempio Pausania), M. Maksimović (Belgrade), L. Nef (Bokrijk-Genk), D. Schvester (Avignon), J.P. Vité (Freiburg/Br.).

APPENDIX

Chapter 21

Apple Trees in the Suburban Forest as Hosts for Insects and Mites

Richard C. Moore[1]

Department of Entomology
The Connecticut Agricultural Experiment Station
New Haven, Connecticut 06504

INTRODUCTION

Apple is the cultivated form of *Malus pumila* Mill. (Angiospermae: Rosaceae) (Encyclopedia Britannica 1967). Its origin is reported to be southern Eurasia in a region lying directly south of the Caucasus and extending from the Caspian Sea to the Black Sea. Like its relative, *Crataegus, Malus* is a taxonomically difficult genus with numerous intergrading variations and hybrids for which many scientific names have been given (Little 1953).

Hundreds of apple varieties were known to exist in Europe and many were brought to North America in colonial times as seed or grafted nursery stock (Encyclopedia Britannica 1967). One of the first actions taken by colonists as they cleared their land was to plant an orchard, which in some areas was considered proof that a person was serious about settling his land (Price 1954). Apple was an essential food crop for the settlers and was a basic part of their diet throughout the year. Early orchards were established mostly from seeds because transporting of grafted or budded stock was difficult and expensive. These wild or naturalized or Johnny Appleseed trees are seldom cultivated today. In considering the role of apple trees in the suburban forest, I have chosen to look primarily at them as hosts for insect and mite species which also are found on other suburban and forest trees in eastern United States.

---

[1] Present address: Uniroyal, Agricultural Chemical Division, Bethany, CT 06525

APPLES IN THE EASTERN UNITED STATES

In New York, cultivated apple trees reached a maximum about 1875 when 18,278,636 trees were recorded (Chapman and Lienk 1971). Shortly after, orchards began to decline in New York, principally due to heavy losses sustained by insect pests and diseases (Beach 1905). Cultivated apple trees were reduced to 2,886,752 in New York by 1966 (Chapman and Lienk 1971). With the development of cold storage and better insect and disease control and horticultural practices, fruit growing became a specialized industry of commercial orchards. The family orchard which was once a requirement on every well-balanced farm has all but disappeared, and apples in the modern diet have been relegated to side dishes and casual eating.

Apples in today's suburban forest consist of commercial orchards, abandoned orchards and homeowner and naturalized trees. In New York, naturalized apple trees occur principally in rural settings or in active or recently abandoned pasturelands where they have been "planted" by dairy cattle (Chapman and Lienk 1971). Naturalized trees can also be found in fence rows, along streams, or in backyards where they apparently were derived from seeds of fallen fruit. Many of these rural areas became suburbanized as people moved from the city. Commercial orchards were sold to developers who constructed homes while maintaining many fruit trees for landscaping. Some commercial orchards have been abandoned. In other instances, homeowners have planted their own apple trees. Most trees in these suburban areas are used for shade, not for fruit production.

Apples and various species of hawthorn, *Crataegus* spp., are often the dominant woody plants in pasturelands (Chapman and Lienk 1971). Other relatives occurring in some numbers are pear, *Pyrus communis* L., wild rose, *Rosa* spp., black cherry, *Prunus serotina* Ehrh., and buckthorn, *Rhamnus* spp. In the suburban forest, cultivated apple trees dominate. These are interspersed with existing native species of forest trees and other cultivated shade trees.

SPECIFICITY OF ARTHROPODS

It is customary to divide phytophagous insects into three groups based on the diversity of food eaten (Brues 1952). The first group, termed polyphagous, includes those which exercise little choice in food selection, depending largely on availability, abundance, texture of foliage and other factors. Most of these insects do, however, have preferred food plants. Insects in the second group restrict their feeding to a small and discrete number of usually similar plants and are termed oligophagous. Members of the third group are restricted to a single species of food plant and are termed monophagous. They are the most highly specialized, and truly monophagous species are few in number. Although there are other definitions for these terms (Dethier 1947), I have chosen to use the more customary definition given by Brues.

When considering whether an insect is monophagous or oligophagous, it may also be important to determine how closely related are the species of plants on which they feed. Apple appears to be most closely related to native crab apple, *Pyrus coronavia L.*, followed by hawthorn (Chapman and Lienk 1971). Wellhouse (1920, 1922) refers to over 100 species of insects which feed on apple and hawthorn. In this review, I have chosen to classify insects as monophagous if they have been reported to feed only on apple. Oligophagous species were classified as those feeding on apple and other members of the Rosaceae, primarily in the genera, *Pyrus, Crataegus, Sorbus, Amelanchier* and *Prunus*, or those using a very restricted series of plant hosts, some of which were not Rosaceae. Polyphagous species are those with a wide host range, including apple.

Chapman and Lienk (1971) divided the tortricid fauna of apple in New York into three groups depending on their use of apple as a host. In the first group, apple is considered a primary or preferred host for those insects which consistently select it for oviposition and whose resultant larvae complete their development in an apparently normal manner. In another group, those species established by accidental and/or associational circumstances and which complete their development in an apparently normal manner are considered using apple as a secondary host. The third group includes those which use apple as a casual or incidental host. It consists primarily of species which feed on apple as last instar larvae.

Several major references were used in compiling the species which use apple and other forest trees as hosts (Forbes 1923, Craighead 1950, Metcalf and Flint 1962, Prentice 1965, Chapman and Lienk 1971, Baker 1972, Jeppson et al. 1975). The material included in this paper was gathered from these references, from personal communications with others, and from my own observations. The classifications of insects by Borror and DeLong (1971) and of mites by Jeppson et al. (1975) are used in this review.

INSECT AND MITE–HOST ASSOCIATION

As shown in Table 1, 171 species which are found on apple and on other tree hosts in the eastern United States were considered in this study. They are represented in 47 families and 7 orders. Lepidoptera (67.5%) are by far the most commonly found insects on apple and other suburban trees. Coleoptera (13.0%), Acariformes (9.5%) and Homoptera (7.0%), were next in abundance followed by Hemiptera (1.2%), Hymenoptera (1.2%), and least abundant Diptera (0.6%).

Monophagous Species

It is difficult to find species of insects which are truly monophagous on

TABLE 1   *Numbers of orders, families and species of insects and mites using apple and other suburban forest trees as a host.*

Orders	Families No.	%	Species No.	%
Hemiptera	1	2.1	3	1.2
Homoptera	6	12.8	12	7.0
Coleoptera	9	19.2	22	13.0
Lepidoptera	25	53.2	115	67.5
Diptera	1	2.1	1	0.6
Hymenoptera	2	4.2	2	1.2
Acariformes	3	6.4	16	9.5
Totals	47	100.0	171	100.0

apple. Three Lepidoptera and one mite species are placed in this category. Included are *Exartema malamum* Fernald, the slender brown budworm, *Pseudexentera mali* Freeman, the pale apple budworm and *Pseudotelphusa incana* Hodges, the two-leaf tier. It seems probable that these species may use other Rosaceae as a host. *Aculus schlechtendali* (Nalepa), the apple rust mite, also appears to be monophagous. Although it has been reported from pear, Jeppson et al. (1975) believe that the report is erroneous.

Oligophagous Species

Almost 36% of the species were classified as oligophagous (Table 2). Among the Hemiptera, *Lygidea mendax* Reuter and *Heterocordylus malinus* Reuter, the apple redbugs, are reported to be found abundantly on hawthorn, crab apple and quince, *Chaenomeles oblonga* Mill. (Knight 1915). Since the entire life cycle may be spent on apple, hawthorn and crab apple, these plants may

TABLE 2   *Specificity of insects and mites using apple as a host.*

	Numbers of species using apple as a host					
	Preference			Selectivity		
Orders	Primary	Secondary	Incidental	Monophagous	Oligophagous	Polyphagous
Hemiptera	2	1	0	0	2	1
Homoptera	8	4	0	0	3	9
Coleoptera	16	6	0	0	9	13
Lepidoptera	77	21	17	3	41	71
Diptera	1	0	0	0	1	0
Hymenoptera	2	0	0	0	1	1
Acariformes	10	5	1	1	4	11
Totals	116	37	18	4	61	106
%	67.8	21.7	10.5	2.3	35.7	62.0

now serve as reservoirs from which they move into unsprayed apple trees (Schaefer 1974). Both bugs use apple as a primary host.

A host alternation occurs in aphids which move during the course of the season from one kind of plant to another. The woolly apple aphid, *Eriosoma lanigerum* (Hausm.), uses apple, pear, hawthorn, and mountain-ash, *Sorbus* spp., as a summer host and elm, *Ulmus americana* L., as an overwintering host. *Anuraphis roseus* Baker, the rosy apple aphid, uses narrow leaf plantain, *Plantago lanceolata* L., as a host during the summer and apple and other related trees as hosts for the remainder of the year. The apple grain aphid, *Rhopalosiphum fitchii* (Sanderson), overwinters on apple and other Rosaceae and migrates in early summer to various grasses.

Several beetles feed on apple and a few other hardwood species. *Scolytus sulcatus* LeC. also has been reported on plum, *Prunus* spp., and elm, and *S. mali* (Bechstein) on cherry and elm. Both species are apparently vectors of Dutch elm disease, *Ceratocystis ulmi* (Buis.) C. Moreau. *S. rugulosus* (Ratzeburg) is found commonly on most cultivated fruit trees, and there is one record of this species on elm (Craighead 1950). *Lymantor decipiens* (LeConte) breeds also in hickory, *Carya* spp., and maple, *Acer* spp. Other wood-boring beetles, *Agrilus vittaticolis* (Randall), *Saperda cretata* (Newman), and *S. candida* (F.), occur on other Rosaceae. Two species of Curculionidae, *Tachypterellus quadrigibbus* (Say) and *Conotrachelus nenuphar* (Herbst) also feed on other members of this family.

Forty-one Lepidoptera were classified as oliogophagous. As shown in Table 3, twenty-two species are restricted to feeding on Rosaceae. Seventeen of these species use apple and/or other Rosaceae as preferred hosts, while 5 species use Rosaceae as a primary host and apple as a secondary host. The remaining 19 species use apple and one or two deciduous tree hosts other than Rosaceae. Many of these insects use suburban forest trees as a preferred host and feed secondarily or incidentally on apple. Others use apple as well as other deciduous trees as preferred hosts.

In the Diptera, *Rhagoletis pomonella* (Walsh), the apple maggot, feeds almost exclusively on the fruit of apple and other Rosaceae. Wellhouse (1922) lists 5 species of *Crataegus* from which flies have been obtained. While *Crataegus* is believed to be this insect's original host, it has also been reported from plum (Herrick 1920), peaches, *P. persica* (L.) Batsch (Millar 1929), sour cherry, *P. cerasus* L. (Shervis et al. 1970), apricot, *P. armeniaca* L. (Lienk 1970), pear (Prokopy and Bush 1972), and chokecherry, *P. virginiana* L. (Baker 1972).

The European apple sawfly, *Hoplocampa testudinea* (Klug), feeds within the berries and fruits of the Rosaceae (Pyenson 1943).

Three species of mites were classified as oligophagous: *Phytoptus pyri* Pagenstecher, the pear leaf blister mite, *Bryobia arborea* Morgan and Anderson, the brown mite, and *Oligonychus newcomeri* (McGregor). A fourth species, *Cecidophyes malifoliae* (Parrott), was found on apple (Parrott el al. 1906), but

TABLE 3 *Feeding preferences of oligophagous Lepidoptera which feed on apple and other suburban forest trees.*

Family	Species	Reference[a]
	Restricted to Rosaceae–Apple preferred host	
Sphingidae	*Sphinx drupiferarum* J. E. Smith	1
Pyralididae	*Psorosina hammondi* (Riley)	2
Olethreutidae	*Anchylopera nubeculana* (Clemens)	2
	Laspeyresia pomonella (L.)	2
Tortricidae	*Acleris nivisellana* (Walsingham)	2
	Argyrotaenia quadrifasciana (Fernald)	2, 3, 4
Gelechiidae	*Recurvaria nanella* (Hübner)	2
	Filatima epulatrix Hodges	2
Glyphipterygidae	*Anthophila pariana* (Clerck)	1
Aegeriidae	*Synanthedon pyri* (Harris)	1
Yponomeutidae	*Argyresthia conjugella* Zeller	1
Heliozelidae	*Coptodisca splendoriferella* (Clemens)	1
Coleophoridae	*Coleophora serratella* (L.)	1
Gracilariidae	*Callisto geminatella* (Packard)	1
	Lithocolletis crataegella Clemens	1
	L. blancardella Clemens	6
Lyonetiidae	*Bucculatrix pomifoliella* Clemens	1
	Restricted to Rosaceae–Apple secondary host	
Olethreutidae	*Ancylis apicana* Walker	2
	Grapholitha molesta (Busck)	2, 11
	G. packardi (Zeller)	2
Tortricidae	*Archips cerasivoranus* (Fitch)	2
	Sparganothis directana Walker	2
	Not restricted to Rosaceae–	
	Apple preferred, secondary or incidental host	
Sphingidae	*Smerinthus jamaicensis* (Drury)	3
	Paonias excaecatus (J. E. Smith)	1
Arctiidae	*Haploa clymene* (Brown)	1
Lymantriidae	*Dasychira atomaria* (Walker)	3
	D. basiflava (Packard)	3
	D. vagans Barnes and McDunnough	3
Geometridae	*Synchlora aerata* (F.)	1
	Euchlaena serrata (Drury)	3
Olethreutidae	*Anchylopera fuscociliana* (Clemens)	2, 5
	Grapholitha prunivora (Walsh)	2, 10
	Hedia chionosema (Zeller)	2, 9
	H. nubiferana (Haworth)	2, 7
	H. separatana (Kearfott)	2
Tortricidae	*Acleris minuta* (Robinson)	2, 12
	A. chalybeana (Fernald)	2, 8
	Archips griseus (Robinson)	2, 4
	A. semiferanus (Walker)	2, 4
	Sparganothis pettitana (Robinson)	2
Gracilariidae	*Marmara elotella* (Busck)	4, 5

[a]Species compiled from the following references:
1. Baker (1972) 2. Chapman and Lienk (1971) 3. Craighead (1950) 4. Freeman (1958) 5. Forbes (1923) 6. Garman and Townsend (1952) 7. Heinrich (1926) 8. MacKay (1962) 9. Prentice (1965) 10. Quaintance (1908) 11. Schoene et al. (1937) and 12. Webster (1909).

apparently had been blown onto it from its primary host, oak, *Quercus spp.* (Jeppson et al. 1975).

Polyphagous Species

Most insect and mite species using apple and other suburban forest trees as hosts are polyphagous; however, many have preferred food plants. Among hemipterous insects, the tarnished plant bug, *Lygus lineolaris* (Palisot de Beauvois), feeds on many flowering plants as well as most deciduous and small fruits. It is particularly injurious to peach (Metcalf and Flint 1962), and often to forest nursery trees (Baker 1972). It appears to use apple as a secondary host.

Homopterous species such as *Magicicada septendecim* L., the periodical cicada, *Stictocephala bubalus* (F.), the buffalo treehopper, *Empoasca maligna* (Walsh), the common apple leafhopper, *Typhlocyba pomaria* McAtee, the white apple leafhopper, *Aspidiotus perniciosus* Comstock, the San Jose scale, *Lepidosaphes ulmi* L., the oystershell scale, *Chionaspis furfura* (Fitch), scurfy scale and *Pseudococcus comstocki* (Kuwana), the Comstock mealybug, are general feeders on many species of deciduous trees. *M. septendecim, E. maligna, T. pomaria* and *A. perniciosus* use apple as a primary host while *S. bubalus, L. ulmi, C. furfura,* and *P. comstocki* appear to use apple as a secondary host and other deciduous trees as primary hosts.

The apple aphid, *Aphis pomi* De Geer, has continuous generations on apple throughout the summer; however, there is continual migration from other plants in or near an orchard which are used as alternate hosts.

In the Coleoptera, several species of borers including *Chrysobothris femorata* (Olivier), *Amphicerus bicaudatus* (Say), *Pseudolucanus capreolus* (L.) *Lichenophanes bicornis* (Weber) and *Knulliana cincta* (Drury), and two species of curculionids, *Rhynchaenus pallicornis* (Say) and *Polydrusus impressifrons* Gyll., use apple as well as other trees as preferred hosts. Several species of the comb-clawed beetles, *Hymenorus* spp., use apple as a secondary host while preferring other shade trees. *R. rufipes* (LeConte) prefers willow, *Salix* spp., as a host, while *Phyllobius oblongus* (L.) feeds on a wide variety of hardwoods and on apple secondarily. The basswood and locust leafminer, *Baliosus ruber* (Weber) and *Odontota dorsalis* (Thunb.), also use apple as a secondary host and as their names imply, they feed primarily on basswood, *Tilia americana* L., or black locust, *Robinia pseudoacacia* L. The adult Japanese beetle, *Popillia japonica* Newman, attacks many deciduous fruits, shade trees and shrubs.

The majority of the lepidopterous species using apple and other suburban forest trees as hosts are polyphagous, and most have preferred food plants. They include at least 71 species represented in 18 families. A list of the species is shown in Table 4 as well as their preferences for apple.

The pigeon tremex, *Tremex columba* (L.), a hymenopteran, is a borer in apple, pear and a number of deciduous trees (Baker 1972).

Eleven species of mites are polyphagous including 6 which use apple as a

TABLE 4 *Polyphagous Lepidoptera which feed on apple and other suburban forest trees.*

Family	Species	Host Preference for Apple[a]			Reference[b]
		P	S	I	
Papilionidae	*Papilio glaucus* L.		X		6
Nymphalidae	*Limenitis arthemis* (Drury)		X		1, 6
	L. astyanax (F.)		X		1, 6
Sphingidae	*Sphinx gordius* Cram	X			6
Saturniidae	*Automeris io* (F.)	X			1
	Hyalophora cecropia L.			X	1
Arctiidae	*Hyphantria cunea* (Drury)		X		3,12,17
	Halisidota maculata (Harris)	X			6
	H. caryae (Harris)	X			6
Notodontidae	*Heterocampa manteo* (Dbldy.)		X		1,18
	H. guttivitta (Walker)		X		1
	Schizura concinna (J.E. Smith)	X			1,6
	S. unicornis (J.E. Smith)	X			1
	S. ipomaeae Dbldy.	X			1
	S. leptinoides (Grote)	X			1
	Datana ministra (Drury)	X			1
	D. major G.&R.	X			1
Phalaenidae	*Acronicta oblinita* (J.E. Smith)			X	1
	A. distans (Grote)		X		1
	A. interrupta Guen.		X		1
	A. americana (Harris)		X		1, 6
	Lithophane antennata (Walker)	X			1, 6, 12
	Orthosia hibisci (Guen.)	X			1, 6, 12
Lymantriidae	*Hemerocampa definita* (Packard)	X			1
	Hemerocampa leucostigma (J.E. Smith)	X			1
	Nygmia phaeorrhoea (Donov.)	X			1
	Lymantria dispar (L.)	X			1, 13
Lasiocampidae	*Malacosoma americanum* (F.)	X			1
	M. californicum pluviale (Dyar)	X			1
	M. disstria (Hubner)	X			1
	Tolype velleda (Stoll.)	X			1
Geometridae	*Ennomos subsignarius* (Hübner)	X			1, 5, 6
	Operophtera brumata (L.)	X			1
	Paleacrita vernata (Peck)	X			1
	Alsophila pometaria (Harris)	X			1
	Biston cognataria (Guen.)	X			1
	Erannis tiliaria (Harris)	X			1
	Lycia ursaria (Walker)		X		6
	Nematocampa limbata (Haw.)	X			1
	Prochoerodes transversata (Drury)	X			1
Limacodidae	*Cnidocampa flavescens* (Walker)	X			1
Megalopygidae	*Lagoa crispata* (Packard)	X			1
Pyralididae	*Euzophera semifuneralis* (Walker)	X			1
	Oreana unicolorella Hulst		X		4, 15
Olethreutidae	*Spilonota ocellana*(Denis&Schiff.)	X			1, 4, 14

318

TABLE 4. (*cont.*)

Family	Species	Host Preference for Apple[a]			Reference[b]
		P	S	I	
Tortricidae	*Amorbia humerosana* Clemens	X			1, 4, 10, 15
	Aphelia alleniana Fernald			X	4
	Archips argyrospilus (Walker)	X			4
	A. mortuanus Kearfott	X			4, 8
	A. purpuranus (Clemens)			X	4, 8
	A. rosanus (L.)	X			4
	Argyrotaenia mariana (Fernald)	X			4, 11
	A. velutinana (Walker)	X			1, 4, 14
	Choristoneura fractivittana (Clemens)		X		4, 15
	C. rosaceana (Harris)	X			4, 15, 16
	Clepsis melaleucana Walker			X	4
	C. pallorana Robinson		X		4
	C. persicana Fitch		X		4, 15
	Pandemis lamprosana (Robinson)	X			4, 8, 15
	P. limitata (Robinson)	X			4, 15
	Platynota flavedana Clemens			X	4, 7
	P. idaesusalis (Walker)	X			4, 9
	Sparganothis diluticostana Walsingham	X			4, 7, 15
	S. reticulatana Clemens			X	4
	S. sulfureana Clemens		X		1, 2, 4, 15
	S. unifasciana Clemens			X	4
	Syndemis afflictana Walker	X			4, 7, 15
Cossidae	*Zeuzera pyrina* (L.)	X			1
Gelechiidae	*Dichomeris ligulella* Hübner	X			1, 4
Stenomidae	*Antaeotricha leucillana* Zeller	X			4, 15
Oecophoridae	*Machimia tentoriferella* Clemens		X		4, 15

[a]P = primary   S = secondary   I = incidental
[b]Species compiled from the following references:
1. Baker (1972) 2. Beckwith (1938) 3. Berger (1906) 4. Chapman and Lienk (1971) 5. Ciesla (1964a) 6. Craighead (1950) 7. Forbes (1923) 8. Freeman (1958) 9. Frost (1923) 10. Frost (1926) 11. Gilliatt (1929) 12. Metcalf and Flint (1962) 13. Mosher (1915) 14. Porter (1924) 15. Prentice (1965) 16. Schuh and Mote (1948) 17. Warren and Tadic (1970) and 18. Wilson (1961)

primary host and 5 as a secondary host. Those using apple as a preferred host include such economically important species as the European red mite, *Panonychus ulmi* (Koch), two-spotted mite, *Tetranychus urticae* Koch, the McDaniel mite, *T. mcdanieli* McGregor, Schoenei spider mite, *T. schoenei* McGregor, the four-spotted mite, *T. canadensis* (McGregor), and *Eotetranychus uncatus* Garman. These species are widely distributed and are injurious on many other deciduous fruits, shade trees, and shrubs. Species like the strawberry spider mite, *T. turkestani* (Ugarov and Nikolski) (=*T. atlanticus* McGregor), the avocado red mite, *Oligonychus yothersi* (McGregor), *E. pruni* (Oudemans), *E. carpini carpini* (Oudemans) and *Tarsonemus smithi* Ewing, use tree species other than apple as preferred hosts.

DISCUSSION AND SUMMARY

The specificity of insects and mites using apple and other trees in the suburban forest is shown in Table 2. Of the species reviewed, only 2.3% were classified as monophagous; however, these species may use other closely related hosts from which they have not been reported. As apple is an introduced plant, it may be that the monophagous species are introduced rather than native. As suggested by Dethier (1947), these species may be attracted to apple by a single chemical or a group of closely related chemicals produced by apple. Populations of introduced or native insects have been found which prefer different hosts but are morphologically indistinguishable (Brues 1924). Others appear to retain their distinct host preferences and other biological traits while shifting hosts. Examples are the codling moth, *L. pomonella*, which was introduced into North America from Europe and shifted from apple to walnuts, and the apple maggot, *R. pomonella*, which moved from its native host, hawthorn, to apples and cherries (Bush 1974). These two species are among the 37.5% classified as oligophagous and use apple as well as other closely related plants in the Rosaceae. According to Dethier (1947), oligophagous species may be attracted to their host plants by a few specific and different chemicals which they are capable of distinguishing. Most species reviewed (65.0%) were general feeders which accept apple as well as a variety of other trees. These species are not particularly attracted by chemicals but accept as food any plant that is not repellent (Dethier 1947).

There are obvious relationships between phytophagous insects divided into groups based on diversity of food eaten and on their use of apple as a host (Table 2). For example, most species using apple as a secondary host (21.7%) are also general feeders, while some are oligophagous species preferring deciduous fruit or other trees in the family Rosaceae. Those insects using apple as a primary host (67.8%) would by definition include monophagous and most oligophagous species; however, some polyphagous arthropods are also found in this group.

As shown in Table 5, the host range of these arthropod species is quite diverse. Interactions can occur between apple and apple, apple and other Rosaceae, apple and other deciduous hardwoods or apple and conifers. Only 10.5% of these species use apple and conifers as hosts, with trees in the family Pinaceae being preferred. A large percentage (72.5%) of the species reviewed use deciduous broadleaf trees other than Rosaceae as hosts. Trees in the families

TABLE 5 *Host range of insects and mites found on apple.*

Trees	Arthropods on hosts other than apple	
	%	% by family or genus
Conifers	10.5	93.3 Pinaceae (Pine)
		13.3 Cupressaceae (Cedar)
		6.7 Taxaceae (Yews)
Deciduous Broadleafs (other than Rosaceae)	72.5	40.8 Salix (Willow)
		38.8 Betulaceae (Birch)
		38.3 Fagacae (Beech)
		33.3 Ulmaceae (Elm)
		32.6 Aceraceae (Maple)
		20.4 Juglandaceae (Walnut)
		15.0 Tiliaceae (Linden)
		12.9 Oleaceae (Olive)
		8.8 Leguminosae (Legume)
		5.4 Platanaceae (Sycamore)
Rosaceae (other than apple)	80.1	60.0 *Prunus*
		33.3 *Crataegus*
		23.1 *Pyrus (Pear)*
		13.6 *Amelanchier*
		11.6 *Sorbus*

Salicaceae, Betulaceae, Fagaceae, Ulmaceae, and Aceraceae are most commonly used as hosts. Most of the arthropod species (80.1%) will feed on both apple and other closely related trees in the Rosaceae. Tree species in the genus *Prunus* such as cherry, plum and peach are favored hosts. All oligophagus species and many polyphagous species feed on Rosaceae other than apple.

Apple trees in the suburban forest consist of commercial, abandoned, homeowner and naturalized trees. Abandoned, homeowner and naturalized trees may overlap in their description; however, most are not treated with pesticides and furnish a continuing reservoir of insect and mite pests which can move to commercial trees. Additionally, many other deciduous and a few coniferous trees serve as a reservoir for arthropod pests of apples. For these reasons, commercial apple trees in the eastern forest regions require seasonal application of pesticides to provide adequate control of pest species. On the other hand, the untreated apple trees are also a source of parasitoids and predators of some of these pests which attack apple as well as other host trees.

At least 170 species of insects and mites which can use apple and other tree species as hosts are found in the eastern suburban forest. Most are polyphagous in the order Lepidoptera, and most use deciduous broadleaf trees, primarily in the Rosaceae, as hosts other than apple.

Chapter 22

Entomology and the State Agricultural Experiment Stations

Kenneth L. Knight[1]

Department of Entomology
North Carolina State University
Raleigh, North Carolina, 27607

By signing the Morrill Act into law on July 2, 1862, President Lincoln formally initiated governmentally supported agriculture, an action which prominently assisted during the next century in carrying the United States to unchallenged world leadership in the production of food. Passed only when the States Rightists from the South were excluded from Congress by the onset of the Civil War (Conover 1924, p. 18), this Act, along with the Act establishing the U. S. Department of Agriculture, adapted education, experimentation and the scientific method to the improvement of farming. The passage of the Hatch Act in 1887 brought agricultural experiment stations to each state. Combined with the research personnel of the U. S. Department of Agriculture this resulted by 1969 in a tax-supported agricultural research force in this country of approximately 10,500 scientists (Hightower 1972, p. 37). The following account highlights the development of entomology against the backdrop of U. S. agriculture (Table 1) with special attention being given to the interrelationships existing between entomology and the state agricultural experiment stations, and the contributions of the latter to the growth and welfare of the former. Consideration of this subject is especially appropriate in 1975, the centennial anniversary of the founding of the state agricultural experiment station system.

It is difficult today to visualize the problems that beset the explorers and colonists of the lands now comprising the United States. None of the necessities,

[1] Contribution from the North Carolina State University Agricultural Experiment Station, Raleigh, North Carolina.

let alone the niceties, laid readily at hand. In addition to coming into violent competition with an indigenous human population, Europeans landing on the shores of America faced almost insurmountable problems in supplying such fundamental physical needs as food and protection from the elements. Yet slowly and at great cost in terms of human suffering, the initial toe-hold on the Eastern Seaboard was widened and the tide of colonization moved slowly towards full flood. Agriculture played a dominant role in making this possible.

TABLE 1   *Highlights of entomology and the state agricultural experiment station movement*

Date	Event
1622	James I fostered experiments in growing mulberry trees and silkworms in the American colonies.
1668	Agricultural education in North America began in Canada with establishment of the Lesser Seminary.
1781	Formation of the New Jersey Society for Promotion of Agriculture. Marked beginning of an extended period of agricultural societies and the growth of an active interest in improving agricultural practices.
1792	Experimental agriculture treated in anonymous volume entitled "Rural Economy," published in Burlington, Vermont. Essentially no agricultural publications available previously.
1792	Professor Samuel L. Mitchell began teaching agriculture at Columbia College, City of New York.
1804	Farm school opened on Thompson's Island, near Boston. First *bona fide* agricultural school established in the United States.
1805	William Dandridge Peck (1763–1822), entomologist, became first Harvard professor in natural history.
1809	Columbian Agriculture Society for the Promotion of Rural and Domestic Economy organized. Forerunner of a national agricultural society.
1810	Columbian Agricultural Society held a livestock exhibition.
1819	Secretary of the Treasury directed consuls to collect seeds, plants, and agricultural inventions for introduction into this country.
1839	First money, $1,000, appropriated for agriculture by Congress. Given to the Patent Office.
1846	Professor John P. Norton began providing instruction in agricultural chemistry at Yale.
1854	Asa Fitch (1809–1879) appointed State Entomologist of New York. First such appointment in the United States.
1857	Nation's first agricultural college founded, the Michigan Agricultural College.
1862	The U. S. Department of Agriculture created.
1862.	Passage of the Morrill Act. Established the land-grant college system.
1862	Passage of the Homestead Act. Provided freehold farms from public lands west of the Mississippi to anyone who would farm them for 5 years.
1863	Townend Glover (1813–1883) appointed first entomologist in the U. S. Department of Agriculture.

1874   John Henry Comstock (1849–1931) appointed assistant professor of entomology at Cornell University, the first such appointment in the United States.

1875   Connecticut provided money "to carry on appropriate work of an agricultural experiment station."

1876   The United States Entomological Commission created to study the Rocky Mountain locust and other serious insect pests. Ceased operations in 1880.

1887   Passage of the Hatch Act. An act to establish agricultural experiment stations in connection with the land-grant colleges.

1887   Formation of the American Association of Agricultural Colleges and Experiment Stations (now the National Association of State Universities and Land-Grant Colleges–NASULGC).

1888   Office of Experiment Stations organized in the U. S. Department of Agriculture to distribute and administer the Hatch funds (named the Cooperative State Research Service in 1961).

1889   Creation by the American Association of Agricultural Colleges and Experiment Stations of 6 committees (later termed sections) for the conduct of business. Entomology constituted one of these.

1889   The U. S. Department of Agriculture raised to cabinet rank.

1889   Founding of the Association of Economic Entomologists.

1890   Passage of the second Morrill Act. An act to increase the endowment of colleges of agricultural and mechanical arts with the proviso that no money be paid out for the support of a college where a distinction of race or color is made (establishment of separate but equal institutions was accepted as compliance with this).

1904   Bureau of Entomology created in the U. S. Department of Agriculture (abolished its functions and transferred to the Agricultural Research Service in 1953. (Baker et al. 1963).

1906   Passage of Adams Act. An act to provide for an increased annual appropriation for state agricultural experiment stations.

1906   Entomological Society of America established.

1914   Passage of Smith-Lever Act. An act establishing the agricultural extension service in connection with the first Morrill Act land-grant colleges.

1925   Passage of Purnell Act. An act to authorize the more complete endowment of the agricultural experiment stations.

1934   Bureau of Entomology enlarged to Bureau of Entomology and Plant Quarantine.

1935   Passage of Bankhead-Jones Act. An act to provide for agricultural research and more complete endowment and support of the land-grant colleges.

1946   Amendment of Bankhead-Jones Act and the Agricultural Marketing Act of 1946.

1953   The Agricultural Research Service established to administrate the USDA inhouse research program. The Bureau of Entomology and Plant Quarantine was abolished and its functions transferred to the ARS.

1953   American Association of Economic Entomologists and Entomological Society of America amalgamated under name of the latter.

1955   An Act consolidating the Hatch Act and laws supplementary thereto.

1962   Passage of McIntyre-Stennis Bill. Provided for the funding of forestry research through the land-grant colleges and the state agricultural experiment stations.

1973   Reorganization of the Agricultural Research Service with a resultant horizontal integration of disciplines. Unit identification of entomology in U. S. D. A. lost.

Certainly in more than the first century of colonization there were no indications that U. S. agriculture would one day reach the preeminence it has today. Vivid descriptions of the primitive nature of agriculture during the founding decades of our country's development can be found in a report prepared by Charles L. Flint, secretary to the Massachusetts Board of Agriculture and read to the members of that body at its annual meeting in 1873. This report, not published until 1973, was written with the design of exciting some interest in the minds of the farming community as a preparation for the national centennial of 1876. It opened with the following words: "There is little need to look beyond the period of the Revolution in search of the first steps of any real progress in the agriculture of this country. The first European settlers upon these shores had to begin life anew, as it were, in the midst of untold hardships, privations, and dangers. They found a climate widely different from any which they had known before; a soil which the foot of civilized man had never trod, and natural productions which they had never seen. They brought with them little or no experience which could have fitted them for the rude struggle with nature in which they were about to engage. This they were forced to gain, painfully and laboriously enough, with the axe in hand to clear the forest, and the gun by their side to defend their lives. That progress in agriculture should have been slow is not, therefore, a matter of surprise. We must rather wonder that they got on at all in the struggle for life."

Even with a foothold securely gained on the continent, the colonists were extremely slow in improving any aspects of their agricultural technologies. They had no knowledge of cultivating grass or hay for their animals. As a result death from starvation was common, with sometimes the entire herd falling victim to the severity of the season. Superstitions or traditions handed down through generations very often dictated courses of action, even in the face of direct observations to the contrary.

Because livestock was commonly allowed to wander, little manure was produced for application to the land. As a result, cropped areas quickly became exhausted, requiring that additional areas be cleared and put into cultivation. Because of the seemingly endless availability of land, this practice was followed without questioning (probably serving to expedite the westward expansion and settlement of the United States). The implements of husbandry were few and crude. Slow and laborious hand-labor for nearly all of the processes of the farm was the rule. The concepts of improving plants and animals through selective breeding did not exist and strains then in use were poorly adapted to man's need for food production.

There were no agricultural journals during this period; as for newspapers, it is reported that there was not one in New England in 1700 and only four in 1750 (Flint 1973). Even these had very limited circulation in the rural districts. Books were extremely scarce. The facilities for travel were depressingly limited.

Everything was favorable to the growth of prejudice and the maintenance of narrow-minded views.

Following the American Revolution, statesmen and public-spirited private citizens quickly began to seek means to resuscitate farming from the deplorable condition in which the war had left it. Particularly interested were those city inhabitants whose economic existence depended upon agriculture. As a result, the agitation for agricultural enlightenment began in the cities rather than rurally.

The most notable result of this new interest was the formation of numerous societies for the encouragement of agricultural improvements. These early agricultural societies, to which men like Washington, Franklin, and Jefferson belonged, were links in the sequence from which subsequently grew the U. S. Department of Agriculture, the land-grant colleges, and the state agricultural experiment stations. The first of these societies, the New Jersey Society for the Promotion of Agriculture, was founded in 1781. By 1860 more than 900 state, county, and municipal societies existed in the United States (Knoblauch et al. 1962).

The principal goal of these societies was to assist in bringing about agricultural improvements. Unfortunately, because they were city rather than rural organizations, the common people were not initially involved. As Flint (1973) stated, "The average farmer of that day was not up to their [agricultural societies] standard of thought and observation. Their example, their teachings, their entreaties for aid, their reports and papers, fell comparatively dead upon the mass of the people. Farmers were not to be taught by men who had never held the plough. They did not want anything to do with theories. Custom had marked out a road for them, and it was smooth and easy to travel, and, though it might be a circle that brought up just where it had started, it had the advantage, in the old farmer's mind, that in it he never lost his way . . . His field of vision was bounded and narrow, and his work was strictly imitative, so far as he could see, and in no way experimental."

However, time brings changes. In 1810, the Columbian Agricultural Society for the Promotion of Rural and Domestic Economy held a livestock exhibition with the offer of liberal premiums for the best sheep (Flint 1973). It was an innovation and as such was the recipient of much ridicule and contempt from the farmers of that day. But it was the germ of an idea that was to grow and to become a potent force in the move towards scientific agriculture. As this innovation gradually gained support it inevitably led to the improvement of livestock, cultural methods, and farming equipment.

In line with the growing postwar awareness of the need for sustaining and promoting the welfare of agriculture, an early interest developed in bringing governmental support to agriculture. President Washington, a noted farmer in his own right, urged in his first inaugural address the advancement of agriculture by all proper means (Conover 1924, p. 8). In his eighth and last annual message to Congress on December 7, 1796, Washington suggested the creation of a national board of agriculture (Baker et al. 1963, p. 2).

Although interest at state and county levels in improved agriculture continued to develop, federal support for agriculture was disappointingly slow in coming and extremely meager in quantity when it did.

One of the earliest, if not the earliest, gestures made by the national government to support agriculture was that of Secretary of the Treasury, William H. Crawford, who on March 26, 1819 sent a circular letter to U. S. consuls requesting them to ship useful seeds and plants to the collectors of American ports for distribution to interested persons (Conover 1924, p. 8). Later in 1827, a similar request was initiated by President John Quincy Adams (Baker et al. 1963, p. 4).

Although these happenings served a useful purpose, the action that finally led to sustained governmental support of agriculture came from Henry Leavitt Ellsworth, Commissioner of the Patent Office from 1836 to 1845. Keenly interested in the improvement of agriculture, Ellsworth succeeded in getting Congress to appropriate $1,000 to his office in 1839 for "the collection of agricultural statistics, and for other agricultural purposes." Following this, Congress was prevailed upon to support Ellsworth's work by annually appropriating similarly small sums from 1842 to 1845 and yearly from 1847. Prior to 1854, the largest appropriation from Congress had been $5,500 a year. This was meager support but extremely important in the conditioning of Congress to the concept of federal support for the betterment of agriculture.

In addition to agriculture's need for continuous and enlarged federal funding, it had also become apparent that solving the problems of farming was going to require the work of specially educated individuals. In the period following the Revolution, sporadic efforts were made in the various states to provide formal agricultural education. These were generally unsuccessful. Apparently, the first *bona fide* agricultural school established in the United States was a farm school opened on Thompson's Island near Boston in 1804 (Conover 1924, p. 13). After this, little of consequence happened for many years. Real progress began in 1846 when Professor John P. Norton began providing instruction in agricultural chemistry at Yale. Two years later he opened a laboratory there for the purpose of giving practical instruction in the application of science to agriculture. Finally, in 1857, the Nation's first agricultural college was founded, that of Michigan (Knoblauch et al. 1962, p. 13).

At last, the stage seemed to be set for making definitive progress in the direction of scientific agriculture, and indeed, action wasn't long in coming. The year 1862 saw passage by Congress of three acts which have been fundamental to the development of scientific agriculture in this country: the Morrill Act, the

Homestead Act, and the Act creating the Department of Agriculture. The land-grant institutions created by the Morrill Act provided the sites for agricultural science education which had previously been lacking. The creation of the Department of Agriculture brought federal funding to the support of agricultural research. The Homestead Act provided a great and rapidly expanded land base for agriculture. Collectively, these three acts were a milestone of unparalleled importance in the history of United States agriculture.

In the extended congressional debates that preceded passage of the Acts of 1862, Senator Wright of Indiana made a statement which epitomized a *raison d'etre* for the land-grant colleges, the Department of Agriculture, and the state agricultural experiment stations which were to result from these actions. In this statement, he made the point that government support would make possible the conduct of experiments entirely beyond the means of private individuals, yet which would result in immense benefits to the entire nation because of increased production made possible by the use of scientific methods of farming. That the importance of insects to agriculture was already realized is evidenced by the Senator's referral later in his statement to "the necessity of being able to prevent the ravages of the army worm" and "the devastation of the wheat fly" (Conover 1924, p. 24).

Isaac Newton from the Patent Office became the first Commissioner of Agriculture. In his initial annual report, he listed as one of the seven major objectives for the new department, the promotion of "botany and entomology" (Deering 1945, p. 29). Townend Glover (1813-1883) was appointed as the first entomologist of the new department in 1863 (Mallis 1971, p. 66). With this event, entomology officially entered the national scene.

The founding of the land-grant agricultural and mechanical arts colleges which followed the passage of the Morrill Act provided opportunities for applying the scientific method to the improvement of agriculture, and further, set the stage for the introduction of the agricultural experiment station concept.

The man succeeding in bringing the agricultural experiment station concept to fruition was Samuel W. Johnson. Entering the Yale Analytical Laboratory in 1850, he became an enthusiastic champion of Professor Norton's unsuccessful efforts to establish an agricultural college and an agency for agricultural experimentation. From this time on, Johnson dedicated his life to overcoming the difficulties obstructing the creation and successful operation of public institutions for the scientific investigation of agricultural problems.

Initially, he proposed that this be accomplished by each county agricultural society establishing an "Agricultural Institute," since it seemed obvious that state legislatures would continue to balk at funding a state college. In 1853 he traveled to Europe to continue his studies in German laboratories, and in 1854 visited the village of Moeckern on the outskirts of Leipzig to visit a new institution, not yet 2 years old, which its founders called an "Agricultural

Experiment-Station" (Knoblauch et al. 1962, p. 15). This was a tax-supported experimental farm with a chemist and an experienced farmer for staff. It concentrated in one location all necessary facilities for the conduct of research in the laboratory and in the field. Upon his return, Johnson became America's first advocate calling for the creation of similar institutions in the United States. Support came from many of the young men who had been students of Norton and Johnson at New Haven and who subsequently became leaders in the land-grant agricultural college movement.

Johnson's efforts bore fruit in 1875 when the Connecticut State Legislature passed a simple measure contributing $2,800 a year to matching contributions of space and services by Wesleyan University at Middletown, Connecticut "to be used in employing competent scientific men to carry on the appropriate work of an *agricultural experiment station*." Shortly afterwards, a bill for a permanent station was drafted and became law in 1877, creating The Connecticut Agricultural Experiment Station, which is now in New Haven.

About 1875, the U. S. Commissioner of Agriculture asked for land at Washington, D. C. on which to conduct experiments and urged that auxiliary experimental farms be established in each of the states. His desires were not fully realized. However, the New Haven beginning, the Commissioner's efforts, and the continuing general desire for the application of science to agriculture produced the desired effects. Synergistically, the basic pattern of the modern agricultural experiment station was established by these happenings and by the expanding intellectual climate of the day. As a result, within the short space of 10 years, 15 state agricultural experiment stations were in operation (Conover 1924, p. 33), and overall, 28 states had adopted the concept in one form or another (Trullinger 1937). The enthusiasm generated by these events resulted in Congress passing the Hatch Act on March 2, 1887. This Act authorized the annual payment of federal funds to each state that would create an agricultural experiment station.

Following the passage of the Hatch Act, land-grant college presidents and experiment station directors cooperatively founded the Association of American Agricultural Colleges and Experiment Stations. The Association's objective was to promote the successful operation and administration of the member colleges and agricultural experiment stations. This organization has undergone some changes in structure and names since that time, but continues to the present as a dynamic policy-making force in land-grant college and agricultural experiment station operations.

After the enactment of the Hatch Act in 1887, the payment of federal funds to each of the states for the conduct of agricultural research became routine, with the U. S. Department of Agriculture having responsibility for ensuring that all such funds were used as had been directed by Congress. To accomplish the latter, the Office of Experiment Stations was established within the U. S. Department of Agriculture in the same year as the passage of the Hatch Act (Conover 1924, p. 2). This Office comes down to us today as the Cooperative State Research Service.

With the linkage brought about by the Hatch Act between the land-grant colleges, the state agricultural experiment stations and the U. S. Department of Agriculture, Congress contributed to the welfare of this country to an extent undreamt of at that time. The unique organizational structure created by these enabling acts not only integrated the functions of teaching, research and extension but more importantly also interlocked federal and state programs.

Entomology and the state agricultural experiment station system were first publicly connected in 1889 when the young Association of American Agricultural Colleges and Experiment Stations created six committees (later termed sections) for the conduct of their business. One of these committees was for entomology. The remaining five were designated for agriculture, botany, chemistry, horticulture and college management, respectively (Knoblauch et al. 1962, p. 69). How did entomology come to be singled out from the other plant and animal protection professions for special attention at such an early date? Quite possibly the greater visibility of insects accounted for this. Damage by insects was immediately detectable and in most cases easily associated with the causal agents. This was not equally true in the earlier days with diseases and nematodes. Weed control was considered part of normal cultural procedures and weeds were not even considered a pest in the present sense of the word.

Colonial history is replete with accounts of the discomfort caused by biting insects and of course, insect-borne disease was a serious problem during all of that time. However, damage to crops by insects did not get reported as frequently. In this connection, L. O. Howard (1930, p. 9) wrote "The crops of the early colonists in America apparently did not suffer seriously from the attacks of insects. The growth of agriculture was relatively slow. The opportunities for the introduction of new insect pests from other countries were practically non-existent. Apparently very few native insects changed their habits and took to cultivated crops." He also stated that during the Revolutionary War and afterwards, five injurious insects in particular began to attract attention: the Gage bug [?], Hessian fly, codling moth, Angoumois grain moth, and chinch bug.

Probably the biggest factor responsible for the early attention given to entomology was the notoriety brought to our field by the catastrophic grasshopper outbreaks of the seventies (see Howard 1930 for detailed account). From 1874 to 1876 certain of the western states suffered greatly from an invasion of the so-called Rocky Mountain locust. The calamity resulting from these invasions assumed almost national proportions. Because of this, C. V. Riley was able to persuade Congress in 1876 to appropriate money for the establishment of the United States Entomological Commission, and to make him

Chief of the Commission. This was the first federal action that recognized in any broad way the national importance of economic entomology and did much to insure prominent attention being given to entomology when the Hatch Act was finally enacted. The Commission was disestablished in 1880, at which time all federal entomological activity reverted to the U. S. Department of Agriculture.

Following the grasshopper outbreak, attention to entomology by both federal and state governments never waned again—for reasons detailed by Howard (1930, p. 115) in this manner: "Following very soon after the establishment of the Agricultural Experiment Stations in the United States. . . . there occurred four events which fixed the attention of the whole country upon the importance of entomological work. The first of these was the discovery of the gypsy moth in Massachusetts in 1889; the second was the discovery of the San Jose scale in the East in 1893; the third was the discovery of the Mexican cotton boll weevil in Texas in 1894; and the fourth was the discovery by Ross in 1898 of the carriage of malaria by *Anopheles*."

The founding of the land-grant colleges under the Morrill Act in 1862 was responsible for the beginning of the teaching of entomology. However, at that time there were no positions to be filled by entomologists except those for teachers and the demand for teachers was very small. The entomology taught by these early individuals was principally concerned with how to handle insect problems met in the practice of agriculture. In other words, this training was primarily for men planning to become farmers. The first entomological training known to have been given in the land-grant institutions was by A. J. Cook (1842-1916) at Michigan Agricultural College in 1867; in 1869, he was made a Professor of Zoology and Entomology. Lectures were given in entomology by C. V. Riley (1843–1895) at Kansas State Agricultural College in 1870–71, by H. A. Hagen (1817–1893) at Harvard in 1870, by C. H. Fernald (1838–1921) at Maine State College in 1871, and by B. F. Mudge at Kansas State College during 1871–72. J. H. Comstock (1849–1931) gave lectures in entomology at Cornell University in 1873 and founded the Department of Entomology there when he became an Assistant Professor of Entomology in 1874 (Howard 1930, p. 70).

With the enactment of the Hatch Act in 1887, a demand immediately developed for the conduct of entomological research at the diverse state agricultural experiment stations. The effect of this was that very quickly there were not enough trained men to meet the demand. Because of this, many of the positions ended up being filled by individuals who had had little or no training in entomology. Prior to 1887, New York, Illinois, and Missouri were the only states to support distinct and consecutive investigations in economic entomology; although of course, a number of the state horticultural and agricultural societies had published reports on injurious insects.

However, conditions quickly changed. The education of entomologists began in earnest. By 1894, only 7 years after the passage of the Hatch Act, 42 states and territories had employed persons to do entomological work and 311 station publications containing agricultural entomology had been published (Howard 1930, p. 107). Between 1887 and 1905, the stations published nearly 4,000 bulletins or reports dealing exclusively with insect control (Fletcher 1937, p. 140). In marked contrast to all of this, in the period from 1771 until 1880 there were only 60 men in the whole of North America who wrote worthwhile notes or articles on injurious insects. Comparatively few of these first writers were competent entomologists. Some were farmers or fruit-growers, others were physicians, and some were teachers. None received compensation for his work until Thaddeus W. Harris (1795–1856) was given a small sum for the preparation of a report in 1841.

I should not neglect pointing out that another early event of importance to entomology resulting from the Hatch Act was the founding of the Association of Economic Entomologists in the summer of 1889. The state agricultural experiment stations had been active under the new act for little more than a year, but so many entomologists had been hired by the new stations that the desirability of having an association for them had already become evident. This organization was later renamed the American Association of Economic Entomologists and in 1953 joined with the Entomological Society of America to become our present organization of that name.

As stated previously many of the first entomological appointments in the state agricultural experiment stations were of men who varied widely in their preparation or qualifications for experimental work. As would be expected, this led initially to the conduct of some rather superficial studies. Nonetheless, useful work did appear and over a period of a few years most of the less qualified individuals were replaced by ones better trained for the accomplishment of meaningful entomological research.

In the period between 1887 and 1906, when the Adams Act was enacted, Hatch Act monies constituted the principal source of support for agricultural research within the States. As late as 1903, 27 out of 52 state agricultural experiment stations received no direct state aid whatever, 6 received less than $1,000 a year, and only 8 received a sum equal to or in excess of the Hatch funds (Fletcher 1937, p. 136). Because of this situation, the stations were sometimes referred to in those days as the "Hatch Experiment Stations."

It was inevitable that most of the investigations of the formative years were highly applied in character, since they were undertaken for the most part in response to farmers' needs for answers to immediate practical problems. Even so, a surprising amount of fundamental research was done. This was particularly true in entomology where very extensive life history and ecological-type studies were made of the many species of economically important insects. From the beginning of economic entomological work in the United States until the availability of the persistent chlorinated hydrocarbon insecticides in the mid-forties, truly adequate chemical control means were not available for most of the insect pests of the United States. As a result, the entomologists of those years were very ecologically oriented and worked diligently to supplement and integrate into a reasonably adequate control program all environmental forces found to play a part in the reduction of pest insect populations.

With the state agricultural experiment station movement and the profession of entomology both well established and inextricably integrated by the advent of the 20th century, the story of their genesis is essentially told. What then can be said for the 75 years that have elapsed since that time?

Entomologically speaking, the period from 1900 to 1975 has been largely devoted to the "Development of the Science of Entomology." This can be contrasted with the 19th Century in which the "Development of the Practice of Entomology" occurred. Within the 20th Century, the science of entomology has successively given birth to: medical and veterinary entomology (1900–1909), insect physiology, genetics, and behavior (1910-1919), insect toxicology (1920-1929), the synthetic organic insecticides (1930-1945), the chlorinated hydrocarbon insecticides (1946-1955), the public environmental concern for the impact of chemical insect control (1956-1965), integrated insect control (1960-1968), and pest management (1969 to the present).[2] State agricultural experiment station entomology has shared prominently in all of these accomplishments.

In a treatment of the inter-relationships of the state agricultural experiment stations and the profession of entomology, it would be most negligent not to acknowledge how greatly entomology has benefited from the intramural federal agricultural research organization. From the days when Townend Glover was appointed as the first entomologist in the U. S. Department of Agriculture, entomology has been a strong integral part of the Department. Presently, the number of entomologists employed within the USDA research organization is approximately equal to the number employed in the entire state agricultural experiment station system (Table 2). Figures shown in Table 2 are in Scientific Man Years (SMY's), each of which represent a full-time professional scientist who has project leadership for planning and execution of research. It does not represent professional support personnel and technicians. These SMY data are from Inventories of Agricultural Research issued by the Current Research Information System (CRIS) of the Cooperative State Research Service, USDA. Appreciation is expressed to Dr. Robert C. Riley, Principal Entomologist, CSRS, for making this information available.

---

[2] This classification has been synthesized from a series of articles published together under the title "Fifty Years of Entomological Progress" by Caesar, Essig, Marlatt, Metcalf, and Rohwer (1940).

TABLE 2 *Summary by agency for entomology research, scientific man-years for FY 1967-1974*

Government	Agency	Years							
		1967	1968	1969	1970	1971	1972	1973	1974
Federal	ARS	532.9	555.7	553.7	524.3	531.1	537.6	554.7	552.6
	FS	87.2	96.8	148.8	111.0	111.3	113.7	108.7	123.7
	ARS+FS	620.1	652.5	702.5	635.3	642.4	651.3	663.4	676.3
State	CSRS	269.8	278.2	273.8	300.2	302.9	342.6	389.6	442.8
	SAES	235.9	264.7	299.8	282.6	259.5	254.4	254.2	256.4
	CSRS+SAES	505.7	542.9	573.6	582.8	562.4	597.0	643.8	699.2
Grand Total		1125.8	1195.4	1276.1	1218.1	1204.8	1248.3	1307.2	1375.5

ARS = Agricultural Research Service
FS = Forest Service
CSRS= Cooperative State Research Service
SAES= State Agricultural Experiment Station

As for the future, I envision that a major preoccupation of all agricultural scientists in the days ahead will be a search for knowledge breakthroughs which will permit a quantum jump in food production coincident with a lesser use of nonrenewable resources. Entomologists must remain alert to every opportunity to participate in this life-sustaining process.

LITERATURE CITED

Abrahamson, L. P. and J. D. Harper. 1973. Microbial insecticides control forest tent caterpillar in southwestern Alabama. *U. S. For. Serv. Res. Note SO-157.* 3 pp.

Aizawa, K. 1963. The nature of infections caused by nuclear-polyhedrosis viruses. Pages 381-412 in E. A. Steinhaus, ed. "Insect Pathology, an Advanced Treatise." Vol. 1. Academic Press, N.Y. 661 pp.

Aizawa, K. 1973. Development of microbial insecticides in Japan. *Botyu-Kagaku.* *38*:114-24. (In Japanese).

Aizawa, K. 1975. Selection and strain improvement of insect pathogenic micro-organisms for microbial control. Pages 99-105 in K. Yasumatsu and H. Mori, eds. "Approaches to Biological Control." Vol 7. Japan Int. Biol. Program. Univ. Tokyo Press, Tokyo. 142 pp.

Aizawa, K. and Y. Furuta. 1964. Resistance to polyhedrosis in F_1 hybrids between resistant and original strains in the silkworm, *Bombyx mori. J. Seric. Sci. Jap. 33*:403-6.

Allen, D.C. 1972. Insect parasites of the saddled prominent, *Heterocampa guttivitta* (Lepidoptera: Notodontidae) in the northeastern United States. *Can. Entomol. 104:* 1609-22.

Allen, L. H., Jr. 1968. Turbulence and wind speed spectra within a Japanese larch plantation. *J. Appl. Meteorol. 7*:73-8.

Amargier, A., G. Meynadier, and C. Vago. 1968. Un complex de viroses: polyédrie nucléare et densonucléose chez le Lépidoptére *Galleria mellonella* L. *Mikroskopie 23*:245-51.

Ambros, W. 1938. Einige spezielle Beobachtungen und Untersuchungen während der Nonnenkontrolle im Jahre 1937. *Zentralbl. Gesamte Forstwes. 64*:49-50.

Ambros, W. 1940. Einige Beobachtungen und Untersuchungen an der Nonne im Jahre 1938. *Zentralbl. Gesamte Forstwes. 66*:131-47, 166-9.

American Forests. 1974. Forestry to fit the future—an examination of the Weyerhaeuser high yield forest. *Am. For. 80*:17-32.

Anagnostakis, S. L. and R. A. Jaynes. 1973. Chestnut blight control: use of hypovirulent cultures. *Plant Dis. Rep. 57*:225-6.

Anderson, J. F. and S. W. Gould. 1974. Defoliation in Connecticut 1969-1974. *Conn. Agric. Exp. Stn. Bull. (New Haven) 749.* 25 pp.

Anderson, J. F. and H. K. Kaya. 1973a. Influence of elm spanworm oviposition sites on parasitism by *Ooencyrtus clisiocampae* and *Telenomus alsophilae. Environ. Entomol. 2*:705-11.

Anderson, J. F. and H. K. Kaya 1973b. Release and recovery of the elm spanworm egg parasitoid *Ooencyrtus clisiocampae* in Connecticut. *Environ. Entomol. 2*:722-4.

Anderson, J. F. and H. K. Kaya. 1974a. Parasitism of the elm spanworm by *Telenomus alsophilae* and *Actia ontario* in Connecticut. Pages 267-76 in R. L. Beard, ed. "25th Anniversary Memoirs Connecticut Entomological Society." Conn. Entomol. Soc., New Haven, Conn. 322 pp.

Anderson, J. F. and H. K. Kaya. 1974b. Diapause induction by photoperiod and temperature in the elm spanworm egg parasitoid, *Ooencyrtus* sp. *Ann. Entomol. Soc. Am. 67*:845-9.

Anderson, J. F. and H. K. Kaya. 1975. Influence of temperature on diapause termination in *Ooencyrtus ennomus*, an elm spanworm egg parasitoid. *Ann. Entomol. Soc. Am. 68*:671-2.

Anderson, P. J. 1913. The morphology and life history of the chestnut blight fungus. *Pa. Chestnut Tree Blight Comm. Publ. Bull. 7.* 44 pp.

Anderson, P. J. and W. H. Rankin. 1914. Endothia canker of chestnut. *N.Y. Agric. Exp. Stn. Cornell Bull. 347.* pp. 533-618.

Anderson, R. F. 1944. The relation between host condition and attacks by the bronzed birch borer. *J. Econ. Entomol. 37*:588-96.

Andrews, G. L. and P. P. Sikorowski. 1973. Effects of cotton leaf surfaces on the nuclear polyhedrosis virus of *Heliothis zea* and *Heliothis virescens* (Lepidoptera: Noctuidae). *J. Invertebr. Pathol. 22*:290-1.

Andrews, G. L., F. A. Harris, P. P. Sikorowski, and R. E. McLaughlin. 1975. Evaluation of *Heliothis* nuclear polyhedrosis virus in a cottonseed oil bait for control of *Heliothis virescens* and *H. zea* on cotton. *J. Econ. Entomol. 68*:87-90.

Andriescu, I., V. Ciochia, and V. Sauciniteanu. 1972/73. Studies on the possibilities of biological control of *Hyphantria cunea* Drury in the conditions of the Subkarpathian zone of Moldavia. I. The biology of the butterfly in the studied zone and the testing of some biopreparations based on *Bacillus thuringiensis* Berl. *Lucr. Stat. "Stejarul", Ecol. Terestra, Genet.* pp. 253-64.

Angus, T. A. and P. Luthy. 1971. Formulation of microbial insecticides. Pages 623-38 in H. D. Burges and N. W. Hussey, eds. "Microbial Control of Insects and Mites." Academic Press, N.Y. 861 pp.

Anonymous. 1916. Current notes. *J. Econ. Entomol. 9*:323.

Anonymous. 1954. Chestnut blight and resistant chestnuts. *U.S. Dep. Agric. Farmers Bull. 2068.* 21 pp.

Anonymous. 1968a. Connecticut: no loss without some small gain. Pages 230-1 in R. R. Widner, ed. "Forests and Forestry in the American States." Natl. Assoc. State For. 594 pp.

Anonymous. 1968b. Meteorological fundamentals for atmospheric transport and diffusion studies. Pages 13-63 in D. H. Slade, ed. "Meteorology and Atomic Energy." U.S.A.E.C., Oak Ridge, Tenn. 445 pp.

Anonymous. 1971. Summary of fire statistics 1910-1970. Pages 44-5 in "Fire Warden Directory 1971." For. Div. State Park and For. Comm. Hartford, Conn. 56 pp.

Anonymous. 1973. "1972-1973 Annual Report," Bureau of Plant Laboratory, Div. Plant Industry, N.J. Dep. Agric. 148 pp.

Anonymous. 1975. Mechanized line for large-scale propagation of insects. *Plant Protection-75, International Exhibition, Soviet Section Moscow, USSR Exhibition of Economic Achievements. Aug. 20-Sep. 2.* 12 pp.

Aoki, J. 1974. Mixed infection of the gypsy moth, *Lymantria dispar japonica* Motschulsky (Lepidoptera: Lymantriidae), in a larch forest by *Entomophthora aulicae* (Reich.) Sorok. and *Paecilomyces canadensis* (Vuill.) Brown et Smith. *Appl. Entomol. Zool. 9*:185-90.

Aratake, Y. and T. Kayamura. 1973. Pathogenicity of a nuclear-polyhedrosis virus of the silkworm, *Bombyx mori*, for a number of lepidopterous insects. *Jap. J. Appl. Entomol. Zool. 17*:121-6.

Aratake, Y., T. Kayamura, and H. Watanabe. 1974. Inactivation of a cytoplasmic-polyhedrosis virus by gut-juice of the silkworm, *Bombyx mori* L. *J. Seric. Sci. Jap. 43*:41-4.

Arthur, A. P. 1962a. Influence of host tree on abundance of *Itoplectis conquisitor* (Say) (Hymenoptera), a polyphagous parasite of the European pine shoot moth, *Rhyacionia buoliana* (Schiff.) (Lepidoptera: Olethreutidae). *Can. Entomol. 94*:337-47.

Arthur, A. P. 1962b. The influence of associative learning on host selection by the female of *Itoplectis conquisitor* (Say) (Hymenoptera: Ichneumonidae). *Proc. Entomol. Soc. Ont. 93*:133.

Arthur, A. P. 1966. Associative learning in *Itoplectis conquisitor* (Say) (Hymenoptera: Ichneumonidae). *Can. Entomol. 98*:213-23.

Arthur, A. P. 1967. Influence of position and size of host shelter on host-searching by *Itoplectis conquisitor* (Hymenoptera: Ichneumonidae). *Can. Entomol. 99*:877-86.

Arthur, A. P. and J. A. Juillet. 1961. The introduced parasites of the European pine shoot moth, *Rhyacionia buoliana* (Schiff.) (Lepidoptera: Olethreutidae), with a critical evaluation of their usefulness as control agents, *Can. Entomol. 93*:297-312.

Arthur, A. P., J. E. R. Stainer, and A. L. Turnbull. 1964. The interaction between *Orgilus obscurator* (Nees) (Hymenoptera: Braconidae) and *Temelucha interruptor* (Grav.) (Hymenoptera: Ichneumonidae), parasites of the pine shoot moth *Rhyacionia buoliana* (Schiff.) (Lepidoptera: Olethreutidae). *Can. Entomol. 96*:1030-4.

Arthur, A. P., B. M. Hegdekar, and L. Rollins. 1969. Component of the host haemolymph that induces oviposition in a parasitic insect. *Nature (Lond.) 223*:966-7.

Arthur, A. P., B. M. Hegdekar, and W. W. Batsch. 1972. A chemically defined, synthetic medium that induces oviposition in the parasite *Itoplectis conquistor* (Hymenoptera: Ichneumonidae). *Can. Entomol. 104*:1251-8.

Aruga, H. 1963. Induction of virus infections. Pages 499-530 in E. A. Steinhaus, ed. "Insect Pathology, an Advanced Treatise." Vol. 1. Academic Press, N.Y. 661 pp.

Aruga, H. 1968. Induction of polyhedroses and interaction among viruses in insects. *Proc. Joint U.S.-Japan Seminar Microbial Control Insect Pests, Fukuoka, Apr. 21-23, 1967.* pp. 33-6.

Aruga, H. and Y. Hashimoto. 1965. Interference between the UV-inactivated and active cytoplasmic-polyhedrosis viruses in the silkworm, *Bombyx mori* (Linnaeus). *J. Seric. Sci. Jap. 34*:351-4.

Aruga, H. and Y. Tanada. 1971. "The Cytoplasmic-polyhedrosis Virus of the Silkworm." Univ. Tokyo Press, Tokyo. 234 pp.

Aruga, H. and H. Watanabe. 1964. Resistance to *per os* infection with cytoplasmic-polyhedrosis virus in the silkworm, *Bombyx mori* (Linnaeus). *J. Insect Pathol. 6*:387-94.

Aruga, H. and H. Watanabe. 1965. The effect of high temperature on the infection with cytoplasmic polyhedrosis viruses and on interference between viruses in the silkworm, *Bombyx mori* L. *J. Seric. Sci. Jap. 34*:391-4.

Aruga, H., T. Hukuhara, N. Yoshitake, and I. N. Ayudhya. 1961a. Interference and latent infection in the cytoplasmic polyhedrosis of the silkworm, *Bombyx mori* (Linnaeus). *J. Insect Pathol. 3*:81-92.

Aruga, H., N. Yoshitake, H. Watanabe, T. Hukuhara, E. Nagashima, and T. Kawai. 1961b. Further studies on polyhedroses of some Lepidoptera. *Jap. J. Appl. Entomol. Zool. 5*:141-4.

Aruga, H., T. Hukuhara, S. Fukuda, and Y. Hashimoto. 1963a. Interference between cytoplasmic-polyhedrosis viruses of the silkworm, *Bombyx mori* (Linnaeus), and of the pine caterpillar, *Dendrolimus spectabilis* (Butler). *J. Insect Pathol. 5*:415-21.

Aruga, H., H. Watanabe, and H. Nagano. 1963b. Interference by the heat-inactivated virus on the active virus of the cytoplasmic polyhedrosis in the silkworm, *Bombyx mori* L. *J. Seric. Sci. Jap. 32*:51-7.

Aruga, H., N. Yoshitake, and H. Watanabe. 1963c. Interference between cytoplasmic polyhedrosis viruses in *Bombyx mori* (Linnaeus). *J. Insect Pathol. 5*:1-10.

Aruga, H., S. Tanaka, and T. Shimizu. 1965. Interference by the infectious flacherie virus on the cytoplasmic-polyhedrosis virus in the silkworm, *Bombyx mori* (Linnaeus). *J. Seric. Sci. Jap. 34*:385-90.

Ashley, T. R., D. Gonzalez, and T. F. Leigh. 1973. Reduction in effectiveness of laboratory-reared *Trichogramma. Environ. Entomol. 2*:1069-73.

Ashley, T. R., D. Gonzalez, and T. F. Leigh. 1974. Selection and hybridization of *Trichogramma. Environ. Entomol. 3*:43-8.

Askew, R. R. 1971. "Parasitic Insects." American Elsevier Publ. Co., N.Y. 316 pp.

Association of Official Analytical Chemists. 1970. "Official Methods of Analysis." 11th ed., Wash. D.C. 1015 pp.

Atger, P. 1962. Virose intestinale chez la Noctuelle du chou *Mamestria brassicae* L. (Lepidoptera). *Ann. Épiphyt. (Paris) 13*:263-5.

Auer, C. 1974. Ein Feldversuch zur gezielten Veränderung zyklischer Insektenpopulationsbewegungen. *Schweiz. Z. Forstwes. 125*:353-8.

Ayuzawa, C. and Y. Furuta. 1966. Susceptibility of the silkworm (*Bombyx mori* L.) to the nuclear polyhedrosis virus and the role of the inhibiting activity of the gut-juice. *J. Seric. Sci. Jap. 35*:65-70.

Baerg, W. J. 1928. Three shade tree insects. *Arkansas Agric. Exp. Stn. Bull. 224.* 25 pp.

Bailey, L. 1963. "Infectious Diseases of the Honeybee." Land Books Ltd., London. 176 pp.

Bailey, L. 1973. Control of invertebrates by viruses. Pages 533-53 in A. J. Gibbs, ed. "Viruses and Invertebrates." North-Holland Publ. Co., Amsterdam. 673 pp.

Bailey, L. and E. F. W. Fernando. 1972. Effect of sacbrood virus on adult honeybees. *Ann. Appl. Biol. 72*:27-35.

Bailey, L. and R. D. Woods. 1974. Three previously undescribed viruses from the honeybee. *J. Gen. Virol. 25*:175-86.

Baird, A. B. 1918. Some notes on the natural control of the cherry-tree ugly nest tortricid, *Archips cerasivorana* (Fitch). *Agric. Gaz. Can. 5*:766-71.

Baird, A. B. 1958. Biological control of insect and plant pests in Canada. *Proc. 10th Int. Congr. Entomol. (Montreal) 4*:483-5.

Baker, G. L., W. D. Rasmussen, V. Wiser, and J. M. Porter. 1963. "Century of Service: the First 100 Years of the United States Department of Agriculture." U.S. Gov. Printing Office, Wash. D.C. 560 pp.

Baker, T. 1975. "Male Behavioral and Neurophysiological Responses in *Argyrotaenia velutinana* (Lepidoptera: Tortricidae), to Components of its Sex Pheromone." M.S. Thesis. Cornell University, Ithaca. 58 pp.

Baker, T., R. Cardé, and W. Roelofs. 1976. Behavioral responses of male *Argyrotaenia velutinana* (Lepidoptera: Tortricidae) to components of its sex pheromone. *J. Chem. Ecol. 2*: Ms. submitted.

Baker, W. L. 1941. Effect of gypsy moth defoliation on certain forest trees. *J. For. 39*:1017-22.

Baker, W. L. 1972. "Eastern Forest Insects." U.S. Dep. Agric., For. Serv. Misc. Publ. 1175. 642 pp.

Bakke, A. 1967. Pheromone in the bark beetle, *Ips acuminatus* Gyll. *Z. Angew. Entomol. 59*:49-53.

Bakke, A. 1970. Evidence of a population aggregating pheromone in *Ips typographus* (Coleoptera: Scolytidae). *Contrib. Boyce Thompson Inst. 24*:309-10.

Bakke, A. 1973. Bark beetle pheromones and their potential use in forestry. *EPPO Bull. No. 9*:5-15.

Bakke, A. 1975. Aggregation pheromone in the bark beetle *Ips duplicatus* (Sahlberg). *Norw. J. Entomol. 22*:67-9.

Balch, R. E. 1958. Control of forest insects. *Annu. Rev. Entomol. 3*:449-68.

Balch, R. E. and F. T. Bird. 1944. A disease of the European spruce sawfly, *Gilpinia hercyniae* (Htg.), and its place in natural control. *Sci. Agric. 25*:65-80.

Baltensweiler, W. 1968. The cyclic population dynamics of the grey larch tortrix, *Zeiraphera griseana* Hübner (= *Semasia diniana* Guenée) (Lepidoptera: Tortricidae). Pages 88-97 in T. R. E. Southwood, ed. "Insect Abundance." Symp. R. Entomol. Soc. Lond. Vol. 4 Blackwell Sci. Publ., Oxford, England. 168 pp.

Barbosa, P., J. L. Capinera, and E. A. Harrington. 1975. The gypsy moth parasitoid complex in western Massachusetts, a study of parasitoids in areas of high and low host density. *Environ. Entomol. 4*:842-6.

Bartels, J. M. and G. N. Lanier. 1974. Emergence and mating in *Scolytus multistriatus* (Coleoptera: Scolytidae). *Ann. Entomol. Soc. Am. 67*:364-70.

Barter, G. W. 1957. Studies of the bronze birch borer, *Agrilus anxius* Gory, in New Brunswick. *Can. Entomol. 89*:12-36.

Barter, G. W. 1965. Survival and development of the bronze poplar borer *Agrilus liragus* Barter & Brown (Coleoptera: Buprestidae). *Can. Entomol. 97*:1063-8.

Batchelor, G. K. 1952. Diffusion in a field of homogeneous turbulence II. The relative motion of particles. *Proc. Cambridge Phil. Soc. 48*:345-62.

Beach, S. A. 1905. "The Apples of New York." Vol. 1. N.Y. Agric. Exp. Stn. Geneva Annu. Rep. 1903. 409 pp.

Beal, F. E. L. 1915. Food habits of the thrushes of the United States. *U.S. Dep. Agric. Bull. 280*. 23 pp.

Beal, J. A. 1943. Relation between tree growth and outbreaks of the Black Hills beetle. *J. For. 41*:359-66.

Beattie, R. K. and J. D. Diller. 1954. Fifty years of the chestnut blight in America. *J. For. 52*:323-9.

Beavers, J. B. and D. K. Reed. 1972. Susceptibility of seven tetranychids to the nonoccluded virus of the citrus red mite and the correlation of the carmine spider mite as a vector. *J. Invertebr. Pathol. 20*:279-83.

Beckwith, C. S. 1938. *Spargonthis sulfureana* Clem., a cranberry pest in New Jersey. *J. Econ. Entomol. 31*:253-6.

Bedard, W. D. 1965. The biology of *Tomicobia tibialis* (Hymenoptera: Pteromalidae) parasitizing *Ips confusus* (Coleoptera: Scolytidae) in California. *Contrib. Boyce Thompson Inst. 23*:77-81.

Bedford, G. O. 1973. Experiments with the virus *Rhabdionvirus oryctes* against the coconut palm rhinoceros beetles *Oryctes rhinoceros* and *Scapanes australis gossepunctatus* in New Guinea. *J. Invertebr. Pathol. 22*:70-4.

Bedny, V. D. and B. G. Kovalev. 1975. On disorientation caused in gypsy moth males by disparlure. *Proc. II All Union Symposium, No. 2.* pp. 177-9. (In Russ., Engl. summ.).

Beegle, C. C. and .E. R. Oatman. 1974. Differential susceptibility of parasitized and nonparasitized larvae of *Trichoplusia ni* to a nuclear polyhedrosis virus. *J. Invertebr. Pathol. 24*:188-95.

Beegle, C. C. and E. R. Oatman. 1975. Effect of a nuclear polyhedrosis virus on the relationship between *Trichoplusia ni* (Lepidoptera: Noctuidae) and the parasite, *Hyposoter exiguae* (Hymenoptera: Ichneumonidae). *J. Invertebr. Pathol. 25*:59-71.

Beirne, B. P. 1974. Status of the biological control procedures that involve parasites and predators. Pages 69-76 in F. G. Maxwell and F. A. Harris, eds. "Proceedings of the Summer Institute on Biological Control of Plant Insects and Diseases." Univ. Press of Miss. Jackson, Miss. 647 pp.

Bejer-Petersen, B. 1974. Bekämpfung von Nonnen (*Lymantria monacha* L.) in Dänemark. *Dan. Skovforen. Tidsskr. 59*:59-80. (In Danish).

Bell, M. R. and R. F. Kanavel. 1975. Potential of bait formulations to increase effectiveness of nuclear polyhedrosis virus against the pink bollworms. *J. Econ. Entomol.* 68:389-91.

Benham, G. S., Jr. and G. O. Poinar, Jr. 1973. Tabulation and evaluation of recent field experiments using the DD-136 strain of *Neoaplectana carpocapsae* Weiser: a review. *Exp. Parasitol.* 33:248-52.

Benjamin, D. M. and A. T. Drooz. 1954. Parasites affecting the jack-pine budworm in Michigan. *J. Econ. Entomol.* 47:588-90.

Bennett, W. H. 1965. Silvicultural control of southern forest insects. Pages 51-63 in C. B. Marlin, ed. "Insects in Southern Forests." Proc. 14th Annu. For. Symp., La. State Univ. Press. 129 pp.

Benz. G. 1961. Ueber eine Polyedrose als Begrenzungsfaktor einer Population von *Malacosoma alpicola* Stg. (Lepid. Lasiocampidae). *Mitt. Schweiz. Entomol. Ges.* 34:382-92.

Benz, G. 1971. Synergism of micro-organisms and chemical insecticides. Pages 327-55 in H. D. Burges and N. W. Hussey, eds. "Microbial Control of Insects and Mites." Academic Press, N.Y. 861 pp.

Benz, G. 1973. Role of sex pheromone and its insignificance for heterosexual and homosexual behaviour of larch bud moth. *Experientia* 29:553-4.

Benz, G. 1974. Negative Rückkoppelung durch Raum-und Nahrungskonkurrenz sowie zyklische Veränderung der Nahrungsgrundlage als Regelprinzip in der Populationsdynamik des Grauen Lärchenwicklers, *Zeiraphera diniana* (Guenée) (Lep., Tortricidae). *Z. Angew. Entomol.* 76:196-228.

Benz, G. 1975. Action of *Bacillus thuringiensis* preparations against larch bud moth, *Zeiraphera diniana* (Gn.), enhanced by β-exotoxin and DDT. *Experientia* 31:1288-90.

Benz, G. and G. von Salis. 1973. Use of synthetic sex attractant of larch bud moth, *Zeiraphera diniana* (Gn.) in monitoring traps under different conditions and antagonistic action of *cis*-isomere. *Experientia* 29:729-30.

Bergen, J. D. 1974. Vertical air temperature profiles in a pine stand: spatial variation and scaling problems. *For. Sci.* 20:64-73.

Berger, E. W. 1906. Observations upon the migrating, feeding and nesting habits of the fall webworm (*Hyphantria cunea* Dru.). Pages 41-51 in *Proc. 18th Annu. Meeting Assoc. Econ. Entomol. U.S. Dep. Agric. Bur. Entomol. Bull. 60.* 206 pp.

Bergold, G. H. 1943. Über Polyederkrankheiten bei Insekten. *Biol. Zentralbl.* 63:1-55.

Bergold, G. H. 1958. Viruses of insects. Pages 60-142 in C. Hallauer and K. F. Meyer, eds. "Handbuch der Virusforschung." Vol. 4. Springer-Verlag, Vienna. 688 pp.

Berisford, C. W., H. M. Kulman, R. L. Pienkowski, and H. J. Heikkenen. 1971. Factors affecting distribution and abundance of hymenopterous parasites of *Ips* spp. bark beetles in Virginia (Coleoptera: Scolytidae). *Can. Entomol.* 103:235-9.

Beroza, M. and F. Acree, Jr. 1964. A new technique for determining chemical structure by gas chromatography. *J. Assoc. Off. Agric. Chem.* 47:1-14.

Beroza, M. and E. F. Knipling. 1972. Gypsy moth control with the sex attractant pheromone. *Science (Wash. D.C.)* 177:19-27.

Beroza, M., B. A. Bierl, E. F. Knipling, and J. G. R. Tardif. 1971a. The activity of the gypsy moth sex attractant disparlure vs. that of the live female moth. *J. Econ. Entomol.* 64:1527-9.

Beroza, M., B. A. Bierl, J. G. R. Tardif, D. A. Cook, and E. C. Paszek. 1971b. Activity and persistence of synthetic and natural sex attractants of the gypsy moth in laboratory and field trials. *J. Econ. Entomol.* 64:1499-508.

Beroza, M., L. J. Stevens, B. A. Bierl, F. M. Philips, and J. G. R. Tardif. 1973. Pre- and postseason field tests with disparlure, the sex pheromone of the gypsy moth, to prevent mating. *Environ. Entomol.* 2:1051-7.

Beroza, M., C. S. Hood, D. Trefrey, D. E. Leonard, E. F. Knipling, W. Klassen, and L. J. Stevens. 1974a. Large field trial with microencapsulated sex pheromone to prevent mating of the gypsy moth. *J. Econ. Entomol. 67*:659-64.

Beroza, M., E. C. Paszek, E. R. Mitchell, B. A. Bierl, J. R. McLaughlin, and D. L. Chambers. 1974b. Tests of a 3-layer laminated plastic bait dispenser for controlled emission of attractants from insect traps. *Environ. Entomol. 3*:926-8.

Beroza, M., C. S. Hood, D. Trefrey, D. E. Leonard, E. F. Knipling, and W. Klassen. 1975. Field trials with disparlure in Massachusetts to suppress mating of the gypsy moth. *Environ. Entomol. 4*:705-11.

Berthelay-Sauret, S. 1973. Utilization de mutants auxotrophes dan les recherches sur le determinisme de "l'hypovirulence exclusive". (Abst.) *Ann. Phytopathol. 5*:318.

Besemer, A. F. H. 1964. The available data on the effect of spray chemicals on useful arthropods in orchards. *Entomophaga 9*:263-9.

Bess, H. A. 1961. Population ecology of the gypsy moth. *Conn. Agric. Exp. Stn. Bull. (New Haven) 646.* 43 pp.

Bess, H. A., S. H. Spurr, and E. W. Littlefield. 1947. Forest site conditions and the gypsy moth. *Harv. For. Bull. 22.* 56 pp.

Bevan, D. 1974. Control of forest insects: there is a porpoise close behind us. Pages 302-12 in D. P. Jones and M. E. Solomon, eds. "Biology in Pest and Disease Control." Blackwell Sci. Publ., Oxford, England. 398 pp.

Bierl, B. A., M. Beroza, and C. W. Collier. 1970. Potent sex attractant of the gypsy moth: its isolation, identification and synthesis. *Science (Wash. D.C.) 170*:87-9.

Bingham, R. T., R. J. Hoff, and G. I. McDonald. 1971. Disease resistance in forest trees. *Annu. Rev. Phytopathol. 9*:433-52.

Biraghi, A. 1951. Caratteri di resistenza in *Castanea sativa* nei confronti di *Endothia parasitica. Inst. Patologia For. Agraria, Firenge, Italy.* 5 pp.

Biraghi, A. 1953. Possible active resistance to *Endothia parasitica* in *Castanea sativa. Rep. 11th Congr. Int. Union For. Res. Organ. Rome, Italy.* pp. 643-5.

Biraghi, A. 1966. Aspetti fitopathologici della conservazione del castangno. Pages 120-218 in "Atti conegno internazionale sul castagno." Camera Commer. Ind. Artigianato Agric., Cuneo, Italy. 432 pp.

Birch, M. C. 1974. "Pheromones." North-Holland Publ. Co., Amsterdam. 495 pp.

Bird, F. T. 1953a. The effect of metamorphosis on the multiplication of an insect virus. *Can. J. Zool. 31*:300-3.

Bird, F. T. 1953b. The use of a virus disease in the biological control of the European pine sawfly, *Neodiprion sertifer* (Geoffr.). *Can. Entomol. 85*:437-46.

Bird, F. T. 1955. Virus diseases of sawflies. *Can. Entomol. 87*:124-7.

Bird, F. T. 1959. Polyhedrosis and granulosis viruses causing single and double infections in the spruce budworm, *Choristoneura fumiferana* Clemens. *J. Insect Pathol. 1*:406-30.

Bird, F. T. 1961. Transmission of some insect viruses with particular reference to ovarial transmission and its importance in the development of epizootics. *J. Insect Pathol. 3*:352-80.

Bird, F. T. 1964. The use of viruses in biological control. *Entomophaga, Mem. Hors. Ser. No. 2.* pp. 465-73.

Bird, F. T. 1969. Infection and mortality of spruce budworm, *Choristoneura fumiferana*, and forest tent caterpillar, *Malacosoma disstria*, caused by nuclear and cytoplasmic polyhedrosis viruses. *Can. Entomol. 101*:1269-85.

Bird, F. T. and J. M. Burk. 1961. Artifically disseminated virus as a factor controlling the European spruce sawfly, *Diprion hercyniae* (Htg.) in the absence of introduced parasites. *Can. Entomol. 93*:228-38.

Bird, F. T. and D. E. Elgee. 1957. A virus disease and introduced parasites as factors controlling the European spruce sawfly, *Diprion hercyniae* (Htg.), in central New Brunswick. *Can. Entomol. 89*:371-8.

Bird, F. T. and J. R. McPhee. 1970. Susceptibility of spruce budworm to pure nuclear polyhedrosis virus (NPV) sprays. *Can. For. Serv. Bi-mon. Res. Notes. 26* (4):35.

Bird, F. T., J. C. Cunningham, and G. M. Howse. 1972. The possible use of viruses in the control of spruce budworm. *Proc. Entomol. Soc. Ont. 103*:69-75.

Blewett, M. B. and J. E. Potzger. 1951. The forest primeval of Marion and Johnson Counties, Indiana, in 1819. *Butler Univ. Bot. Study 10*:40-52.

Block, B. C. 1960. Laboratory method for screening compounds as attractants to gypsy moth males. *J. Econ. Entomol. 53*:172-3.

Bobb, M. L. 1964. Apparent loss of sex attractiveness by the female of the Virginia-pine sawfly, *Neodiprion pratti pratti. J. Econ. Entomol. 57*:829-30.

Bobb, M. L. 1972. Influence of sex pheromones on mating behavior and populations of Virginia-pine sawfly. *Environ. Entomol. 1*:78-80.

Bogenschütz, H. 1975. Parasitenstudien als Entscheidungshilfen bei der integrierten Bekämpfung von Forstschädlingen. *Z. Angew. Entomol. 78*:1-5.

Boldaruyev, V. O. 1969. Results and prospects of research on biological control of insect pests in Eastern Siberia. Pages 98-9 in A. I. Cherepanov, ed. "Biological Control of Agriculture and Forest Pests." Isr. Prog. Sci. Transl. (Jerusalem). 179 pp.

Boldaruyev, V. O. 1971. The silkworm moth, *Telenomus* and forest fires. (Trans. from Russ.) *Priroda (Mosc.) No. 12.* 7 pp.

Boldaruyev, V. O. 1972. *Erannis jacobsoni* (Djak) (Lepidoptera, Geometridae) a serious larch pest in Transbaykalia. *Entomol. Rev. 51*:29-34.

Boller, E. 1972. Behavioral aspects of mass-rearing insects. *Entomophaga 17*:9-25.

Boness, M. 1975. Disparlure: comparison of effectiveness in *Lymantria dispar* and *Lymantria monacha* as shown in field tests. *8th Int. Plant Prot. Congr. Moscow. Sec. V*: 41-7.

Boness, M., W. Schulze, and U. Skatulla. 1974. Versuche zur Bekämpfung der Nonne *Lymantria monacha* L. mit dem synthetischen Pheromon Disparlure. *Anz. Schaedlingskd. Pflanzen-Umweltschutz. 47*:119-22.

Bonifacio, A. and T. Turchetti. 1973. Differenze morfologiche e fisiologiche in isolati di *Endothia parasitica* (Murr.) And. *Ann. Acad. Ital. Sci. For. 22*:111-31.

Bonnemaison, L. 1972. Diapause et superparasitisme chez *Trichogramma evanescens* Westwood. (Hym. Trichogrammatidae). *Bull. Soc. Entomol. Fr. 77*:122-32.

Borden, J. H. and E. Stokkink. 1971. Secondary attraction in the Scolytidae: an annotated bibliography. *Can. Dep. Fish. For. Inf. Rep. BC-X-57.* 77 pp.

Borden, J. H., R. G. Brownlee, and R. M. Silverstein. 1968. Sex pheromone of *Trypodendron lineatum* (Coleoptera: Scolytidae): production, bioassay, and partial isolation. *Can. Entomol. 100*:629-36.

Borror, D. J. and D. M. DeLong. 1971. "An Introduction to the Study of Insects." 3rd ed. Holt, Rinehart and Winston, N.Y. 812 pp.

Bossert, W. H. and E. O. Wilson. 1963. The analysis of olfactory communication among animals. *J. Theor. Biol. 5*:443-69.

Braun, E. L. 1950. "Deciduous Forests of Eastern North America." The Blakiston Co., Philadelphia. 596 pp.

Brender, E. V. 1974. Impact of past land use on the Lower Piedmont forest. *J. For. 72*:34-6.

Britton, W. E. 1906. Fifth report of the state entomologist of Connecticut. Pages 189-262 in *29th Annu. Rep. Conn. Agric. Exp. Stn. (New Haven).* 368 pp.

Britton, W. E. 1908. Eighth report of the state entomologist of Connecticut. Pages 763-848 in *31st and 32nd Annu. Rep. Conn. Agric. Exp. Stn. (New Haven)*. 934 pp.

Britton, W. E. 1914. Thirteenth report of the state entomologist of Connecticut. Pages 181-256 in *37th Annu. Rep. Conn. Agric. Exp. Stn. (New Haven)*. 441 pp.

Britton, W. E. 1939. Connecticut state entomologist thirty-eighth report 1938. *Conn. Agric. Exp. Stn. Bull. (New Haven) 428*. 122 pp.

Bromley, S. W. 1935. The original forest types of southern New England. *Ecol. Monogr. 5*:62-89.

Broome, J. R., P. P. Sikorowski, and W. W. Neel. 1974. Effect of sunlight on the activity of nuclear polyhedrosis virus from *Malacosoma disstria. J. Econ. Entomol. 67*:135-6.

Brown, E. A. 1974. "Vision in *Porthetria dispar* (L.) Males: Physiological Spectral Sensitivity and Behavioral Implications." M.S. Thesis. Pa. State Univ., University Park. 38 pp.

Brown, R. A., G. E. McVehil, R. L. Peace, Jr., and R. W. Coakley. 1969. "Characterization of Forest Vegetation Analogs." Cornell Aeronautical Lab., Inc., Buffalo, N.Y. 64 pp.

Brown, R. C. 1931. Observations on the satin moth and its natural enemies in central Europe. *U.S. Dep. Agric. Circ. 176*. 19 pp.

Brown, W. L., Jr. 1961. Mass insect control programs: four case histories. *Psyche. 68*:75-111.

Brues, C. T. 1924. The specificity of food plants in the evolution of phytophagous insects. *Am. Nat. 58*:127-44.

Brues, C. T. 1952. How insects choose their food plants. Pages 37-42 in "Insects." U.S. Dep. Agric. Yearb. Agric. Gov. Printing Office, Wash. D.C. 780 pp.

Brumbach, J. J. 1965. The climate of Connecticut. *State Geol. Nat. Hist. Surv. Conn. Bull. 99*. 215 pp.

Bucher, G. E. 1963. Nonsporulating bacterial pathogens. Pages 117-43 in E. A. Steinhaus, ed. "Insect Pathology, an Advanced Treatise." Vol. 2. Academic Press, N.Y. 689 pp.

Bull, H. 1939. Increased growth of loblolly pine as a result of cutting and girdling large hardwoods. *J. For. 37*:642-5.

Bulla, L. A., Jr. 1973. "Regulation of Insect Populations by Microorganisms." Ann. N.Y. Acad. Sci. Vol. 217. 243 pp.

Burgerjon, A. and G. Biache. 1964. The activity of the heat-stable toxin of *Bacillus thuringiensis* Berliner used in nature against larvae of *Diprion pini* (Linnaeus). *J. Insect Pathol. 6*:538-41.

Burges, H. D. 1973. Enzootic diseases of insects. Pages 31-49 in L. A. Bulla, Jr., ed. "Regulation of Insect Populations by Microorganisms." Ann. N.Y. Acad. Sci. 217. 243 pp.

Burges, H. D. and N. W. Hussey. 1971. "Microbial Controls of Insects and Mites." Academic Press, N.Y. 861 pp.

Burgess, A. F. 1916. The work carried on in the United States against the gipsy and brown-tail moths. *Annu. Rep. Entomol. Soc. Ont. 46*:153-5.

Burgess, A. F. and S. S. Crossman. 1927. The satin moth, a recently introduced pest. *U.S. Dep. Agric. Bull. 1469*. 23 pp.

Burgess, A. F. and S. S. Crossman. 1929. Imported insect enemies of the gipsy moth and the brown-tail moth. *U.S. Dep. Agric. Tech. Bull. 86*. 147 pp.

Burgess, E. D. 1950. Development of gypsy moth sex-attractant traps. *J. Econ. Entomol. 43*:325-8.

Burke, H. E. 1917. Flat-headed borers affecting forest trees in the United States. *U.S. Dep. Agric. Bull. 437*. 8 pp.

Burks, B. D. 1960. The establishment of *Brachymeria intermedia* (Nees) in North America (Hymenoptera: Chalcididae). *Entomol. News. 71*:62.

Bush, G. L. 1974. Sympatric speciation in phytophagous parasitic insects. Pages 187-206 in P. W. Price, ed. "Evolutionary Strategies of Parasitic Insects and Mites." Plenum Press, N.Y. 224 pp.

Butler, C. G. 1967. A sex attractant acting as an aphrodisiac in the honeybee (*Apis mellifera* L.). *Proc. R. Entomol. Soc. Lond. Ser. A. 42*:71-6.

Butler, C. G. 1970. Chemical communication in insects: behavioral and ecological aspects. Pages 35-78 in J. W. Johnston, Jr., D. G. Moulton, and A. Turk, eds. "Advances in Chemoreception. Vol. 1. Communication by Chemical Signals." Appleton-Century-Crofts, N.Y. 412 pp.

Caesar, L. 1940. Fifty years of entomological progress, Part II, 1899 to 1909. *J. Econ. Entomol. 33*:15-21.

Caffrey, D. J.'1921. Biology and economic importance of *Anastatus semiflavidus*, a recently described egg parasite of *Hemileuca oliviae. J. Agric. Res. 21*:373-84.

Cameron, E. A. 1973. Disparlure: a potential tool for gypsy moth population management. *Bull. Entomol. Soc. Am. 19*:15-9.

Cameron, E. A. 1974. Programs utilizing pheromones in survey or control. The gypsy moth. Pages 431-5 in M. C. Birch, ed. "Pheromones." North-Holland Publ. Co., Amsterdam. 495 pp.

Cameron, E. A., C. P. Schwalbe, M. Beroza, and E. F. Knipling. 1974. Disruption of gypsy moth mating with microencapsulated disparlure. *Science (Wash. D.C.) 183*:972-3.

Cameron, E. A., C. P. Schwalbe, L. J. Stevens, and M. Beroza. 1975. Field tests of the olefin precursor of disparlure for suppression of mating in the gypsy moth. *J. Econ. Entomol. 68*:158-60.

Cameron, J. W. M. 1963. Factors affecting the use of microbial pathogens in insect control. *Annu. Rev. Entomol. 8*:265-86.

Cameron, J. W. M. 1972. Implementation of biological control programs against forest pests. *Proc. North Cent. Branch, Entomol. Soc. Am. 27*:43-7.

Camors, F. B., Jr. and T. L. Payne. 1972. Response of *Heydenia unica* (Hymenoptera: Pteromalidae) to *Dendroctonus frontalis* (Coleoptera: Scolytidae) pheromones and a host-tree terpene. *Ann. Entomol. Soc. Am. 65*:31-3.

Campbell, R. W. 1963a. Some ichneumonid-sarcophagid interactions in the gypsy moth, *Porthetria dispar* (L.) (Lepidoptera: Lymantriidae). *Can. Entomol. 95*:337-45.

Campbell, R. W. 1963b. The role of disease and desiccation in the population dynamics of the gypsy moth *Porthetria dispar* (L.) (Lepidoptera: Lymantriidae). *Can. Entomol. 95*:426-34.

Campbell, R. W. 1963c. Some factors that distort the sex ratio of the gypsy moth *Porthetria dispar. Can. Entomol. 95*:465-74.

Campbell, R. W. 1967. The analysis of numerical change in gypsy moth populations. *For. Sci. Monogr. 15.* 33 pp.

Campbell, R. W. 1973a. Forecasting gypsy moth egg-mass density. *U.S. For. Serv. Res. Pap. NE-268.* 19 pp.

Campbell, R. W. 1973b. Numerical behavior of a gypsy moth population system. *For. Sci. 19*:162-7.

Campbell, R. W. 1974. The gypsy moth and its natural enemies. *U.S. Dep. Agric., For. Serv. Agric. Infor. Bull. 381.* 27 pp.

Campbell, R. W. and J. D. Podgwaite. 1971. The disease complex of the gypsy moth. I. Major components. *J. Invertebr. Pathol. 18*:101-7.

Campbell, R. W. and R. J. Sloan. 1975. Forest stand responses to heavy, repeated defoliation by the gypsy moth. *Manuscript, Northeast. For. Exp. Stn. Pap.* 27 pp.

Campbell, R. W., D. L. Hubbard, and R. J. Sloan. 1975. Patterns of gypsy moth occurrence within a sparse and numerically stable population. *Environ. Entomol. 4*:535-42.

Capinera, J. L. and P. Barbosa. 1975. Transmission of nuclear-polyhedrosis virus to gypsy moth larvae by *Calosoma sycophanta. Ann. Entomol. Soc. Am. 68*:593-4.

Cardé R. T., W. L. Roelofs, and C. C. Doane. 1973. Natural inhibitor to the gypsy moth sex attractant. *Nature (Lond.) 241*:474.

Cardé R. T., C. C. Doane, and W. L. Roelofs. 1974. Diel periodicity of male sex pheromone response and female attractiveness in the gypsy moth (Lepidoptera: Lymantriidae). *Can. Entomol. 106*:479-84.

Cardé R. T., T. C. Baker, and W. L. Roelofs. 1975a. Ethological function of components of a sex attractant system for oriental fruit moth males, *Grapholitha molesta* (Lepidoptera: Tortricidae). *J. Chem. Ecol. 1*:475-91.

Cardé, R. T., C. C. Doane, J. Granett, and W. L. Roelofs. 1975b. Disruption of pheromone communication in the gypsy moth and some behavioral effects of disparlure and an attractant modifier. *Environ. Entomol. 4*:793-6.

Cardinal, J. A. and W. A. Smirnoff. 1973. Introduction experimentale de la polyédrie nucléaire de *Porthetria dispar* L. (Lepidopteres: Lymantriidae) en forêt. *Phytoprotection 54*:48-50.

Carlson, R. W. and F. B. Knight. 1969. Biology, taxonomy, and evolution of four sympatric *Agrilus* beetles (Coleoptera: Buprestidae). *Contrib. Am. Entomol. Inst. 4*:1-105.

Carolin, V. M. and W. K. Coulter. 1959. The occurrence of insect parasites of *Choristoneura fumiferana* (Clem.), in Oregon. *J. Econ. Entomol. 52*:550-5.

Casida, J. E., H. C. Coppel, and T. W. Watanabe. 1963. Purification and potency of the sex attractant from the introduced pine sawfly, *Diprion similis. J. Econ. Entomol. 56*:18-24.

Champlain, A. B. and J. N. Knull. 1923. Fragmentary notes on forest Coleoptera. *Can. Entomol. 55*:112-5.

Chapman, P. J. and S. E. Lienk. 1971. "Tortricid Fauna of Apple in New York." N.Y. State Agric. Exp. Stn. Geneva. Special Publ. 122 pp.

Chapman, P. J., G. W. Pearce, and A. W. Avens. 1941. The use of petroleum oils as insecticides. III. Oil deposit and the control of fruit tree leafroller and other apple pests. *J. Econ. Entomol. 34*:639-47.

Chapman, R. N. 1915. Observations on the life history of *Agrilus bilineatus. J. Agric. Res. 3*:283-97.

Chapman, R. N. 1931. "Animal Ecology." McGraw-Hill Book Co., N.Y. 464 pp.

Chittenden, F. H. 1897. Insect injury to chestnut and pine trees in Virginia and neighboring states. *U.S. Dep. Agric., Div. Entomol. Bull. 7, n.s.* pp. 67-75.

Chittenden, F. H. 1900. Food plants and injury of North American species of *Agrilus. U.S. Dep. Agric., Div. Entomol. Bull. 22, n.s.* pp. 64-8.

Chittenden, F. H. 1909. The two-lined chestnut borer. *U.S. Dep. Agric., Bur. Entomol. Circ. 24.* 7 pp.

Chumakova, B. M. 1960. Complementary feeding as a factor to increase effectiveness of the parasites of injurious insects (Trans. from Russ.) *Trans. Inst. Plant Prot. 15*:57-70.

Ciesla, W. M. 1964a. The feeding preference for hardwoods by elm spanworm in the southern Appalachian Mountains. *J. Econ. Entomol. 57*:604.

Ciesla, W. M. 1964b. Egg parasites of the elm spanworm in the southern Appalachian Mountains. *J. Econ. Entomol. 57*:837-8.

Ciesla, W. M. 1965. Observations on the life history of *Telenomus alsophilae*, an egg parasite of the elm spanworm, *Ennomos subsignarius. J. Econ. Entomol. 58*:702-4.

Cionco, R. M. 1965. A mathematical model for air flow in a vegetative canopy. *J. Appl. Meteorol. 4*:517-22.

Clapper, R. B. 1954. Chestnut breeding, techniques and results. *J. Hered. 45*:106-14, 201-8.

Clapper, R. B., G. F. Gravatt, and D. C. Stout. 1946. Endothia canker on post oak. *Plant Dis. Rep. 30*:381.

Clark, E. C. 1955. Observations on the ecology of a polyhedrosis of the Great Basin tent caterpillar, *Malacosoma fragilis. Ecology 36*:373-6.

Clark, E. C. 1956. Survival and transmission of a virus causing polyhedrosis in *Malacosoma fragile. Ecology 37*:728-32.

Clark, E. C. 1958. Ecology of the polyhedroses of tent caterpillars. *Ecology 39*:132-9.

Clark, E. C. and C. E. Reiner. 1956. The possible use of a polyhedrosis virus in the control of the Great Basin tent caterpillar. *J. Econ. Entomol. 49*:653-9.

Clark, E. C. and C. G. Thompson. 1954. The possible use of microorganisms in the control of the Great Basin tent caterpillar. *J. Econ. Entomol. 47*:268-72.

Clark, G. L. 1914. "A History of Connecticut." G. P. Putnam's Sons, N.Y. 609 pp.

Clark, T. B. and T. Fukuda. 1971. Field and laboratory observations of two viral diseases in *Aedes sollicitans* (Walker) in southwestern Louisiana. *Mosq. News 31*:193-8.

Clausen, C. P. 1956. Biological control of insect pests in the continental United States. *U.S. Dep. Agric. Tech. Bull. 1139.* 151 pp.

Clausen, C. P. 1962. "Entomophagous Insects." Hafner Publ. Co., N.Y. 688 pp.

Clement, G. E. 1917. Control of the gipsy moth by forest management. *U.S. Dep. Agric Bull. 484.* 54 pp.

Clinton, G. P. 1908a. Report of the botanist for 1907. Pages 339-96 in *31st and 32nd Annu. Rep. Conn. Agric. Exp. Stn.* (*New Haven*). 934 pp.

Clinton, G. P. 1908b. Report of the botanist for 1908. Pages 849-907 in *31st and 32nd Annu. Rep. Conn. Agric. Exp. Stn.* (*New Haven*). 934 pp.

Clinton, G. P. 1913. Report of the botanist for 1911 and 1912. Pages 359-453 in *36th Annu. Rep. Conn. Agric. Exp. Stn.* (*New Haven*). 531 pp.

Clinton, G. P. and F. A. McCormick. 1919. Infection experiments of *Pinus strobus* with *Cronartium ribicola. Conn. Agric. Exp. Stn. Bull.* (*New Haven*) *214.* pp. 428-59.

Clinton, G. P. and F. A. McCormick. 1936. Dutch elm disease *Graphium ulmi. Conn. Agric. Exp. Stn. Bull.* (*New Haven*) *389.* 54 pp.

Cole, L. R. 1970. Observations on the finding of mates by male *Phaeogenes invisor* and *Apanteles medicaginis* (Hymenoptera: Ichneumonidea). *Anim. Behav. 18*:184-9.

Collins, C. W. 1926. Observations on a recurring outbreak of *Heterocampa guttivitta* Walker and natural enemies controlling it. *J. Agric. Res. 32*:689-99.

Collins, C. W. and S. F. Potts. 1932. Attractants for the flying gipsy moths as an aid in locating new infestations. *U.S. Dep. Agric. Tech. Bull. 336.* 43 pp.

Compere, H. 1969. The role of systematics in biological control: a backward look. *Isr. J. Entomol. 4*:5-10.

Conover, M. 1924. "The Office of Experiment Stations: its History, Activities and Organization." Serv. Monogr. U.S. Gov. 32. Inst. Gov. Res. Johns Hopkins Press, Baltimore. 178 pp.

Corrsin, S. 1961. Turbulent flow. *Am. Sci. 49*:300-25.

Cosenza, B. J. and F. B. Lewis. 1965. Occurrence of motile, pigmented streptococci in lepidopterous and hymenopterous larvae. *J. Invertebr. Pathol. 7*:86-91.

Côté, W. A. and D. C. Allen. 1973. Biology of the maple trumpet skeletonizer, *Epinotia aceriella* (Lepidoptera: Olethreutidae), in New York. *Can. Entomol. 105*:463-70.

Cottam, G. 1949. The phytosociology of an oak woods in southwestern Wisconsin. *Ecology 30*:271-87.

Craighead, F. C. 1915. Current notes. *J. Econ. Entomol. 8*:440.

Craighead, F. C. 1924. Part II. General bionomics and possibilities of prevention and control. Pages 28-57 in Studies on the spruce budworm (*Cacoecia fumiferana* Clem.). *Dom. Can. Dep. Agric.* (*Tech.*) *Bull. 37, n.s.* 91 pp.

Craighead, F. C. 1950. "Insect Enemies of Eastern Forests." U.S. Dep. Agric. Misc. Publ. 657. 679 pp.

Crist, C. R. and D. F. Schoeneweiss. 1975. The influence of controlled stresses on susceptibility of European white birch stems to attack by *Botryosphaeria dothidea*. *Phytopathology 65*:369-73.

Crossman, S. S. 1917. Some methods of colonizing imported parasites and determining their increase and spread. *J. Econ. Entomol. 10*:177-83.

Crossman, S. S. 1925. Two imported egg parasites of the gypsy moth, *Anastatus bifasciatus* Fonsc. and *Schedius kuvanae* Howard. *J. Agric. Res. 30*:643-75.

Csanady, G. T. 1973. "Turbulent Diffusion in the Environment." D. Reidel Publ. Co., Boston. 248 pp.

Cunningham, J. C. 1968. Serological and morphological identification of some nuclear-polyhedrosis and granulosis viruses. *J. Invertebr. Pathol. 11*:132-41.

Cunningham, J. C. and T. W. Tinsley. 1968. A serological comparison of some iridescent non-occluded insect viruses. *J. Gen. Virol. 3*:1-8.

Cuthbert, R. A. and J. W. Peacock. 1975. Attraction of *Scolytus multistriatus* to pheromone-baited traps at different heights. *Environ. Entomol. 4*:889-90.

Cuvier, B. 1832. "Animal Kingdom, Class Insecta." Vol. II. Whittaker, Treacher, and Co., London. 796 pp.

Dahlsten, D. L. and G. M. Thomas. 1969. A nucleopolyhedrosis virus in populations of the Douglas-fir tussock moth, *Hemerocampa pseudotsugata*, in California. *J. Invertebr. Pathol. 13*:264-71.

Dana, S. T. and E. W. Johnson. 1963. "Forestry Education in America Today and Tomorrow." Soc. Am. For., Wash. D.C. 401 pp.

Danilevskii, A. S. 1965. "Photoperiodism and Seasonal Development of Insects." Oliver and Boyd, London. 283 pp.

David, W. A. L. 1975. The status of viruses pathogenic for insects and mites. *Annu. Rev. Entomol. 20*:97-117.

David, W. A. L. and B. O. C. Gardiner. 1960. A *Pieris brassicae* (Linnaeus) culture resistant to a granulosis. *J. Invertebr. Pathol. 2*:106-14.

David, W. A. L. and B. O. C. Gardiner. 1965. Resistance of *Pieris brassicae* (Linnaeus) to granulosis virus and the virulence of the virus from different host races. *J. Invertebr. Pathol. 7*:285-90.

David, W. A. L. and B. O. C. Gardiner. 1966. Persistence of a granulosis virus of *Pieris brassicae* on cabbage leaves. *J. Invertebr. Pathol. 8*:180-3.

David, W. A. L. and B. O. C. Gardiner. 1967. The persistence of a granulosis virus of *Pieris brassicae* in soil and in sand. *J. Invertebr. Pathol. 9*:342-7.

David, W. A. L. and I. A. Magnus. 1967. Preliminary observations on the *in vitro* photoreactivation of an insect virus inactivated with ultra-violet radiation. *J. Invertebr. Pathol. 9*:266-8.

David, W. A. L., S. J. Ellaby, and G. Taylor. 1971. The stability of a purified granulosis virus of the European cabbageworm, *Pieris brassicae*, in dry deposits of intact capsules. *J. Invertebr. Pathol. 17*:228-33.

David, W. A. L., S. J. Ellaby, and G. Taylor. 1972. The effect of reducing the content of certain ingredients in a semi-synthetic diet on the incidence of granulosis virus disease in *Pieris brassicae*. *J. Invertebr. Pathol. 20*:332-40.

Davis, K. P. 1966. "Forest Management: Regulation and Valuation." 2nd ed. McGraw-Hill Book Co., N.Y. 519 pp.

Day, G. M. 1953. The Indian as an ecological factor in the northeastern forest. *Ecology 34*:329-46.

Day, M. F. and M. L. Dudzinski. 1966. The effect of temperature on the development of *Sericesthis* iridescent virus. *Aust. J. Biol. Sci. 19*:481-93.

DeBach, P. 1964a. Successes, trends, and future possibilities. Pages 673-713 in P. DeBach, ed. "Biological Control of Insect Pests and Weeds." Reinhold Publ. Corp., N.Y. 844 pp.

DeBach, P. 1964b. "Biological Control of Insect Pests and Weeds." Reinhold Publ. Corp., N.Y. 844 pp.

DeBach, P. 1966. The competitive displacement and coexistence principles. *Annu. Rev. Entomol. 11*:183-212.

DeBach, P. 1971. The use of imported natural enemies in insect pest management ecology. *Proc. Tall Timbers Conf. Ecol. Anim. Control Habitat Manage. 3*:211-33.

DeBach, P. 1974. "Biological Control by Natural Enemies." Cambridge Univ. Press, London. 323 pp.

DeBach, P. and K. S. Hagen. 1964. Manipulation of entomophagous species. Pages 429-58 in P. DeBach, ed. "Biological Control of Insect Pests and Weeds." Reinhold Publ. Corp., N.Y. 844 pp.

DeBach, P., D. Rosen, and C. E. Kennett. 1971. Biological control of coccids by introduced natural enemies. Pages 165-94 in C. B. Huffaker, ed. "Biological Control." Plenum Press, N.Y. 511 pp.

Decker, G. C. 1933. The two-lined chestnut borer and its control. *Trans. Iowa State Hortic. Soc. 68*:151-6.

Deering, F. 1945. "USDA: Manager of American Agriculture." Univ. of Oklahoma Press, Norman. 213 pp.

DeLeon, D. 1935. The biology of *Coeloides dendroctoni* (Cushman) (Hymenoptera: Braconidae) an important parasite of the mountain pine beetle (*Dendroctonus monticolae* Hopk.). *Ann. Entomol. Soc. Am. 28*:411-24.

Demolin, G. 1970. Programa ecológico internacional sobre la "procesionaria del pino" *Thaumetopoea pityocampa* Schiff. Mora de Rubielos, 1970. *Bol. Serv. Plagas For. 13*:111-7.

Dethier, V. G. 1947. "Chemical Insect Attractants and Repellents." The Blakiston Co., Philadelphia. 289 pp.

Devauchelle, G. and M. Durchon. 1973. Sur la présence d'un virus, du type Iridovirus, dans les cellules mâles de *Nereis diversicolor* (O. F. Müller). *C. R. Hebd. Seances Acad. Sci. Paris (Ser. D). 277*: 463-6.

Dimond, A. E., G. H. Plumb, E. M. Stoddard, and J. G. Horsfall. 1949. An evaluation of chemotherapy and vector control by insecticides for combating Dutch elm disease, *Conn. Agric. Exp. Stn. Bull. (New Haven) 531*. 69 pp.

Dimond, J. B. 1972. A demonstration of *Bacillus thuringiensis,* plus the enzyme chitinase, against the spruce budworm in Maine, Part I. Efficacy. *Maine Agric. Exp. Stn. Misc. Rep. 144.* 26 pp.

Dixon, J. C. and D. M. Benjamin. 1963. Natural control factors associated with the jack-pine budworm, *Choristoneura pinus. J. Econ. Entomol. 56*:266-70.

Doane, C. C. 1961. Field tests with gyplure, 1961. *Conn. Agric. Exp. Stn. Prog. Rep. 1.* 3 pp.

Doane, C. C. 1967. Bioassay of nuclear-polyhedrosis virus against larval instars of the gypsy moth *J. Invertebr. Pathol. 9*:376-86.

Doane, C. C. 1968a. Aspects of mating behavior of the gypsy moth. *Ann. Entomol. Soc. Am. 61*:768-73.

Doane, C. C. 1968b. Changes in egg mass density, size, and amount of parasitism after chemical treatment of a heavy population of the gypsy moth. *J. Econ. Entomol. 61*:768-73.

Doane, C. C. 1969. Trans-ovum transmission of a nuclear-polyhedrosis virus in the gypsy moth and the inducement of virus susceptibility. *J. Invertebr. Pathol. 14*:199-210.

Doane, C. C. 1970. Primary pathogens and their role in the development of an epizootic in the gypsy moth. *J. Invertebr. Pathol. 15*:21-33.

Doane, C. C. 1971a. Field applications of a *Streptococcus* causing brachyosis in larvae of *Porthetria dispar. J. Invertebr. Pathol. 17*:303-7.

Doane, C. C. 1971b. Transovum transmission of nuclear polyhedrosis virus in relation to disease in gypsy moth populations. *Proc. 4th Int. Colloq. Insect Pathol. College Park, Md. Aug. 1970.* pp. 285-91.

Doane, C. C. 1971c. A high rate of parasitization by *Brachymeria intermedia* (Hymenoptera: Chalicidae) on the gypsy moth. *Ann. Entomol. Soc. Am. 64*:753-4.

Doane, C. C. 1975. Infectious sources of nuclear polyhedrosis virus persisting in natural habitats of the gypsy moth. *Environ. Entomol. 4*:392-4.

Doane, C. C. and R. T. Cardé. 1973. Competition of gypsy moth males at a sex-pheromone source and a mechanism for terminating searching behavior. *Environ. Entomol. 2*:603-5.

Doane, C. C. and J. J. Redys. 1970. Characteristics of motile strains of *Streptococcus faecalis* pathogenic to larvae of the gypsy moth. *J. Invertebr. Pathol. 15*:420-30.

Doane, C. C. and P. W. Schaefer. 1971. Aerial application of insecticides for control of the gypsy moth. *Conn. Agric. Exp. Stn. Bull. (New Haven) 724.* 23 pp.

Doane, C. C. and R. C. Wallis. 1964. Enhancement of the action of *Bacillus thuringiensis var. thuringiensis* Berliner on *Porthetria dispar* (Linnaeus) in laboratory tests. *J. Insect Pathol. 6*:423-9.

Doane, R. W., E. C. Van Dyke, W. J. Chamberlin, and H. E. Burke. 1936. "Forest Insects." McGraw-Hill Book Co., N.Y. 463 pp.

Donaubauer, E. 1973. Results of polyhedral virus applications against *Neodiprion sertifer* Geoffr. *EPPO Bull. 3*(3):105-10.

Donaubauer, E. 1974. Ergebnisse von Polyedervirus-Applikationen gegen *Neodiprion sertifer* Geoffr. *Centralbl. Gesamte Forstwes. 91*:152-7.

Donaubauer, E. and J. Schönherr. 1972. Neue Ergebnisse einer Bekämpfung von *Neodiprion sertifer* Geoffr. mit Virus-Suspension (*Borrelinavirus*) an Schwarzkiefern (*Pinus nigra austriaca*). *Centralbl. Gesamte Forstwes. 89*:26-33.

Dorsey, C. K. and J. G. Leach. 1956. The bionomics of certain insects associated with oak wilt with particular reference to the Nitidulidae. *J. Econ. Entomol. 49*:219-30.

Doutt, R. L. 1959. The biology of parasitic Hymenoptera. *Annu. Rev. Entomol. 4*:161-82.

Doutt, R. L. 1964. Biological characteristics of entomophagous adults. Pages 145-67 in P. DeBach, ed. "Biological Control of Insect Pests and Weeds." Reinhold Publ. Co., N.Y. 844 pp.

Dowden, P. B. 1933. *Lydella nigripes* and *L. piniariae*, fly parasites of certain tree-defoliating caterpillars. *J. Agric. Res. 46*:963-95.

Dowden, P. B. 1934. *Zenillia libatrix* Panzer, a tachinid parasite of the gipsy moth and the brown-tail moth. *J. Agric. Res. 48*:97-114.

Dowden, P. B. 1935. *Brachymeria intermedia* (Nees), a primary parasite, and *B. compsilurae* (Cwfd), a secondary parasite of the gypsy moth. *J. Agric. Res. 50*:495-523.

Dowden, P. B. 1961a. The gypsy moth egg parasite, *Ooencyrtus kuwanai*, in southern Connecticut in 1960. *J. Econ. Entomol. 54*:876-8.

Dowden, P. B. 1961b. The persistence of gypsy moth parasites in heavily sprayed areas on Cape Cod, Massachusetts. *J. Econ. Entomol. 54*:873-5.

Dowden, P. B. 1962. Parasites and predators of forest insects liberated in the United States through 1960. *U.S. Dep. Agric. Handb. 226.* 70 pp.

Dowden, P. B. and H. B. Girth. 1953. Use of a virus disease to control European pine sawfly. *J. Econ. Entomol. 46*:525-6.

Dowden, P. B., W. D. Buchanan, and V. M. Carolin. 1948. Natural-control factors affecting the spruce budworm. *J. Econ. Entomol. 41*:457-64.

Dowden, P. B., V. M. Carolin, and C. O. Dirks. 1950. Natural control factors affecting the spruce budworm in the Adirondacks during 1946-1948. *J. Econ. Entomol. 43*:774-83.

Drooz, A. T. 1964. A source of elm spanworm egg parasites. *U.S. For. Serv. Res. Note SE-34.* 3 pp.

Drooz, A. T. 1970. The elm spanworm (Lepidoptera: Geometridae): how several natural diets affect its biology. *Ann. Entomol. Soc. Am. 63*:391-7.

Drooz, A. T. 1971. The elm spanworm (Lepidoptera: Geometridae): natural diets and their effect on the F$_2$ generation. *Ann. Entomol. Soc. Am. 64*:331-3.

Drooz, A. T. In press. Current research with *Telenomus alsophilae* Viereck, an egg parasite of the fall cankerworm *Alsophila pometaria* (Harris). *J. N.Y. Entomol. Soc.*

Dunbar, D. M. and G. R. Stephens. 1974a. The two-lined chestnut borer, killer of oaks in Connecticut. *Front. Plant Sci. 27*(1):4-5.

Dunbar, D. M. and G. R. Stephens. 1974b. Twolined chestnut borer: effects of storage conditions, processing, and insecticides on its survival in oak logs. *J. Econ. Entomol. 67*:427-9.

Dunbar, D. M. and G. R. Stephens. 1975. Association of twolined chestnut borer and shoestring fungus with mortality of defoliated oak in Connecticut. *For. Sci. 21*:169-74.

Dunbar, D. M., H. K. Kaya, C. C. Doane, J. F. Anderson, and R. M. Weseloh. 1973. Aerial application of *Bacillus thuringiensis* against larvae of the elm spanworm and gypsy moth and effects on parasitoids of the gypsy moth. *Conn. Agric. Exp. Stn. Bull. (New Haven) 735.* 23 pp.

DuPorte, E. M. 1917. The eye-spotted bud-moth (*Eucosma (Spilonota) ocellana* (Schiff.)). *Annu. Rep. Que. Soc. Prot. Plants. 9*:118-37.

Eaves, G. N. and J. O. Mundt. 1960. Distribution and characterization of streptococci from insects. *J. Insect Pathol. 2*:289-98.

Ehler, L. E. and R. van den Bosch. 1974. An analysis of the natural biological control of *Trichoplusia ni* (Lepidoptera, Noctuidae) on cotton in California. *Can. Entomol. 106*:1067-73.

Eidmann, H. H. 1976. Aspects of biological control of forest insects in Sweden. *Ambio 5*:23-6.

Eidmann, H. H. and B. Ehnström. 1975. Einbürgerung von *Scymnus impexus* Muls. (Col. Coccinellidae) in Schweden. *Entomol. Tidskr. 96*:14-6.

Elgee, D. E. 1971. Disease in forest tent caterpillar larvae hatching from egg bands contaminated with virus. *Can. For. Serv. Bi-mon. Res. Notes. 27*(4):41.

El-Ibrashy, M. T. and M. Sadek. 1973. Hormonal control of larval sensitivity to a nuclear-polyhedrosis virus in noctuids. *Appl. Entomol. Zool. 8*:44-6.

Elliott, E. W., G. N. Lanier, and J. B. Simeone. 1975. Termination of aggregation by the European elm bark beetle *Scolytus multistriatus. J. Chem. Ecol. 1*:283-6.

Elliott, J. C. 1953. Composition of upland second growth hardwood stands in the tension zone of Michigan as affected by soils and man. *Ecol. Monogr. 23*:271-88.

Elmore, J. C. and A. F. Howland. 1964. Natural versus artificial dissemination of nuclear-polyhedrosis virus by contaminated adult cabbage loopers. *J. Insect Pathol. 6*:430-8.

Elsey, K. D. and R. L. Rabb. 1970. Biology of *Voria ruralis* (Diptera: Tachinidae). *Ann. Entomol. Soc. Am. 63*:216-22.

Embree, D. G. 1971. The biological control of the winter moth in eastern Canada by introduced parasites. Pages 217-26 in C. B. Huffaker, ed. "Biological Control." Plenum Press, N.Y. 511 pp.

Embree, D. G. and P. Sisojevic. 1965. The bionomics and population density of *Cyzenis albicans* (Fall.) (Tachinidae: Diptera) in Nova Scotia. *Can. Entomol. 97*:631-9.

Encyclopedia Britannica. 1967. Apple. *2*:138-40.

Entwistle, P. F. 1974. New perspectives in pest control with pathogenic viruses. *Land, Oxford 1* (1):84-8.

Escherich, K. 1914. "Die Forstinsekten Mitteleuropas." Bd. I. P. Parey, Berlin. 432 pp.

Essig, E. O. 1940. Fifty years of entomological progress, Part IV, 1919 to 1929. *J. Econ. Entomol. 33*:30-57.

Etzel, L. K. and L. A. Falcon. 1976. Studies of transovum and transstadial transmission of a granulosis virus of the codling moth. *J. Invertebr. Pathol. 27*:13-26.

Evans, J. W. 1952. "The Injurious Insects of the British Commonwealth." Commonw. Inst. Entomol. London. 242 pp.

Fairchild, D. 1913. The discovery of the chestnut bark disease in China. *Science (Wash. D.C.) 38*:297-9.

Falcon, L. A. 1971. Microbial control as a tool in integrated control programs. Pages 346-64 in C. B. Huffaker, ed. "Biological Control." Plenum Press, N.Y. 511 pp.

Farkas, S. R. and H. H. Shorey. 1972. Chemical trail-following by flying insects: a mechanism for orientation to a distant odor source. *Science (Wash. D.C.) 178*:67-8.

Farkas, S. R. and H. H. Shorey. 1974. Mechanisms of orientation to a distant pheromone source. Pages 81-95 in M. C. Birch, ed. "Pheromones." North-Holland Publ. Co., Amsterdam. 495 pp.

Farkas, S. R., H. H. Shorey, and L. K. Gaston. 1974. Sex pheromones of Lepidoptera. Influence of pheromone concentration and visual cues on aerial odor-trail following by males of *Pectinophora gossypiella. Ann. Entomol. Soc. Am. 67*:633-8.

Fassett, N. C. 1944. Vegetation of the Brule Basin, past and present. *Trans. Wis. Acad. Sci., Arts and Lett. 36*:33-56.

Faull, J. H. 1936. Pathological studies on beech at the Arnold Arboretum. *Proc. Natl. Shade Tree Conf. 12*:25-9.

Fedde, G. F. 1975. Unpublished report. *U.S. For. Serv. Southeast. For. Exp. Stn., Research Triangle Park, N.C.*

Fedde, G. F., C. L. Morris, and A. T. Drooz. 1973. Delayed parasitism of fall cankerworm eggs in Virginia. *Environ. Entomol. 2*:1123-5.

Federici, B. A., R. R. Granados, D. W. Anthony, and E. I. Hazard. 1974. An entomopoxvirus and nonoccluded virus-like particles in larvae of the chironomid *Goeldichironomus holoprasinus. J. Invertebr. Pathol. 23*:117-20.

Felt, E. P. 1924. "Manual of Tree and Shrub Insects." Macmillan Co., N.Y. 382 pp.

Felt, E. P. 1933. Beech injured by borers. *J. Econ. Entomol. 26*:977.

Felt, E. P. 1935. The imporant shade tree insects in 1934. *J. Econ. Entomol. 28*:390-3.

Felt, E. P. and S. W. Bromley. 1930. Shade tree problems. *Proc. Natl. Shade Tree Conf. 6*:13-23.

Felt, E. P. and S. W. Bromley. 1931. Observations on shade tree insects. *J. Econ. Entomol. 24*:157-62.

Felt, E. P. and S. W. Bromley. 1932. Observations on shade tree insects. *J. Econ. Entomol. 25*:39-46.

Fernando, H. E. 1972. Concluding report on control of *Promecotheca cumingi*, the introduced pest of coconut. December (1972). *Ceylon Coconut Q. 23*:116-22.

Filley, W. O. 1917. Report of the forester for 1916. Pages 379-82 in *40th Annu. Rep. Conn. Agric. Exp. Stn. (New Haven)*. 450 pp.

Finney, G. L. and T. W. Fisher. 1964. Culture of entomophagous insects and their hosts. Pages 328-56 in P. DeBach, ed. "Biological Control of Insect Pests and Weeds." Reinhold Publ. Corp., N.Y. 844 pp.

Fisher, W. S. 1928. A revision of the North American species of buprestid beetles belonging to the genus *Agrilus. U.S. Natl. Mus. Bull. 145.* 347 pp.

Fiske, W. F. and A. F. Burgess. 1910. The natural control of *Heterocampa guttivitta. J. Econ.˙Entomol. 3*:389-94.

Flanders, S. E. 1930. Mass production of egg parasites of the genus *Trichogramma. Hilgardia 4*:465-501.

Fletcher, J. 1893. Report of the entomologist and botanist. *Annu. Rep. Can. Dep. Agric. Exp. Farms.* pp. 144-67.

Fletcher, S. W. 1937. The major research achievements made possible through grants under the Hatch Act. *Proc. Assoc. Land-Grant Colleges and Univ. 51*:136-44.

Flint, C. L. 1973. The first centennial: a hundred years of progress of American agriculture. *Agric. Sci. Rev. Second Quarter 11*(2):1-17.

Flint, R. F. 1930. The glacial geology of Connecticut. *State Geol. Nat. Hist. Surv. Hartford, Conn. Bull. 47.* 294 pp.

Forbes, W. T. M. 1923. "The Lepidoptera of New York and Neighboring States." N.Y. Agric. Exp. Stn. Ithaca Mem. 68. 729 pp.

Forbush, E. H. and C. H. Fernald. 1896. "The Gypsy Moth. *Porthetria dispar* (Linn.)." Wright and Potter Printing Co., Boston. 495 pp.

Force, D. C. 1974. Ecology of insect host-parasitoid communities. *Science (Wash. D.C.) 184*:624-32.

Forest Service. 1973. The outlook for timber in the United States. *U.S. For. Serv. For. Resour. Rep. 20.* 367 pp.

Fowler, M. E. 1958. Oak wilt. *U.S. Dep. Agric. For. Serv. Pest Leafl.* 29. 7 pp.

Fraenkel, G. S. and D. L. Gunn. 1961. "The Orientation of Animals." Dover Press, N.Y. 376 pp.

Frahm, J. 1973. Verhalten und Nebenwirkungen von Benomyl (Sammelbericht). *Z. Pflanzenkr. Pflanzenschutz. 80*:431-46.

Francke, W. 1973. "Nachweis und Identifizierung von Aggregations-substanzen in dem Ambrosiakäfer *Xyloterus domesticus* L. (Coleoptera Scolytidae)." Diss. Fachbereich Chemie, Univ. Hamburg. 146 pp.

Franz, J. M. 1948. Über die Zonenbildung der Insektenkalamitäten in Urwäldern. *Forstwiss. Centralbl. 67*:38-48.

Franz, J. M. 1961a. Biological control of pest insects in Europe. *Annu. Rev. Entomol.* 6:183-200.

Franz, J. M. 1961b. Biologische Schädlingsbekämpfung. Pages 1-302 in H. Richter, ed. "Handbuch der Pflanzenkrankheiten." Vol. 6. 2nd ed., No. 3. Paul Parey, Berlin. 627 pp.

Franz, J. M. 1964. Dispersion and natural-enemy action. *Ann. Appl. Biol. 53*:510-5.

Franz, J. M. 1970/71. Biological and integrated control of pest organisms in forestry. *Unasylva 24*(4):37-46; *25*(1):45-56.

Franz, J. M. 1973. The role of biological control in pest management. *Boll. Lab. Entomol. Agric. Portici 30*:235-43.

Franz, J. M. 1974. Die Prüfung von Nebenwirkungen der Pflanzenschutz-mittel auf Nutzarthropoden im Laboratorium—Ein Sammelbericht. *Z. Pflanzenkr. Pflanzenschutz. 81*:141-74.

Franz, J. M. 1975. Pesticides and beneficial arthropods. *WHO Pestic. Residues Serv. Bull. 1975/1.* pp. 147-52.

Franz, J. M. and A. M. Huger. 1971. Microsporidia causing the collapse of an outbreak of the green tortrix (*Tortrix viridana* L.) in Germany. *Proc. 4th Int. Colloq. Insect Pathol. College Park, Md. Aug. 1970.* pp. 48-53.

Franz, J. M. and A. Krieg. 1967. *Bacillus thuringiensis*–Präparate gegen Forstschädlinge-Erfahrungen in der Alten Welt. *Gesunde Pflanzen. 19*:1-6.

Franz, J. and O. F. Niklas. 1954. Feldversuche zur Bekämpfung der Roten Kiefernbusch-hornblattwespe (*Neodiprion sertifer* (Geoffr.)) durch künstliche Verbreitung einer Virusseuche. *Nachrichtenbl. Dtsch. Pflanzenschutzdienstes. (Braunschw.).* 6:131-4.

Franz, J. M., D. H. Phillips, and R. W. Stark. 1975. Integrated management of forest insect pests and diseases. *Proc. 2nd FAO/IUFRO World Tech. Consult. For. Diseases and Insects (New Delhi, April 1975).* (in press).

Franz, J. M., A. Krieg, W. Herfs, W. König, and A. Krump. 1970. Richtlinien für die Prüfung von *Bacillus thuringiensis*–Präparaten gegen freifressende Raupen im Forst. In "Richtlinien für die amtliche Prüfung von Pflanzenschutzmitteln 18–23 Aug. 1970." Hrsg. Biolog. Bundesanst. Land-Forstwirtsch., Berlin-Dahlem; bearb. v. Abt. Pflanzen-schutzmittel und-geräte.

Fratian, A. 1975. Rationalization of chemical control as part of integrated control of defoliating insects. *Rev. Padurilor 90*:103-6. (In Romanian).

Frazer, B. D. and R. van den Bosch 1973. Biological control of the walnut aphid in California: the interrelationship of the aphid and its parasite. *Environ. Entomol. 2*:561-8.

Freeman, T. N. 1958. The Archipinae of North America (Lepidoptera: Tortricidae). *Can. Entomol. Suppl. 7.* 89 pp.

Friend, R. B. 1945. The gypsy moth in Connecticut. *Trans. Conn. Acad. Arts Sci. 36*:607-29.

Friend, R. B. and H. W. Hicock. 1933. The European pine shoot moth. *Conn. Agric. Exp. Stn. New Haven Circ. 90.* 4 pp.

Fritschen, L. J., C. H. Driver, C. Avery, J. Buffo, R. Edmonds, R. Kinerson, and P. Schiess. 1970. Dispersion of air tracers into and within a forested area. 3. Res. and Devel. Tech. Rep. *ECOM-68-G8-3, U.S. Army Electronics Command, Fort Huachuca, Ariz.* 44 pp.

Frost, S. W. 1923. A new apple bud-moth in Pennsylvania. *J. Econ. Entomol. 16*:304-7.

Frost, S. W. 1926. The dusky leaf roller. *Pa. Agric. Exp. Stn. Bull. 205.* 15 pp.

Galloway, B. T. 1926. The search in foreign countries for blight-resistant chestnuts and related tree crops. *U.S. Dep. Agric. Circ. 383.* 16 pp.

Gard, I. E. 1975. "Utilization of Light Traps to Disseminate Insect Viruses for Pest Control." Ph.D. Thesis. Univ. Calif., Berkeley. 174 pp.

Garman, P. and J. F. Townsend. 1952. Control of apple insects. *Conn. Agric. Exp. Stn. Bull. (New Haven) 552.* 84 pp.

Garzon, S. and E. Kurstak. 1972. Infection double inhabituelle de cellules d'un arthropode par le virus de la polyédrie nucléaire (VPN) et le virus irisant de *Tipula* (TIV). *C. R. Acad. Sci. Paris. 275*:507-8.

Geiger, G. 1965. "The Climate near the Ground." Harvard Univ. Press, Cambridge, Mass. 611 pp.

Gershenzon, S. M. 1964. Characteristics of the epizootiology of virus diseases in insects. *Biol. Control Agric. For. Pests, Proc. of Symp. 17-20 Nov.* pp. 28-30.

Gibbs, A. J. 1973. "Viruses and Invertebrates." Frontiers of Biology Vol. 31. North-Holland Publ. Co., Amsterdam. 673 pp.

Giese, R. L. and D. M. Benjamin. 1964. Insect complex associated with maple blight. Part II. Pages 20-57 in "Studies of Maple Blight." Univ. Wis. Res. Bull. 250. 128 pp.

Giese, R. L., D. R. Houston, D. M. Benjamin, and J. E. Kuntz. 1964a. A new condition of sugar maple. Part I. Pages 1-19 in "Studies of Maple Blight." Univ. Wis. Res. Bull. 250. 128 pp.

Giese, R. L., J. E. Kapler, and D. M. Benjamin. 1964b. Defoliation and the genesis of maple blight. Part IV. Pages 80-113 in "Studies of Maple Blight." Univ. Wis. Res. Bull. 250. 128 pp.

Gifford, F. A., Jr. 1957. Relative atmospheric diffusion of smoke puffs. *J. Meteorol.* *14*:410-4.

Gifford, F. A., Jr. 1959. Statistical properties of a fluctuating plume dispersion model. Pages 117-37 in F. N. Frenkiel and P. A. Sheppard, eds. "Atmospheric Diffusion and Air Pollution." Academic Press, N.Y. 471 pp.

Gifford, F. 1960. Peak to average concentration ratios according to a fluctuating plume dispersion model. *Int. J. Air Poll.* *3*:253-60.

Gifford, F. A., Jr. 1968. An outline of theories of diffusion in the lower layers of the atmosphere. Pages 65-116 in D. H. Slade, ed. "Meteorology and Atomic Energy." U.S.A.E.C., Oak Ridge, Tenn. 445 pp.

Gilliatt, F. C. 1929. The bionomics of the tortricid moth, *Eulia mariana* Fern. *Trans. R. Soc. Can. 3rd. Ser. Sec. 5.* *23*:69-84.

Gilliatt, F. C. 1932. Four year's observations on the eye-spotted bud moth *Spilonota ocellana* D. and S. in Nova Scotia. *Can. J. Agric. Sci.* *12*:357-71.

Gilliatt, F. C. 1937. Natural control of the grey banded leaf roller, *Eulia mariana* Fern, in Nova Scotia orchards. *Can. Entomol.* *69*:145-6.

Gilmore, J. E. and F. Munger. 1965. Influence of population density on the incidence of a noninclusion virus disease of the citrus red mite in the laboratory. *J. Invertebr. Pathol.* *7*:156-60.

Gilmore, J. E. and H. Tashiro. 1966. Fecundity, longevity, and transinfectivity of citrus red mites (*Panonychus citri*) infected with a noninclusion virus. *J. Invertebr. Pathol.* *8*:334-9.

Glaser, R. W. 1915. Wilt of gipsy-moth caterpillars. *J. Agric. Res.* *4*:101-28.

Glaser, R. W. 1918. A new bacterial disease of the gipsy-moth caterpillars. *J. Agric. Res.* *13*:515-22.

Glaser, R. W. and J. W. Chapman. 1912. Studies on the wilt disease or "flacherie" of the gypsy moth. *Science, n.s.* *36*:219-24.

Glaser, R. W., and J. W. Chapman. 1913. The wilt disease of gipsy moth caterpillars. *J. Econ. Entomol.* *6*:479-88.

Glass, E. H. 1963. Parasitism of the red-banded leaf roller *Argyrotaenia velutinana* by *Trichogramma minutum.* *Ann. Entomol. Soc. Am.* *56*:564.

Glass, E. H. 1975. "Integrated Pest Management: Rationale, Potential, Needs and Implementation." ESA Spec. Publ. 75-2. Entomol. Soc. Am. 141 pp.

Glowacka-Pilot, B. 1973. Wrazliwosc larw L$_2$ borecznika rudego (*Neodiprion sertifer* (Geoffer.)) na infekcje wirusem poliedrozy. *Sylwan. No.* *7*:45-52.

Godwin, P. A. and A. R. Hastings. 1961. Tests of some behavioral effects of gyplure on male gypsy moths. *Northeast. For. Exp. Stn. For. Insect Lab. Office Rep.* 3 pp.

Goodwin, R. H., J. L. Vaughn, J. R. Adams, and S. J. Louloudes. 1973. The influence of insect cell lines and tissue-culture media on *Baculovirus* polyhedra production. *Misc. Publ. Entomol. Soc. Am.* *9*:66-72.

Gordon, R. and J. M. Webster, 1974. Biological control of insects by nematodes. *Helmintho-logical Abstr. Ser. B.* *43*:137-59.

Gore, W. E., G. T. Pearce, and R. M. Silverstein. 1975. Relative stereochemistry of multi-striatin. *J. Org. Chem.* *40*:1705-8.

Gore, W. E., G. T. Pearce, and R. M. Silverstein. 1976. Mass spectrometric studies of the dioxabicyclo (3.2.1) octanes, multistriatin, frontalin, and brevicomin. *J. Org. Chem.*: in press.

Görnitz, K. 1949. Anlockversuche mit dem weiblichen Sexualduftstoff des Schwamm-spinners (*Lymantria dispar*) und der Nonne (*Lymantria monacha*). *Anz. Schädlingskd.* *22*:145-9.

Graham, K. E. 1945. Forest insect conditions in the Quatsino Region. *Can. Dep. Agric. For. Insect Invest. Bi-mon. Prog. Rep.* *1*(4):3.

Graham, S. A. 1956. Forest insects and the law of natural compensations. *Can. Entomol.* *88*:45-55.

Graham, S. A. 1959. Control of insects through silvicultural practices. *J. For.* *57*:281-3.

Graham, S. A. 1963. Making hardwood forests safe from insects. *J. For.* *61*:356-9.

Graham, S. A. 1965. Causes leading to insect outbreaks. Pages 3-14 in C. B. Marlin, ed. "Insects in Southern Forests." Proc. 14th Annu. For. Symp., La. State Univ. Press. 129 pp.

Graham, S. A. and L. G. Baumhofer. 1927. The pine tip moth in the Nebraska National Forest. *J. Agric. Res.* *35*:323-33.

Graham, S. A. and F. B. Knight. 1965. "Principles of Forest Entomology." 4th ed. McGraw-Hill Book Co., N.Y. 417 pp.

Graham, S. A., R. P. Harrison, Jr., and C. E. Westell, Jr. 1963. "Aspens: Phoenix Trees of the Great Lakes Region." Univ. Mich. Press, Ann Arbor. 272 pp.

Granett, J. 1973. A disparlure-baited box trap for capturing large numbers of gypsy moths. *J. Econ. Entomol.* *66*:359-62.

Granett, J. 1974. Estimation of male mating potential of gypsy moths with disparlure traps. *Environ. Entomol.* *3*:383-5.

Granett, J. and C. C. Doane. 1975. Reduction of gypsy moth male mating potential in dense populations by mistblower sprays of microencapsulated disparlure. *J. Econ. Entomol.* *68*:435-7.

Graves, A. H. 1914. The future of the chestnut tree in North America. *Popular Sci. Mon.* *84*:551-66.

Graves, H. S. and C. H. Guise. 1932. "Forest Education." Yale Univ. Press, New Haven Conn. 421 pp.

Greathead, D. J. 1976. A review of biological control in western and southern Europe. *Tech. Commun. No. 7, Commonw. Inst. Biol. Control, Commonw. Agric. Bur. Farnham Royal* (in press).

Grente, M. J. 1965. Les formes hypovirulentes d'*Endothia parasitica* et les espoirs de lutte contre le chancre du chataignier. *C. R. Hebd. Seances Acad. Agric. Fr. 51*:1033-7.

Grente, M. J. 1971. Hypovirulence et lutte biologique dans le cas de l'*Endothia parasitica*. (Abst.) *Ann. Phytopathol. 3*:409-10.

Grente, M. J. and S. Sauret. 1969a. L'hypovirulence exclusive, phénomène original en pathologie vegetale. *C. R. Acad. Sci. Paris (Ser. D) 268*:2347-50.

Grente, M. J. and S. Sauret. 1969b. L' "hypovirulence exclusive" est-elle contrôlée par les determinants cytoplasmiques? *C. R. Acad. Sci. Paris (Ser. D) 268*:3173-6.

Greth, J. W. 1957. Ax girdling kills large cull hardwoods. *Cent. States For. Exp. Stn. Note 107.* 2 pp.

Grison, P. 1970. La lutte biologique en forêt. *Rev. For. Fr. 22 no. spéc.* pp. 193-336.

Grison, P., D. Martouret, and C. Auer. 1971. La lutte microbiologique contre la tordeuse du mélèze. *Ann. Zool. Ecol. Anim. no. hors-sér.* pp. 91-121.

Griswold, N. B. and R. N. Ferguson. 1957. The timber resources of Connecticut. *Northeast. For. Exp. Stn. Upper Darby, Pa.* 37 pp.

Gross, H. L. and M. J. Larsen. 1971. Nutrient content of artificially defoliated branches of *Betula papyrifera*. *Phytopathology 6*:631-5.

Gukasyan, A. B. 1970. "Bacteriological Control Methods of Siberian Silkworm." "Nauka", Moskva. 128 pp. (In Russ.).

Gülü, V. V. 1963. Increasing the effectiveness of parasites of the European pine shoot moth (*Evertria buoliana* Schiff.) in pine stands on the northern slopes of the central Caucasus. *Zool. Zh. 42*:1414-5. (In Russ.).

Györfi, F. 1945. Beobachtungen über die Ernährung der Schlupfwespenimagos. *Erdeszeti Faipari Egy. Tud. Kozl. 45*:100-12.

Györfi, F. 1951. Die Schlupfwespen und der Unterwirchs des Waldes. *Z. Angew. Entomol.* *33*:32-47.

Hagen, K. S. 1964. Developmental stages of parasites. Pages 168-246 in P. DeBach, ed. "Biological Control of Insect Pests and Weeds." Reinhold Publ. Corp., N.Y. 844 pp.

Hall, I. M. 1963. Microbial control. Pages 477-517 in E. A. Steinhaus, ed. "Insect Pathology, an Advanced Treatise." Vol. 2. Academic Press, N.Y. 689 pp.

Hall, I. M. 1964. Use of microorganisms in biological control. Pages 610-28 in P. DeBach, ed. "Biological Control of Insect Pests and Weeds." Chapman and Hall, London. 844 pp.

Haller, H. C., F. Acree, Jr., and S. F. Potts. 1944. The nature of the sex attractant of the female gypsy moth. *J. Am. Chem. Soc. 66*:1659-62.

Harcourt, D. G. and L. M. Cass. 1968. Persistence of a granulosis virus of *Pieris rapae* in soil. *J. Invertebr. Pathol. 11*:142-3.

Harman, D. M. and H. M. Kulman. 1973. A world survey of the parasites and predators of the pine moths of the genus *Rhyacionia*, Parts I to IV. *Univ. Md. Nat. Resour. Inst. Contrib. 527.* 178 pp.

Harper, J. D. 1974. "Forest Insect Control with *Bacillus thuringiensis.* Survey of Current Knowledge." Univ. Printing Serv., Auburn Univ., Auburn, Ala. 64 pp.

Harper, R. M. 1918. Changes in the forest area of New England in three centuries. *J. For. 16*:442-52.

Harrap, K. A. 1973. Virus infection in invertebrates. Pages 272-99 in A. J. Gibbs, ed. "Viruses and Invertebrates." North Holland Publ. Co., Amsterdam. 673 pp.

Harring, C. M., J. P. Vité, and P. R. Hughes. 1975. "Ipsenol"; der Populationslockstoff des krummzähnigen Tannenborkenkäfers. *Naturwissenschaften 62*:488.

Harrington, W. H. 1897. Some beetles occurring upon beech. *Annu. Rep. Entomol. Soc. Ont. 27*:69-75.

Harris, P. 1960. Natural mortality of the pine shoot moth, *Rhycionia buoliana* (Schiff.) (Lepidoptera: Olethreutidae), in England. *Can. J. Zool. 38*:755-68.

Harshbarger, J. C. and R. M. Faust. 1973. Environmental factors internal to the host that affect the success of microbial insecticides. Pages 131-40 in L. A. Bulla, Jr., ed. "Regulation of Insect Populations by Microorganisms." Ann. N.Y. Acad. Sci. 217. 243 pp.

Haseman, L. 1940. The walnut caterpillar. *Univ. Mo. Exp. Stn. Bull. 418.* 14 pp.

Hassan, E. 1967. Untersuchungen über die Bedeutung der Kraut-und Strauchschicht als Nahrungsquelle fuer Imagines entomophager Hymenopteren. *Zool. Zh. 60*:238-56.

Hassell, M. P. 1968. The behavioural response of a tachinid fly (*Cyzenis albicans* (Fall)) to its host, the winter moth (*Operophtera brumata* (L.)). *J. Anim. Ecol. 37*:627-39.

Hassell, M. P. and G. C. Varley. 1969. New inductive population model for insect parasites and its bearing on biological control. *Nature (Lond.) 223*:1133-7.

Hawes, A. F. 1968. Connecticut: scattering the seeds. Pages 100-6 in R. R. Widner, ed. "Forests and Forestry in the American States." Natl. Assoc. State For. 594 pp.

Hawley, R. C. 1913. A working plan for the woodlands of the New Haven Water Company *Yale Univ. For. Bull. 3.* 30 pp.

Hayashiya, K., J. Nishida, and F. Kawamoto. 1971. On the biosynthesis of the red fluorescent protein in the digestive juice of the silkworm larvae. *Jap. J. Appl. Entomol. Zool. 15*:109-14.

Haynes, D. L. and J. W. Butcher. 1962. Studies on host preference and its influence on European pine shoot moth success and development. *Can. Entomol. 94*:690-706.

Heatwole, H. 1964. Detection of mates and hosts by parasitic insects of the genus *Megarhyssa* (Hymenoptera: Ichneumonidae). *Am. Midl. Nat. 71*:374-81.

Heatwole, H. and D. M. Davis. 1965. Ecology of three sympatric species of parasitic insects of the genus *Megarhyssa* (Hymenoptera: Ichneumonidae). *Ecology 46*:140-50.

Heck, W. W., J. A. Dunning, and L. J. Hindawi. 1966. Ozone: nonlinear relation of dose and injury in plants. *Science (Wash. D.C.) 151*:577-8.

Hegdekar, B. M. and A. P. Arthur. 1973. Host haemolymph chemicals that induce oviposition in the parasite *Itoplectis conquisitor* (Hymenoptera: Ichneumonidae). *Can. Entomol. 105*:787-93.

Heichel, G. H., N. C. Turner, and G. S. Walton. 1972. Anthracnose causes dieback of regrowth on defoliated oak and maple. *Plant Dis. Rep. 56*:1046-7.

Heinrich, C. 1926. Revision of the North American moths of the subfamilies Laspeyresiinae and Olethreutinae. *U.S. Natl. Mus. Bull. 132.* 216 pp.

Hendrickson, C. L. 1933. The agricultural land available for forestry. Pages 151-69 in "A National Plan for American Forestry." U.S. Senate Doc. 12, 73rd Congr., 1st Session. 2. 1677 pp.

Hendry, L. B., J. Jugovich, L. Roman, M. E. Anderson, and R. O. Mumma. 1974. *cis*-10-Tetradecenyl acetate, an attractant component in the sex pheromone of the oak leaf roller moth (*Archips semiferanus* Walker). *Experientia 30*:886-8.

Hendry, L. B., M. E. Anderson, J. Jugovich, R. O. Mumma, D. Robacker, and Z. Kosarych. 1975a. Sex pheromone of the oak leaf roller: a complex chemical messenger system identified by mass fragmentography. *Science (Wash. D.C.) 187*:355-7.

Hendry, L. B., J. Jugovich, R. O. Mumma, D. Robacker, K. Weaver, and M. E. Anderson. 1975b. The oak leaf roller (*Archips semiferanus* Walker) sex pheromone complex: field and laboratory evaluation of requisite behavioral stimuli. *Experientia 31*:629-31.

Hendry, L. B., J. K. Wickmann, D. M. Hindenlang, R. O. Mumma, and M. E. Anderson. 1975c. Evidence for origin of insect sex pheromones: presence in food plants. *Science (Wash. D.C.) 188*:59-63.

Hepting, G. H. 1974. Death of the American chestnut. *J. For. Hist. July*:61-7.

Hepting, G. H. and G. G. Hedgcock. 1937. Decay in merchantable oak, yellow poplar, and basswood in the Appalachian Region. *U.S. Dep. Agric. Tech. Bull. 570.* 30 pp.

Herfs, W. 1975. Die Zulassung von Pflanzenschutzmitteln mit Nutzarthropoden schonenden Eigenschaften sowie die für die Zulassung erforderlichen Voraussetzungen in der Bundesrepublik Deutschland. *Nachrichtenbl. Dtsch. Pflanzenschutzdienstes. (Braunsch.) 27*:152-5.

Herrebout, W. M. 1960. Host selection in the parasitic fly, *Eucarcelia rutilla* Vill. *Arch. Neerl. Zool. 13*:626.

Herrebout, W. M. 1967. Habitat selection in *Eucarcelia rutilla* Vill. (Diptera: Tachinidae). I. Observations on the occurrence during the season. *Z. Angew. Entomol. 60*:219-29.

Herrebout, W. M. 1969. Habitat selection in *Ecuarcelia rutilla* Vill. (Diptera: Tachinidae). II. Experiments with females of known age. *Z. Angew. Entomol. 63*:336-49.

Herrick, G. W. 1920. The apple maggot in New York. *N.Y. Agric. Exp. Stn. Ithaca Bull. 402.* pp. 89-101.

Herting, B. 1960. Biologie der westpalaarktischen Raupenfliegen, Dipt., Tachinidae. *Monogr. Angew. Entomol. 16.* 188 pp.

Hewitt, C. G. 1912. Some of the work of the Division of Entomology in 1911. *Annu. Rep. Entomol. Soc. Ont. 42*:25-7.

Hicock, H. W. 1957. The suburban forest. *Front. Plant Sci. 9*(2):2.

Hightower, J. 1972. "Hard Tomatoes, Hard Times: The Failure of the Land Grant College Complex." Preliminary Rep., Task Force on the Land Grant College Complex, Agribusiness Accountability Project, Wash. D.C. 308 pp.

Hill, A. and W. Roelofs. 1975. Sex pheromone components of the omnivorous leafroller moth, *Platynota stultana. J. Chem. Ecol. 1*:91-9.

Hill, A., R. Cardé, A. Comeau, W. Bode, and W. Roelofs. 1974. Sex pheromones of the tufted apple bud moth, *Platynota idaeusalis. Environ. Entomol. 3*:249-52.

Hill, A., R. Cardé, H. Kido, and W. Roelofs. 1975. Sex pheromones of the orange tortrix moth, *Argyrotaenia citrana. J. Chem. Ecol. 1*:215-24.

Hitchcock, S. W. 1958. The orange-striped oakworm. *Conn. Agric. Exp. Stn., New Haven. Circ. 204.* 8 pp.

Hitchcock, S. W. 1961. Egg parasitism and larval habits of the orange-striped oakworm. *J. Econ. Entomol. 54*:502-3.

Hixson, E. 1941. The walnut datana. *Okla. Agric. Exp. Stn. Bull. B-246.* 29 pp.

Hodson, A. C. 1939. Biological notes on the egg parasites of *Malacosoma disstria* Hbn. *Ann. Entomol. Soc. Am. 32*:131-6.

Hodson, A. C. 1941. An ecological study of the forest tent caterpillar, *Malacosoma disstria* Hbn. *Minn. Agric. Exp. Stn. Tech. Bull. 148.* 55 pp.

Holbrook, R. F., M. Beroza, and E. D. Burgess. 1960. Gypsy moth (*Porthetria dispar*) detection with the natural female sex lure. *J. Econ. Entomol. 53*:751-6.

Holling, C. S. 1959. Some characteristics of simple types of predation and parasitism. *Can. Entomol. 91*:385-98.

Hopkins, A. D. 1892. Some bred West Virginia Braconidae. *Insect Life 4*:256-9.

Hopkins, A. D. 1893. Catalogue of West Virginia forest and shade tree insects. *W. Va. Agric. Exp. Stn. Bull. 32*:171-252.

Hopkins, A. D. 1894. Notes on some discoveries and observations of the year in West Virginia. *Insect Life 7*:145-51.

Hopkins, A. D. 1895. Notes on timber worms. *Proc. Entomol. Soc. Wash. 3*:82-3.

Hopkins, A. D. 1903. Insect injuries to hardwood forest trees. Pages 313-28 in "U.S. Dep. Agric., Yearb. Agric." Gov. Printing Office, Wash. D.C. 728 pp.

Horn, G. H. 1891. The species of *Agrilus* of Boreal America. *Trans. Am. Entomol. Soc. 18*:277-336.

Horridge, G. A. 1975. "The Compound Eye and Vision of Insects." Clarendon Press, Oxford. 595 pp.

Hosker, R. P., Jr., C. J. Nappo, Jr., and S. R. Hanna. 1974. Diurnal variation of vertical thermal structure in a pine plantation. *Agric. Meteorol. 13*:259-65.

Hosley, R. A. 1975. "Aspects of the Behavior of *Brachymeria intermedia.*" M. A. Thesis, Univ. N.C., Raleigh. 113 pp.

Hostetter, D. L., R. E. Pinnell, P. A. Greer, and C. M. Ignoffo. 1973. A granulosis virus of *Pieris rapae* as a microbial control agent on cabbage in Missouri. *Environ. Entomol. 2*:1109-12.

House, H. L. 1967. The decreasing occurrence of diapause in the fly *Pseudosarcophaga affinis* through laboratory-reared generations. *Can. J. Zool. 45*:149-53.

Houston, D. R. and J. E. Kuntz. 1964. Pathogens associated with the maple blight. Part III. Pages 58-79 in "Studies of Maple Blight." Univ. Wis. Res. Bull. 250. 128 pp.

Howard, L. O. 1910. Technical results from the gipsy moth parasite laboratory. On some parasites reared or supposed to have been reared from the eggs of the gipsy moth. *U.S. Dep. Agric. Tech. Ser. 19.* 12 pp.

Howard, L. O. 1921. Annual report of the Bureau of Entomology for 1920. *Annu. Rep. U.S. Dep. Agric.* pp. 307-42.

Howard, L. O. 1924. Annual report of the Bureau of Entomology for 1923. *Annu. Rep. U.S. Dep. Agric.* pp. 381-95.

Howard, L. O. 1930. "A History of Applied Entomology (Somewhat Anecdotal)." Smithson. Misc. Collect. 84. 564 pp.

Howard, L. O. and W. F. Fiske. 1911. The importation into the United States of the parasites of the gypsy moths and brown-tailed moth. *U.S. Dep. Agric. Bur. Entomol. Bull. 91.* 108 pp.

Hoy, M. A. 1975a. Hybridization of strains of the gypsy moth parasitoid, *Apanteles melanoscelus*, and its influence upon diapause. *Ann. Entomol. Soc. Am. 68*:261-4.

Hoy, M. A. 1975b. Forest and laboratory evaluations of a hybridized *Apanteles melanoscelus* (Hym.: Braconidae), a parasitoid of *Porthetria dispar* (Lep.: Lymantriidae). *Entomophaga 20*:261-8.

Hsieh, M. L., W. J. Collins, and G. R. Stairs. 1974. Interaction of nuclear polyhedrosis virus, DDT, rotenone, and peanut oil in *Galleria mellonella* larvae. *Environ. Entomol. 3*:567-9.

Huchon, H. and G. Demolin. 1970. La bioécologie de la processionaire du pin: dispersion potentielle–dispersion actuelle. *Rev. For. Fr. 22 no. spec.* pp. 220-34.

Huffaker, C. B. 1958. The concept of balance in nature. *Proc. 10th Int. Congr. Entomol. (Montreal)2*:625-36.

Huffaker, C. B. 1967. A comparison of the status of biological control of St. Johnswort in California and Australia. *Mushi 39 (Suppl.)*:51-73.

Huffaker, C. B. 1971. "Biological Control." Plenum Press, N.Y. 511 pp.

Huffaker, C. B. and C. E. Kennett 1966. Studies of two parasites of olive scale, *Parlatoria oleae* (Colvee) IV. Biological control of *Parlatoria oleae* (Colvee) through the compensatory action of two introduced parasites. *Hilgardia 37*:283-335.

Huffaker, C. B. and P. S. Messenger. 1964. The concept and significance of natural control. Pages 74-117 in P. DeBach, ed. "Biological Control of Insect Pests and Weeds." Chapman and Hall, London. 844 pp.

Huffaker, C. B., P. S. Messenger, and P. DeBach. 1971. The natural enemy component in natural control and the theory of biological control. Pages 16-67 in C. B. Huffaker, ed. "Biological Control." Plenum Press, N.Y. 511 pp.

Huger, A. 1963. Granuloses of insects. Pages 531-75 in E. A. Steinhaus, ed. "Insect Pathology, an Advanced Treatise." Vol. 1. Academic Press, N.Y. 661 pp.

Huger, A. 1973. Grundlagen zur biologischen Bekämpfung des Indischen Nashornkäfers *Oryctes rhinoceros* (L.), mit *Rhabdionvirus oryctes*: Histopathologie der Virose bei Käfern. *Z. Angew. Entomol. 72*:309-19.

Hughes, T. E. 1959. "Mites or the Acari." Athlone Press, Univ. London, London. 225 pp.

Hukuhara, T. 1968. Genetic variations of polyhedrosis viruses of insects. *Proc. Joint U.S.-Japan Seminar Microbial Control Insect Pests, Fukuoka, Apr. 21-23, 1967.* pp. 7-11.

Hukuhara, T. 1973. Further studies on the distribution of a nuclear-polyhedrosis virus of the fall webworm, *Hyphantria cunea*, in soil. *J. Invertebr. Pathol. 22*:345-50.

Hukuhara, T. 1975. Distribution of viruses of the fall webworm in soil. *Proc. 1st Intersection. Congr. Int. Assoc. Microbiol. Soc. Tokyo, Japan. 2*:658-65.

Hukuhara, T. and H. Namura. 1971. Microscopical demonstration of polyhedra in soil. *J. Invertebr. Pathol. 18*:162-4.

Hukuhara, T. and H. Namura. 1972. Distribution of a nuclear-polyhedrosis virus of the fall webworm, *Hyphantria cunea*, in soil. *J. Invertebr. Pathol. 19*:308-16.

Hunter, D. K. and D. F. Hoffman. 1972. Cross infection of a granulosis virus of *Cadra cautella*, with observations on its ultrastructure in infected cells of *Plodia interpunctella. J. Invertebr. Pathol. 20*:4-10.

Hunter, D. K. and D. F. Hoffman. 1973. Susceptibility of two strains of Indian meal moth to a granulosis virus. *J. Invertebr. Pathol. 21*:114-5.

Hurpin, B. 1971. Principes de la lutte microbiologique en agriculture. *Ann. Parasitol. 46*:243-76.

Hurpin, B. and P. Robert. 1968. Experiments on simultaneous infections of the common cockchafer, *Melolontha melolontha. J. Invertebr. Pathol. 11*:203-13.

Hurpin, B. and P. Robert. 1972. Comparison of the activity of certain pathogens of the cockchafer *Melolontha melolontha* in plots of natural meadowland. *J. Invertebr. Pathol. 19*:291-8.

Ignoffo, C. M. 1966. Effects of age on mortality of *Heliothis zea* and *Heliothis virescens* larvae exposed to a nuclear-polyhedrosis virus. *J. Invertebr. Pathol. 8*:279-82.

Ignoffo, C. M. 1968a. Specificity of insect viruses. *Bull. Éntomol. Soc. Am. 14*:265-76.

Ignoffo, C. M. 1968b. Viruses-living insecticides. Pages 129-67 in K. Maramorosch, ed. "Insect Viruses." Curr. Top. Microbiol. Immunol. Vol. 42. Springer-Verlag, N.Y. 192 pp.

Ignoffo, C. M. 1973. Development of a viral insecticide: concept to commercialization. *Exp. Parasitol. 33*:380-406.

Ignoffo, C. M. 1975. Entomopathogens as insecticides. Pages 23-40 in M. Jacobson, ed. "Insecticides of the Future." Marcel Dekker, Inc., N.Y. 93 pp.

Ignoffo, C. M. and G. E. Allen. 1972. Selection for resistance to a nucleo-polyhedrosis virus in laboratory populations of the cotton bollworm. *J. Invertebr. Pathol. 20*:187-92.

Ignoffo, C. M. and C. Garcia. 1966. The relation of pH to the acitivity of inclusion bodies of a *Heliothis* nuclear polyhedrosis. *J. Invertebr. Pathol. 8*:426-7.

Ignoffo, C. M., F. D. Parker, O. P. Boening, R. E. Pinnell, and D. L. Hostetter. 1973. Field stability of the *Heliothis* nucleopolyhedrosis virus on corn silks. *Environ. Entomol. 2*:302-3.

Ignoffo, C. M., D. L. Hostetter, and M. Shapiro. 1974. Efficacy of insect viruses propagated *in vivo* and *in vitro. J. Invertebr. Pathol. 24*:184-7.

Inoue, H. 1974a. Multiplication of an infectious-flacherie virus in the resistant and susceptible strains of the silkworm, *Bombyx mori. J. Seric. Sci. Jap. 43*:318-24.

Inoue, H. 1974b. Double infection of a cytoplasmic-polyhedrosis virus and an infectious-flacherie virus in the silkworm, *Bombyx mori* (Lepidoptera: Bombycidae). *Appl. Entomol. Zool. 9*:167-73.

Inoue, H., C. Ayuzawa, and A. Kawamura, Jr. 1972. Effect of high temperature on the multiplication of infectious flacherie virus in the silkworm, *Bombyx mori. Appl. Entomol. Zool. 7*:155-60.

Irabagon, T. A. and W. M. Brooks. 1974. Interaction of *Campoletis sonorensis* and a nuclear polyhedrosis virus in larvae of *Heliothis virescens. J. Econ. Entomol. 67*:229-31.

Iwaki, S., S. Marumo, T. Saito, M. Yamada, and K. Katagiri. 1974. Synthesis and activity of optically active disparlure. *J. Am. Chem. Soc. 96*:7842-4.

Jacobson, M. 1960. Synthesis of a highly potent gypsy moth sex attractant. *J. Org. Chem. 25*:2074.

Jacobson, M. 1962. Method of attracting male gypsy moth with 12-acetoxy-1-hydroxy-9-octadecene. U.S. Patent 3,0818,219 to Secretary of Agriculture.

Jacobson, M. 1972. "Insect Sex Pheromones." Academic Press, N.Y. 382 pp.

Jacobson, M., M. Beroza, and W. A. Jones. 1960. Isolation, identification and synthesis of the sex attractant of gypsy moth. *Science (Wash. D.C.) 132*:1011-2.

Jacobson, M., M. Schwarz, and R. M. Waters. 1970. Gypsy moth sex attractants: a reinvestigation. *J. Econ. Entomol. 63*:943-5.

Jacsman, J. 1974. Zur methodischen Erforschung der Wohlfahrtsfunktionen des Waldes. *Schweiz. Z. Forstwes. 125*:87-98.

Janisch, E. 1958. Populationsanalyse bei Schadinsekter. *Z. Angew. Entomol. 43*:371-86.

Jaques, R. P. 1962. The transmission of nuclear-polyhedrosis virus in laboratory populations of *Trichoplusia ni. J. Insect Pathol. 4*:433-45.

Jaques, R. P. 1964. The persistence of a nuclear-polyhedrosis virus in soil. *J. Insect Pathol. 6*:251-4.

Jaques, R. P. 1967a. The persistence of a nuclear polyhedrosis virus in the habitat of the host insect, *Trichoplusia ni* I. Polyhedra deposited on the foliage. *Can. Entomol. 99*:785-94.

Jaques, R. P. 1967b. The persistence of a nuclear polyhedrosis virus in the habitat of the host insect, *Trichoplusia ni.* II. Polyhedra in soil. *Can. Entomol. 99*:820-9.

Jaques, R. P. 1969. Leaching of the nuclear-polyhedrosis virus of *Trichoplusia ni* from soil. *J. Invertebr. Pathol. 13*:256-63.

Jaques, R. P. 1970a. Natural occurrence of viruses of the cabbage looper in field plots. *Can. Entomol. 102*:36-41.

Jaques, R. P. 1970b. Application of viruses to soil and foliage for control of the cabbage looper and imported cabbageworm. *J. Invertebr. Pathol. 15*:328-40.

Jaques, R. P. 1971. Tests on protectants for foliar deposits of a polyhedrosis virus. *J. Invertebr. Pathol. 17*:9-16.

Jaques, R. P. 1972. The inactivation of foliar deposits of viruses of *Trichoplusia ni* (Lepidoptera: Noctuidae) and *Pieris rapae* (Lepidoptera: Pieridae) and tests on protectant additives. *Can. Entomol. 104*:1985-94.

Jaques, R. P. 1973a. Methods and effectiveness of distribution of microbial insecticides. Pages 109-19 in L. A. Bulla, Jr., ed. "Regulation of Insect Populations by Microorganisms." Ann. N.Y. Acad. Sci. 217. 243 pp.

Jaques, R. P. 1973b. Tests on microbial and chemical insecticides for control of *Trichoplusia ni* (Lepidoptera: Noctuidae) and *Pieris rapae* (Lepidoptera: Pieridae) on cabbage. *Can. Entomol. 105*:21-7.

Jaques, R. P. 1974a. Occurrence and accumulation of viruses of *Trichoplusia ni* in treated field plots. *J. Invertebr. Pathol. 23*:140-52.

Jaques, R. P. 1974b. Occurrence and accumulation of the granulosis virus of *Pieris rapae* in treated field plots. *J. Invertebr. Pathol. 23*:351-9.

Jaques, R. P. and D. G. Harcourt. 1971. Viruses of *Trichoplusia ni* (Lepidoptera: Noctuidae) and *Pieris rapae* (Lepidoptera: Pieridae) in soil in fields of crucifers in southern Ontario. *Can. Entomol. 103*:1285-90.

Jaques, R. P. and H. T. Stultz. 1966. The influence of a virus disease and parasites on *Spilonota ocellana* in apple orchards. *Can. Entomol. 98*:1035-45.

Jaques, R. P., H. T. Stultz, and F. Huston. 1968. The mortality of the pale apple leafroller and winter moth by fungi and nematodes applied to soil. *Can. Entomol. 100*:813-8.

Jaynes, H. A. 1954. Parasitization of spruce budworm larvae at different crown heights by *Apanteles* and *Glypta. J. Econ. Entomol. 47*:355-6.

Jaynes, H. A. and A. T. Drooz. 1952. The importance of parasites in the spruce budworm infestations in New York and Maine. *J. Econ. Entomol. 45*:1057-61.

Jaynes, R. A. 1974. Genetics of chestnut. *U.S. For. Serv. Res. Pap. WO-17.* 13 pp.

Jaynes, R. A. and N. K. Van Alfen. 1974. Control of American chestnut blight by trunk injection with methyl-2-benzimidazole carbamate (MBC). *Phytopathology 64*:1479-80.

Jenkins, E. H. 1902. The improvement of uncultivated farm land. Pages 350-2 in 25th *Annu. Rep. Conn. Agric. Exp. Stn. (New Haven).* 446 pp.

Jenkins, E. H. 1925. Connecticut agriculture. Pages 287-425 in N. G. Osborn, ed. "History of Connecticut." Vol. 2. The States History Co., N.Y. 601 pp.

Jeppson, L. R., H. H. Keifer, and E. W. Baker. 1975. "Mites Injurious to Economic Plants." Univ. Calif. Press, Berkeley, Calif. 614 pp.

Johnson, C. G. 1969. "Migration and Dispersal of Insects by Flight." Methuen and Co., London. 763 pp.

Jones, H. N. 1910. Further studies on the nature of the wilt disease of the gypsy moth larvae. *7th Annu. Rep. State Forester, Mass. Public Doc. 73.* pp. 101-5.

Jones, T. H., R. T. Webber, and P. B. Dowden. 1938. Effectiveness of imported insect enemies of the satin moth. *U.S. Dep. Agric. Circ. 459.* 24 pp.

Jordan, J. S. 1967. Deer browsing in northern hardwoods after clearcutting. *U.S. Dep. Agric. For. Ser. Res. Pap. NE-57.* 15 pp.

Jorgensen, J. R., C. G. Wells, and L. J. Metz. 1975. The nutrient cycle: key to continuous forest production. *J. For. 73*:400-3.

Josselyn, J. 1672. "New-Englands Rarities Discovered." Reprinted 1972. Mass. Hist. Soc., Boston. 114 pp.

Juillet, J. A. 1960. Some factors influencing the flight activity of hymenopterous parasites. *Can. J. Zool. 38*:1057-61.

Karpel, M. A. 1973. Effects of trichlorfon and carbaryl on gypsy moth, elm spanworm, and related insect populations in Pound Ridge, New York. *J. Econ. Entomol. 66*:271-2.

Katagiri, K. 1969a. Review on microbial control of insect pests in forests in Japan. *Entomophaga 14*:203-14.

Katagiri, K. 1969b. Use of viruses for control of some forest insects in Japan. *Rev. Plant Prot. Res. 2*:31-41.

Katagiri, K. 1975. Control of forest pest insects by virus. *Proc. 1st. Intersection. Congr. Int. Assoc. Microbiol. Soc. Tokyo, Japan. 2*:613-20.

Kawarabata, T. and K. Aizawa. 1968. Immunologic principles in microbial infections in insects. *Proc. Joint U.S.-Japan Seminar Microbial Control Insect Pests, Fukuoka, Apr. 21-23, 1967.* pp. 143-5.

Kaya, H. K. 1970. Toxic factor produced by a granulosis virus in armyworm larva: effect on *Apanteles militaris. Science (Wash. D.C.) 168*:251-3.

Kaya, H. K. 1975. Persistence of spores of *Pleistophora schubergi* (Cnidospora: Microsporida) in the field, and their application in microbial control. *J. Invertebr. Pathol. 26*:329-32.

Kaya, H. K. and J. F. Anderson. 1972. Parasitism of elm spanworm eggs by *Ooencyrtus clisiocampae* in Connecticut. *Environ. Entomol. 1*:523-4.

Kaya, H. K. and J. F. Anderson. 1974a. Collapse of the elm spanworm outbreak: role of *Ooencyrtus* sp. *Environ. Entomol. 3*:659-63.

Kaya, H. K. and J. F. Anderson. 1974b. Flight and ovipositional activity of the elm spanworm egg parasitoid, *Ooencyrtus* sp. *Environ. Entomol. 3*:1028-9.

Kaya, H. K. and J. F. Anderson. 1976. Alternate hosts of the elm spanworm egg parasitoid, *Ooencyrtus ennomophagus* Yoshimoto. *Ann. Entomol. Soc. Am. 69*:35-7.

Kaya, H. K. and D. M. Dunbar. 1972. Effect of *Bacillus thuringiensis* and carbaryl on an elm spanworm egg parasite *Telenomus alsophilae. J. Econ. Entomol. 65*:1132-4.

Kaya, H. K. and Y. Tanada. 1972a. Response of *Apanteles militaris* to a toxin produced in a granulosis-virus-infected host. *J. Invertebr. Pathol. 19*:1-17.

Kaya, H. K. and Y. Tanada. 1972b. Pathology caused by a viral toxin in the parasitoid *Apanteles militaris. J. Invertebr. Pathol. 19*:262-72.

Kaya, H. K. and Y. Tanada. 1973. Hemolymph factor in armyworm larvae infected with a nuclear-polyhedrosis virus toxic to *Apanteles militaris. J. Invertebr. Pathol. 21*:211-4.

Kaya, H., D. Dunbar, C. Doane, R. Weseloh, and J. Anderson. 1974. Gypsy moth aerial tests with *Bacillus thuringiensis* and pyrethroids. *Conn. Agric. Exp. Stn. Bull. (New Haven) 744.* 22 pp.

Keays, J. L. and G. M. Barton. 1975. Recent advances in foliage utilization. *Can. Dep. Environ., Can. For. Serv. Inf. Rep. VP-X-137.* 93 pp.

Keeley, L. L. and S. B. Vinson. 1975. B-ecdysone effects on the development of nucleopolyhedrosis in *Heliothis* sp. *J. Invertebr. Pathol. 26*:121-3.

Keen, F. P. 1938. "Insect Enemies of Western Forests." U.S. Dep. Agric. Misc. Publ. 273. 209 pp.

Keen, F. P. 1943. Ponderosa pine tree classes redefined. *J. For. 41*:249-53.

Keen, F. P. and J. Miller. 1960. "Biology and Control of the Western Pine Beetle." U.S. Dep. Agric. For. Serv. Misc. Publ. 800. 381 pp.

Kegg, J. D. 1971. The impact of gypsy moth: repeated defoliation of oak in New Jersey. *J. For.* 69:852-4.

Kegg, J. D. 1973. Oak mortality caused by repeated gypsy moth defoliations in New Jersey. *J. Econ. Entomol.* 66:639-41.

Keller, S. 1973. Mikrobiologische Bekämpfung des Apfelwicklers (*Laspeyresia pomonella* (L.)) (= *Carpocapsa pomonella*) mit spezifischem Granulosis-virus. *Z. Angew. Entomol.* 73:137-81.

Kelly, D. C. and R. J. Avery. 1974. The DNA content of four small iridescent viruses: genome size, redundancy, and homology determined by renaturation kinetics. *Virology* 57:425-35.

Kennedy, J. S. 1961. A turning point in the study of insect migration. *Nature (Lond.)* 189:785-91.

Kennedy, J. S. 1965. Mechanisms of host plant selection. *Ann. Appl. Biol.* 56:317-22.

Kennedy, J. S. and D. Marsh. 1974. Pheromone-regulated anemotaxis in flying moths. *Science (Wash. D.C.)* 184:999-1001.

Kenoyer, L. A. 1934. Forest distribution in southwestern Michigan as interpreted from the original land survey (1826-32). *Papers, Mich. Acad. Sci., Arts and Lett.* 19:107-11.

Keremidchiev, M. and G. Gantschev. 1973. Artenbestand, Verbreitung, Rolle und Möglichkeiten zum Einsatz der Eierparasiten am Schwammspinner in der Forstschutzpraxis. *Gorskostop. Nauka* 10:37-44. (In Russ., Germ. summ.).

Keys, R. N., F. C. Cech, and W. MacDonald. 1975. Performance of Chinese and hybrid chestnut after 20 years. *Annu. Rep. Northern Nut Growers Assoc.* 66:57-61.

Kim, C. W., J. S. Hyun, T. Y. Lee, S. W. Cha, C. M. Yoo, and S. Y. Cha. 1965. Studies on the control of the pine moth, *Dendrolimus spectabilis* Butler. *Entomol. Res. Bull. Seoul.* 1:1-109.

Kingsley, N. P. 1974. The timber resources of southern New England. *U.S. For. Serv. Resour. Bull. NE-36.* 50 pp.

Kirk, H. B. 1922. Biological notes on Elateridae and Melasidae (Col.). *Entomol. News* 33:236-40.

Klomp, H. 1956. Over het aantal generaties, de gastheerwisseling en de overwintering van *Trichogramma embryophagum* Htg. *Entomol. Ber. (Amst.)* 16:117-20.

Klomp, H. 1966. The dynamics of a field population of the pine looper, *Bupalus piniarius. Adv. Ecol. Res.* 3:207-305.

Klomp, H. 1973. Population dynamics: a key to the understanding of integrated control. Pages 69-79 in P. W. Geier, L. R. Clark, D. J. Anderson, and H. A. Nix, eds. "Insects: Studies in Population Management." Ecol. Soc. Aust. Mem. 1, Canberra. 294 pp.

Knight, H. H. 1915. Observations on oviposition of certain capsids. *J. Econ. Entomol.* 8:293-8.

Knipling, E. F. and J. U. McGuire, Jr. 1966. Population models to test theoretical effects of sex attractants used for insect control. *U.S. Dep. Agric. Infor. Bull. 308.* 11 pp.

Knoblauch, H. C., E. M. Law, and W. P. Meyer. 1962. "State Agricultural Experiment Stations: A History of Research Policy and Procedure." U.S. Dep. Agric. Misc. Publ. 904. 262 pp.

Kobakhidze, D. N. 1965. Some results and prospects of the utilization of beneficial entomophagous insects in the control of insects in Georgian S.S.R. (USSR). *Entomophaga* 10:323-30.

Koehler, W. 1974. Specificity of problems and tasks of forest protection in Poland. *Sylwan No.* 7:23-30. (In Polish).

Kolomiets, N. G. 1957. New data on the parasites of the Siberian silkworm moth. *Lesn. Khoz. No.* 7:57-8. (Abstr. in *Biol. Abstr. 35,* No. 30566) (In Russian).

Kolomiets, N. G. 1958. Parasites of harmful forest insects in Siberia. *Entomol. Rev.* *37*:522-34.

Komárek, J. and V. Breindl. 1924. Die Wipfelkrankheit der Nonne und der Erreger derselben. *Z. Angew. Entomol. 10*:99-162.

Korstian, C. F. and P. W. Stickel. 1927. The natural replacement of blight-killed chestnut. *U.S. Dep. Agric. Misc. Circ. 100.* 15 pp.

Kotinsky, J. 1921. Insects injurious to deciduous shade trees and their control. *U.S. Dep. Agric. Farmers Bull. 1169.* 100 pp.

Koyama, R. and K. Katagiri. 1959. On the virus disease of *Lymantria fumida* Butler. I. On a virus epizootic in an outbreaking population of *Lymantria fumida* Butler. *J. Jap. For. Soc. 41*:4-10.

Koyama, R. and K. Katagiri. 1967. An application of nuclear and cytoplasmic polyhedrosis viruses against *Lymantria fumida* Butler (Lepidoptera: Lymantridae). *Bull. Gov. For. Exp. Stn. 207.* 10 pp.

Koyama, R. and K. Katagiri. 1968. Use of cytoplasmic-polyhedrosis virus for the control of the pine caterpillars, *Dendrolimus spectabilis* Butler (Lepidoptera: Lasiocampidae). *Proc. Joint U.S.-Japan Seminar on Microbial Control of Insect Pests, Fukuoka, Apr. 21-23, 1967.* pp. 63-9.

Kozlov, M. A. 1967. Palearctic species of egg parasites of the genus *Telenomus* Haliday (Hymenoptera, Scelionidae, Telenominae). *Entomol. Rev. 46*:215-24.

Kozlowski, T. T. 1971. "Growth and Development of Trees." Vol. I. Academic Press, N.Y. 443 pp.

Krieg, A. 1957. "Toleranzphänomen" und Latenzproblem. *Arch. Gesamte Virusforsch.* 7:212-9.

Krieg, A. 1961. "Grundlagen der Insektenpathologie. Viren-, Rickettsien-und Bakterien-Infektionen." Dr. D. Steinkopff Publ., Darmstadt. 304 pp.

Krieg, A. 1971a. Interactions between pathogens. Pages 459-68 in H. D. Burges and N. W. Hussey, eds. "Microbial Control of Insects and Mites." Academic Press, N.Y. 861 pp.

Krieg, A. 1971b. Key publications. Pages 711-5 in H. D. Burges and N. W. Hussey, eds. "Microbial Control of Insects and Mites." Academic Press. N.Y. 861 pp.

Krieg, A. 1973. "Arthropodenviren." Georg. Thomas, Stuttgard, Germany. 328 pp.

Krombein, K. V. 1958. "Hymenoptera of America, North of Mexico Synoptic Catalog." Agric. Monogr. 2 1st Suppl., U.S. Gov. Printing Office, Wash. D.C. 303 pp.

Krombein, K. V. and B. D. Burks. 1967. "Hymenoptera of America North of Mexico Synoptic Catalog." Agric. Monogr. 2. 2nd Suppl., U.S. Gov. Printing Office, Wash. D.C. 584 pp.

Kulinčević, J. M. and W. C. Rothenbuhler. 1975. Selection for resistance and susceptibility to hairless-black syndrome in the honeybee. *J. Invertebr. Pathol. 25*:289-95.

Kulman, H. M. 1965. Oviposition habits of *Trichogramma minutum* on artificial concentrations of eggs of the European pine shoot moth. *Ann. Entomol. Soc. Am. 58*:241-3.

Kunimi, Y. and H. Aruga. 1974. Susceptibility to infection with nuclear- and cytoplasmic-polyhedrosis viruses of the fall webworm, *Hyphantria cunea* Drury, reared on several artificial diets. *Jap. J. Appl. Entomol. Zool 18*:1-4.

Kurstak, E. and C. Vago. 1967. Transmission du virus de la densonucléose par la parasitisme d'un hyménoptère. *Rev. Can. Biol. 26*:311-6.

Kurstak, E., S. Garzon, and P. A. Onji. 1975. Multiple viral infections of insect cells and host pathogenesis: multicomponent viral insecticides. *Proc. 1st Intersection. Congr. Int. Assoc. Microbiol. Soc. Tokyo, Japan. 2*:650-7.

Kushner, D. J. and G. T. Harvey. 1962. Antibacterial substances in leaves: their possible role in insect resistance to disease. *J. Insect Pathol. 4*:155-84.

Laigo, F. M. and J. D. Paschke. 1968. *Pteromalus puparum* L. parasites reared from granulosis and microsporidiosis infected *Pieris rapae* L. chrysalids. *Philipp. Agric. 52*:430-9.

Laigo, F. M. and M. Tamashiro. 1966. Virus and insect parasite interaction in the lawn armyworm, *Spodoptera mauritia acronyctoides* (Guenée). *Proc. Hawaii. Entomol. Soc. 19*:233-7.

Langston, R. L. 1957. A synopsis of hymenopterous parasites of *Malacosoma* in California (Lepidoptera: Lasiocampidae) *Univ. Calif. Publ. Entomol. 14*:1-50.

Lee, P. E. and B. Furgala. 1967. Viruslike particles in adult honeybees (*Apis mellifera* Linnaeus) following injection with sacbrood virus. *Virology 32*:11-7.

Lees, A. D. 1955. "The Physiology of Diapause in Arthropods." Cambridge Monogr. Exp. Biol. IV. Cambridge Univ. Press, London. 151 pp.

Leiby, R. W. 1925. Insect enemies of the pecan in North Carolina. *The Bulletin, N.C. Dep. Agric. Feb.* pp. 19-24.

Leius, K. 1960. Attractiveness of different foods and flowers to the adults of some hymenopterous parasites. *Can. Entomol. 92*:369-76.

Leius, K. 1961. Influence of food on fecundity and longevity of adults of *Itoplectis conquisitor* (Say) (Hymenoptera: Ichneumonidae). *Can. Entomol. 93*:771-80.

Leius, K. 1963. Effects of pollens on fecundity and longevity of adult *Scambus buolianae* (Htg.) (Hymenoptera: Ichneumonidae). *Can. Entomol. 95*:202-7.

Leius, K. 1967a. Influence of wild flowers on parasitism of tent caterpillar and codling moth. *Can. Entomol. 99*:444-6.

Leius, K. 1967b. Food sources and preferences of adults of a parasite, *Scambus buolianae* (Hym.: Ichn.), and their consequences. *Can. Entomol. 99*:865-71.

Leonard, D. E. 1966. *Brachymeria intermedia* (Nees) (Hymenoptera: Chalcididae) established in North America. *Entomol. News 77*:25-7.

Leonard, D. E. 1967. Parasitism of gypsy moth in Connecticut by *Brachymeria intermedia*. *J. Econ. Entomol. 60*:600-1.

Leonard, D. E. 1968. Effects of density of larvae on the biology of the gypsy moth, *Porthetria dispar. Entomol. Exp. Appl. 11*:291-304.

Leonard, D. E. 1970. Effect of starvation on behaviour, number of larval instars, and developmental rate of *Porthetria dispar. J. Insect Physiol. 16*:25-31.

Leonard, D. E. 1971a. *Brachymeria intermedia* (Hymenoptera: Chalcididae) parasitizing the gypsy moth in Maine. *Can. Entomol. 103*:654-6.

Leonard, D. E. 1971b. Effects of larval density on the population biology of the gypsy moth, *Porthetria dispar. Proc. 13th Int. Congr. Entomol. (Moscow). 1*:519-20.

Leonard, D. E. 1971c. Air-borne dispersal of larvae of the gypsy moth and its influence on concepts of control. *J. Econ. Entomol. 64*:638-41.

Leonard, D. E. 1974. Recent developments in ecology and control of the gypsy moth. *Annu. Rev. Entomol. 19*:197-229.

Leonard, D. E. and C. C. Doane. 1966. An artificial diet for the gypsy moth, *Porthetria dispar. Ann. Entomol. Soc. Am. 59*:462-4.

Leonard, D. E., B. A. Bierl, and M. Beroza. 1975. Gypsy moth kairomones influencing behavior of the parasitoids *Brachymeria intermedia* and *Apanteles melanoscelus*. *Environ. Entomol. 4*:929-30.

Leopold, A. 1949. "A Sand County Almanac." Ballantine Books, Inc., N.Y. 295 pp.

LePelley, R. 1951. Annual report of the senior entomologist, 1950. *Annu. Rep. Dep. Agric. Kenya. 2*:60-70.

LeRoux, E. J., R. O. Paradis, and M. Hudon. 1963. Major mortality factors in population dynamics of the eye-spotted bud moth, the pistol casebearer, the fruit-tree leafroller, and the European corn borer in Quebec. Pages 67-82 in E. J. LeRoux, ed. "Population Dynamics of Agricultural and Forest Insect Pests." Mem. Entomol. Soc. Can. 32. 103 pp.

Leutenegger, R. 1964. Development of an icosahedral virus in hemocytes of *Galleria mellonella* (L.). *Virology 24*:200-4.

Lewis, T. and L. R. Taylor. 1964. Diurnal periodicity of flight by insects. *Trans. R. Entomol. Soc. Lond. 116*:393-476.

Lienk, S. E. 1970. Apple maggot infesting apricot. *J. Econ. Entomol. 63*:1684.

Linley, J. R. and H. T. Nielsen. 1968a. Transmission of a mosquito iridescent virus in *Aedes taeniorhynchus*. I. Laboratory experiments. *J. Invertebr. Pathol. 12*:7-16.

Linley, J. R. and H. T. Nielsen. 1968b. Transmission of a mosquito iridescent virus in *Aedes taeniorhynchus*. II. Experiments related to transmission in nature. *J. Invertebr. Pathol. 12*:17-24.

Little, E. L., Jr. 1953. Checklist of native and naturalized trees of the U.S. (including Alaska). *U.S. Dep. Agric. Handb. 41*. 472 pp.

Little, S., G. R. Moorhead, and H. A. Somes. 1958. Forestry and deer in the pine region of New Jersey. *Northeast. For. Exp. Stn. Pap. 109*. 33 pp.

Lloyd, D. C. 1935. Random distribution of parasite progeny. *Nature (Lond.) 135*:472-3.

Lloyd, D. C. 1938. A study of some factors governing the choice of hosts and distribution of progeny by the chalcid. *Ooencyrtus kuwanai* Howard. *Philos. Trans. R. Soc. Lond. Ser. B Biol. Sci. 229*:275-322.

Lochhead, W. 1915. Brief notes on some of the injurious insects of Quebec. *Annu. Rep. Entomol. Soc. Ont. 45*:59-61.

Lühl, R. 1974. Versuche mit insektenpathogenen Polyderviren und chemischen Stressoren zur Bekämpfung forstschädlicher Raupen. *Z. Angew. Entomol. 76*:49-65.

Lumley, J. L. and H. A. Panofsky. 1964. "The Structure of Atmospheric Turbulence." Interscience Publ., N.Y. 239 pp.

Lutz, H. J. 1930. Original forest composition in northwestern Pennsylvania as indicated by early land survey notes. *J. For. 28*:1098-103.

MacAloney, H. J. 1968. The bronze birch borer. *U.S. Dep. Agric. For. Serv. Pest Leafl. 111*. 4 pp.

MacDonald, D. R. 1963. The analysis of egg survival in the sprayed area. Pages 133-8 in R. F. Morris, ed. "The Dynamics of Epidemic Spruce Budworm Populations." Mem. Entomol. Soc. Can. 31. 332 pp.

MacKay, M. R. 1962. "Larvae of the North American Tortricinae (Lepidoptera: Tortricidae)." Can. Entomol. Suppl. 28. 182 pp.

MacKinney, A. L. and C. F. Korstian. 1932. Felling, girdling, and poisoning undesirable trees in forest stands. *J. For. 30*:169-77.

Mackauer, M. 1972. Genetic aspects of insect production. *Entomophaga 17*:27-48.

MacLeod, D. M. 1954. Investigations on the genera *Beauveria* Vuill. and *Tritirachium* Limber. *Can. J. Bot. 32*:818-90.

Madden, J. 1968. Behavioural responses of parasites to the symbiotic fungus associated with *Sirex noctilio* F. *Nature (Lond.) 218*:189-90.

Magnoler, A. 1968. Laboratory and field experiments on the effectiveness of purified and non-purified nuclear polyhedral virus of *Lymantria dispar* L. *Entomophaga 13*:335-44.

Magnoler, A. 1974a. Bioassay of a nucleopolyhedrosis virus of the gypsy moth, *Porthetria dispar*. *J. Invertebr. Pathol. 23*:190-6.

Magnoler, A. 1974b. Field dissemination of a nucleopolyhedrosis virus against the gypsy moth, *Lymantria dispar* L. *Z. Pflanzenkrank. Pflanzenschutz. 81*:497-511.

Magnoler, A. 1974c. Ground application of a *Bacillus thuringiensis* preparation for gypsy moth control. *Z. Pflanzenkrankh. Pflanzenschutz. 81*:575-83.

Maksimović, M. 1959. Traps—A modern method of controlling the numerical strength of gypsy moth populations. *Zašt. Bilja No. 56*:65-70. (In Serb.-Kroat., Engl. summ.).

Maksimović, M., P. Bjegović, and L. Vasiljević. 1970. Maintaining the density of the gypsy moth enemies as a method of biological control. *Zašt. Bilja 21* (107):3-15. (In Serb.-Kroat.)

Maksimović, M., D. Ljesov, and P. Prekajski. 1974. Comparative investigation on synthetic and natural sex lure of the gypsy moth and a trial of mass trapping. *Zašt. Bilja 25*(130):251-64. (In Serb.-Kroat.)

Maksymiuk, B. 1970. Occurrence and nature of antibacterial substances in plants affecting *Bacillus thuringiensis* and other entomogenous bacteria. *J. Invertebr. Pathol. 15*:356-71.

Maleki-Milani, H. 1970. Sur quelques caractères de la virose cytoplasmique de la noctuelle du chou, *Mamestra (Barathra) brassicae* L. (Lep. Noctuidae). *Entomophaga 15*:315-25.

Mallis, A. 1971. "American Entomologists." Rutgers Univ. Press, New Brunswick, N.J. 549 pp.

Malo, F. 1961. Phoresy in *Xenufens* (Hymenoptera: Trichogrammatidae), a parasite of *Caligo eurilochus* (Lepidoptera: Nymphalidae). *J. Econ. Entomol. 54*:465-6.

Manthy, R. S. 1975. Response to future needs for land to produce timber, perspectives on prime lands. *U.S. Dep. Agric. Seminar Retention of Prime Lands.* pp. 100-3.

Marchal, P. 1936. Recherches sur la biologie et le développement des Hyménoptères parasites les Trichogrammes. *Ann. Epiphyt. Phytogenet. 2*:447-550.

Marlatt, C. L. 1940. Fifty years of entomological progress, Part I, 1889 to 1899. *J. Econ. Entomol. 33*:8-15.

Marquis, D. A. 1975. The Allegheny hardwood forests of Pennsylvania. *U.S. Dep. Agric. For. Serv. Gen. Tech. Rep. NE-15.* 32 pp.

Marschall, K. J. 1970. Introduction of a new virus disease of the coconut rhinoceros beetle in Western Samoa. *Nature (Lond.) 225*:288-9.

Martignoni, M. E. 1957. Contributo alla conoscenza di una granulosi di *Eucosma griseana* (Hübner) quale fattore limitante il pullulamento dell'insetto nella Engadina alta. *Mitt. Schweiz. Anst. Forstl. Versuchsw. 32*:371-418.

Martignoni, M. E. and J. E. Milstead. 1962. Trans-ovum transmission of the nuclear polyhedrosis virus of *Colias eurytheme* Boisduval through contamination of the female genitalia. *J. Insect Pathol. 4*:113-21.

Martignoni, M. E. and P. Schmid. 1961. Studies on the resistance to virus infections in natural populations of Lepidoptera. *J. Insect Pathol. 3*:62-74.

Marty, R. J. 1965. How much can you afford to spend in controlling forest insects. Pages 38-50 in C. B. Marlin, ed. "Insects in Southern Forests." Proc. 14th Annu. For. Symp., La. State Univ. Press. 129 pp.

Maslennikova, V. A. 1959. On the problem of the overwintering and diapause of Trichogrammatids (*Trichogramma evanescens*) (Westw.). *Vestn. Leningr. Univ. Ser. Biol. 14*:91-6.

Masner, L. 1958. A new egg-parasite of gipsy moth *Lymantria dispar. Entomophaga 3*:39-44.

Mason, R. R. and C. G. Thompson. 1971. Collapse of an outbreak population of the Douglas-fir tussock moth, *Hemerocampa pseudotsugata* (Lepidoptera: Lymantriidae). *U.S. For. Serv. Res. Note. PNW-139.* 10 pp.

Mathur, Y. K. 1971. Discovery of an interesting type of virus in *Amsacta moorei* Butler (Lepidoptera: Arctiidae). *Sci. Cult. 37*:148.

Mathys, G. and E. Guignard. 1965. Etude de L'efficacité de *Prospaltella perniciosi* Tow. en Suisse parasite du pou de San-Jose. *Entomophaga 10*:193-220.

Matsubara, F. and K. Hayashiya. 1969. The susceptibility to the infection with nuclear-polyhedrosis virus in the silkworm reared on artificial diet. *J. Seric. Sci. Jap. 38*:43-8.

Matsui, M. and H. Watanabe. 1974. Cytopathological studies on the multiplication of a small flacherie virus (SFV) in the midgut epithelium of silkworm, *Bombyx mori* L. *Jap. J. Appl. Entomol. Zool. 18*:133-8.

Matthiessen, J. N. and B. P. Springett. 1973. The food of the silvereye, *Zosterops gouldi* (Aves: Zosteropidae), in relation to its role as a vector of a granulosis virus of the potato moth, *Phthorimaea operculella* (Lepidoptera: Gelechiidae). *Aust. J. Zool. 21*:533-40.

May, C. and R. W. Davidson. 1960. *Endothia parasitica* associated with a canker of live oak. *Plant Dis. Rep. 9*:754.

Mayer, M. S. 1973. Attraction studies of male *Trichoplusia ni* (Lepidoptera: Noctuidae) with new combination of olfactometer and pheromone dispenser. *Ann. Entomol. Soc. Am. 66*:1191-6.

Mazokhin-Porshnyakov, G. A. 1969. "Insect Vision." Plenum Press, N.Y. 306 pp.

McBean, G. A. 1968. An investigation of turbulence within the forest. *J. Appl. Meteorol. 7*:410-6.

McGaughey, W. H. 1975. Compatibility of *Bacillus thuringiensis* and granulosis virus treatments of stored grain with four grain fumigants. *J. Invertebr. Pathol. 26*:247-50.

McGee, C. E. 1975. Change in forest canopy affects phenology and development of northern red and scarlet oak seedlings. *For. Sci. 21*:175-9.

McGuire, J. R. and F. J. Mulhern. 1974. "Final Environmental Statement Cooperative Gypsy Moth Suppression and Regulatory Program 1974 Activities." U.S. Dep. Agric. Environ. Impact Statement. 179 pp.

McIntyre, T. and S. R. Dutky. 1961. Aerial application of virus for control of a pine sawfly, *Neodiprion pratti pratti. J. Econ. Entomol. 54*:809-10.

McKnight, J. S. 1975. Response to future needs for land to produce timber, perspectives on prime lands. *U.S. Dep. Agric. Seminar Retention of Prime Lands.* pp. 91-2.

McLaughlin, R. E. 1973. Protozoa as microbial control agents. *Misc. Publ. Entomol. Soc. Am. 9*:95-8.

McLeod, J. H. 1951. Notes on the lodgepole needle miner, *Recurvaria milleri* Busck (Lepidoptera: Gelechiidae), and its parasites in western North America. *Can. Entomol. 83*:295-301.

McLeod, J. H. and G. L. Ayre. 1956. Parasites of tent caterpillars (Lepidoptera: Lasiocampidae) in the lower Fraser Valley of British Columbia, Canada. *8th Pac. Sci. Congr. Proc. 3A*:1547-60.

McLeod, J. M. 1972. A comparison of discrimination and of density responses during oviposition by *Exenterus amictorius* and *E. diprionis* (Hymenoptera: Ichneumonidae), parasites of *Neodiprion swainei* (Hymenoptera: Diprionidae). *Can. Entomol. 104*:1313-30.

McManus, M. L. 1973. The role of behavior in the dispersal of newly hatched gypsy moth larvae. *U.S. For. Serv. Res. Pap. NE-267.* 10 pp.

Meijer, G. M., F. J. Ritter, C. Persoons, A. Minks, and S. Voerman. 1972. Sex pheromones of summer fruit tortrix moth *Adoxophyes orana*: two synergistic isomers. *Science (Wash. D.C.) 175*:1469-70.

Meroney, R. N. 1968. Characteristics of wind and turbulence in and above model forests. *J. Appl. Meteorol. 7*:780-8.

Mery, C. and H. T. Dulmage. 1975. Transmission, diagnosis and control of cytoplasmic polyhedrosis virus in colonies of *Heliothis virescens. J. Invertebr. Pathol. 26*:75-9.

Messenger, P. S. 1964. The use of life tables in a bioclimatic study of the experimental host parasite system. *Ecology 45*:119-31.

Messenger, P. S. 1968. Bioclimatic studies of the aphid parasite *Praon exsoletum.* 1. Effects of temperature on the functional response of females to varying host densities. *Can. Entomol. 100*:728-41.

Messenger, P. S. 1970. Bioclimatic inputs to biological control and pest management programs. Pages 84-102 in R. L. Rabb and F. E. Guthrie, eds. "Concepts of Pest Management." N.C. State Univ., Raleigh, N.C. 242 pp.

Messenger, P. S. 1971. Climatic limitations to biological controls. *Proc. Tall Timbers Conf. Ecol. Anim. Control Habitat Manage. 3*:97-114.

Messenger, P. S. 1975. Parasites, predators, and population dynamics. Pages 201-23 in D. Pimentel, ed. "Insects, Science and Society." Academic Press, N.Y. 284 pp.

Messenger, P. S. and R. van den Bosch. 1971. The adaptibility of introduced biological agents. Pages 68-92 in C. B. Huffaker, ed. "Biological Control." Plenum Press, N.Y. 511 pp.

Messenger, P. S., E. Billioti, and R. van den Bosch. 1976. The importance of natural enemies in integrated control. In C. B. Huffaker and P. S. Messenger, eds. "The Theory and Practice of Biological Control." Academic Press, N.Y. in press.

Metcalf, C. L. 1940. Fifty years of entomological progress, Part III, 1909 to 1919. *J. Econ. Entomol. 33*:21-9.

Metcalf, C. L. and W. P. Flint. 1962. "Destructive and Useful Insects." 4th ed. McGraw-Hill Book Co., N.Y. 1087 pp.

Metcalf, H. 1908. Immunity of the Japanese chestnut to the bark disease. *U.S. Dep. Agric. Bur. Plant Ind. Bull. 121.* 4 pp.

Metcalf, H. and J. F. Collins. 1911. The control of the chestnut bark disease. *U.S. Dep. Agric. Farmers Bull. 467.* 24 pp.

Meyer, H. J. and D. M. Norris. 1967. Behavioral responses by *Scolytus multistriatus* (Coleoptera: Scolytidae) to host-(*Ulmus*) and beetle-associated chemotactic stimuli. *Ann. Entomol. Soc. Am. 60*:642-7.

Michelbacher, A. E. and J. C. Ortega. 1958. A technical study of insects and related pests attacking walnuts. *Univ. Calif. Div. Agric. Sci. Bull. 764*:5-83.

Millar, P. H. 1929. Apple maggot (*Rhagoletis pomonella* Walsh). *U.S. Dep. Agric. Insect Pest Surv. Bull. 9*:325.

Miller, C. A. 1953. Parasitism of spruce budworm eggs by *Trichogramma minutum* Riley. *Can. Sci. Serv., Div. For. Biol., Bi-Mon. Prog. Rep. 9*(4):1.

Miller, C. A. 1959. The interaction of the spruce budworm, *Choristoneura fumiferana* (Clem.), and the parasite *Apanteles fumiferanae* Vier. *Can. Entomol. 91*:457-77.

Miller, C. A. 1963. Parasites and the spruce budworm. Pages 228-44 in R. F. Morris, ed. "The Dynamics of Epidemic Spruce Budworm Populations." Mem. Entomol. Soc. Can. 31. 332 pp.

Miller, D., A. F. Clark, and L. J. Dumbleton. 1936. Biological control of noxious insects and weeds in New Zealand. *N.Z.J. Sci. Tech. 18*:579-93.

Miller, J. R., T. C. Baker, R. T. Cardé, and W. L. Roelofs. 1976. Reinvestigation of oak leafroller sex pheromone components and the hypothesis that they vary with diet. *Science (Wash. D.C.)* in press.

Miller, W. E. 1959. Preliminary study of European pine shoot moth parasitism in lower Michigan. *J. Econ. Entomol. 52*:768-9.

Miller, W. E. 1967. The European pine shoot moth—ecology and control in the Lake States. *For. Sci. Monogr. 14*:1-72.

Milne, A. 1957. The natural control of insect populations. *Can. Entomol. 89*:193-213.

Minks, A., W. Roelofs, F. Ritter, and C. Persoons. 1973. Reproductive isolation of two tortricid moth species by different ratios of a two-component sex attractant. *Science (Wash. D.C.) 180*:1073-4.

Minnich, D. E. 1922. The chemical sensitivity of the tarsi of the red admiral butterfly *Pyrameis atalanta* L. *J. Exp. Zool. 35*:57-81.

Minott, C. W. and I. T. Guild. 1925. Some results of the defoliation of trees. *J. Econ. Entomol. 18*:345-8.

Mitchell, E. R. 1975. Disruption of pheromonal communication among coexistent pest insects with multichemical formulations. *Bioscience 25*:493-9.

Moffat, J. A. 1900. Notes of the season of 1899. *Annu. Rep. Entomol. Soc. Ont. 30*:98-100.

Moffitt, E. M. and R. M. Lister. 1975. Application of a serological screening test for detecting double-stranded RNA mycoviruses. *Phytopathology 65*:851-9.

Mokrzecki, S. A. and A. P. Bragina. 1916. The rearing of *Trichogramma semblidis*, Aur., and *T. fasciatum*, P. in the laboratory and temperature experiments on them. *Rev. Appl. Entomol. Ser. A. 5*:155-6.

Mokrzecki, Z. and A. A. Ogloblin. 1931. *Hadronotus howardi* n. sp. (Microhymenopt., Proctotrupidae). *Bull. Entomol. Pol. T. X.*:1-8.

Monsarrat, P., G. Croizier, and C. Vago. 1973. Recherches cytopathlogiques sur une maladie virale du Coléoptère *Oryctes rhinoceros* L. *C. R. Hebd. Seances Acad. Sci. Paris. (Ser. D.)278*:3259-61.

Monsarrat, P., J.-L. Duthoit, and C. Vago. 1974. Virions of the baculovirus type in the genital organs of a coleoptera *Oryctes rhinoceros* L. *C. R. Hebd. Seances Acad. Sci. Paris. (Ser. D.) 278*:3259-61.

Monteith, L. G. 1955. Host preferences of *Drino bohemica* Mesn. (Diptera: Tachinidae), with particular reference to olfactory responses. *Can. Entomol. 87*:509-30.

Monteith, L. G. 1956. Influence of host movement on selection of hosts by *Drino bohemica* Mesn. (Diptera: Tachinidae) as determined in an olfactometer. *Can. Entomol. 88*:583-6.

Monteith, L. G. 1958. Influence of food plant of host on attractiveness of the host to tachinid parasites with notes on preimaginal conditioning. *Can. Entomol. 90*:478-82.

Monteith, L. G. 1960. Influence of plants other than food plants of their host on host-finding by tachinid parasites. *Can. Entomol. 92*:641-52.

Monteith, L. G. 1963. Habituation and associative learning in *Drino bohemica* Mesn. (Diptera: Tachinidae). *Can. Entomol. 95*:418-25.

Monteith, L. G. 1966. Influence of new growth on the food plant of the host-finding by *Drino bohemica* (Diptera: Tachinidae). *Can. Entomol. 98*:1205-7.

Montoya, R. 1970. Zona de Mora de Rubielos—descripcion, programas y trabajos efectuados en 1970. *Bol. Serv. Plagas For. 13*:119-29.

Monty, J. 1974. Teratological effects of the virus *Rhabdionvirus oryctes* on *Oryctes rhinoceros* (L.) (Coleoptera, Dynastidae). *Bull. Entomol. Res. 64*:633-6.

Moore, G. E. and R. C. Thatcher. 1973. Epidemic and endemic populations of the southern pine beetle. *U.S. Dep. Agric. For. Serv. Res. Pap. SE-111.* 11 pp.

Moravskaya, A. S. 1973. A new additional host of *Anastatus disparis* (Hymenoptera, Eupelmidae), egg parasite of *Porthetria dispar. Zool. Zh. 52*:147-50.

Morris, O. N. 1963. The natural and artificial control of the Douglas-fir tussock moth, *Orgyia pseudotsugata* McDunnough, by a nuclear-polyhedrosis virus. *J. Insect Pathol. 5*:401-14.

Morris, O. N. 1970. Precocious development of adult characteristics in virus-infected Lepidoptera. *J. Invertebr. Pathol. 16*:173-9.

Morris, O. N. 1971. The effect of sunlight, ultraviolet and gamma radiations, and temperature on the infectivity of a nuclear polyhedrosis virus. *J. Invertebr. Pathol. 18*:292-4.

Morris, O. N. 1972. Susceptibility of some forest insects to mixtures of commercial *Bacillus thuringiensis* and chemical insecticides, and sensitivity of the pathogen to the insecticides. *Can. Entomol. 104*:1419-25.

Morris, O. N. 1975. Susceptibility of the spruce budworm, *Choristoneura fumiferana*, and the white-marked tussock moth, *Orgyia leucostigmata*, to *Bacillus thuringiensis*: chemical insecticide combinations. *J. Invertebr. Pathol. 26*:193-8.

Morris, O. N., J. A. Armstrong, G. M. Howse, and J. C. Cunningham. 1974. A 2-year study of virus-chemical insecticide combination in the integrated control of the spruce budworm, *Choristoneura fumiferana* (Tortricidae: Lepidoptera). *Can. Entomol. 106*:813-24.

Morris, R. F. 1951. The importance of insect control in a forest management program. *Can. Entomol. 83*:176-81.

Morris, R. F. 1963. The Dynamics of Epidemic Spruce Budworm Populations. Mem. Entomol. Soc. Can. 31. 332 pp.

Mors, H. 1938. Stellungnahme zu einigen Arbeiten über eine neue Methode zur Nonnenbefallsermittlung und Nonnenbekämpfung. *Forstarchiv 14*:296-9.

Mosher, F. H. 1915. Food plants of the gipsy moth in America. *U.S. Dep. Agric. Bull. 250.* 39 pp.

Muesebeck, C. F. W. 1931. *Monodontomerus aereus* Walker, both a primary and a secondary parasite of the brown-tail moth and the gipsy moth. *J. Agric. Res. 43*:445-60.

Muesebeck, C. F. W. and S. M. Dohanian. 1927. A study in hyperparasitism with particular reference to the parasites of *Apanteles melanoscelus* (Ratzeburg). *U.S. Dep. Agric. Bull. 1487.* 35 pp.

Muesebeck, C. F. W. and D. L. Parker. 1933. *Hyposoter disparis* Viereck, an introduced ichneumonid parasite of the gipsy moth. *J. Agric. Res. 46*:335-47.

Muesebeck, C. F. W., K. V. Krombein, and H. E. Townes. 1951. "Hymenoptera of America North of Mexico Synoptic Catalog." U.S. Dep. Agric. Monogr. No. 2. 1420 pp.

Mulford, W. 1902. First annual report of the forester. Pages 353-64 in *25th Annu. Rep. Conn. Agri. Exp. Stn. (New Haven).* 446 pp.

Müller-Kögler, E. 1965. "Pilzkrankheiten bei Insekten." Paul Parey, Berlin. 444 pp.

Mundt, J. O. 1963. Occurrence of enterococci on plants in a wild environment. *Appl. Microbiol. 11*:141-4.

Murrill, W. A. 1906. A serious chestnut disease. *N.Y. Bot. Garden. 7*:143-53.

Nagaraja, H. and S. Nagarkatti. 1973. A key to some new world species of *Trichogramma* (Hymenoptera: Trichogrammatidae), with descriptions of four new species. *Proc. Entomol. Soc. Wash. 75*:288-97.

Nagarkatti, S. and H. Nagaraja. 1971. Redescriptions of some known species of *Trichogramma* (Hym., Trichogrammatidae), showing the importance of the male genitalia as a diagnostic character. *Bull. Entomol. Res. 61*:13-31.

Nagy, B., G. Reichart, and C. Ubrizy. 1953. Der amerikanische weisse Barenspinner, *Hyphantria cunea* Drury, in Ungarn. *Forschungs-Inst. Pflanzenschutz. 33*:191-5.

Nef, L. 1971. Influence de traitements insecticides chimiques et microbiens sur une population de *Stilpnotia* (= *Leucoma*) *salicis* L. et sur ses parasites. *Z. Angew Entomol. 69*:357-67.

Nef, L. 1975. Microorganismes pathogénes dans la lutte contre les Lymantriidés défoliateurs. *Bull. Rech. Agron. Gembloux, No. hors sér.* (in press).

Neilson, M. M. 1963a. The analysis of egg survival in the unsprayed area. Pages 37-41 in R. F. Morris, ed. "The Dynamics of Epidemic Spruce Budworm Populations." Mem. Entomol. Soc. Can. 31. 332 pp.

Neilson, M. M. 1963b. Disease and the spruce budworm. Pages 272-87 in R. F. Morris, ed. "The Dynamics of Epidemic Spruce Budworm Populations." Mem. Entomol. Soc. Can. 31. 332 pp.

Neilson, M. M. 1965. Effects of a cytoplasmic polyhedrosis on adult Lepidoptera. *J. Invertebr. Pathol. 7*:306-14.

Neilson, M. M. and F. G. Cuming. 1958. Egg parasitism of the fall cankerworm. *Can. Sci. Serv. Div. For. Biol. Bi-mon. Prog. Rep. 14*(6):1.

Neilson, M. M. and D. E. Elgee. 1968. The method and role of vertical transmission of a nucleopolyhedrosis virus in the European spruce sawfly, *Diprion hercyniae. J. Invertebr. Pathol. 12*:132-9.

Neilson, M. M. and R. F. Morris. 1964. The regulation of European spruce sawfly numbers in the Maritime provinces of Canada from 1937 to 1963. *Can. Entomol. 96*:773-84.

Nichols, G. E. 1913. The vegetation of Connecticut. II. Virgin forests. *Torreya 13*:199-215.

Nichols, J. O. 1968. Oak mortality in Pennsylvania: a ten year study. *J. For. 66*:681-94.

Nicholson, A. J. 1933. The balance of animal populations. *J. Anim. Ecol. II(1)(Suppl.)*:132-78.

Nicholson, A. J. 1954. An outline of the dynamics of animal populations. *Aust. J. Zool. 2*:9-65.

Nicholson, A. J. and V. A. Bailey. 1935. The balance of animal populations. Part 1. *Proc. Zool. Soc. London 3*:551-98.

Niklas, O. F. 1939. Zum Massenwechsel der Tachine *Parasetigena segregata* Rond. in der Rominter Heide. *Z. Angew. Entomol. 26*:63-103.

Nikol'skaya, M. N. 1963. "The Chalcid Fauna of the USSR Chalcidoidea" (Transl. from Russ.). Isr. Prog. Sci. Trans. (Jerusalem). National Science Foundation, Wash. D.C. 593 pp.

Nixon, G. E. J. 1974. A revision of the north-western European species of the *glomeratus*-group of *Apanteles* Förster (Hymenoptera, Braconidae). *Bull. Entomol. Res. 64*:453-524.

Nolte, H. W. 1940. Neue Erfahrungen zur Dykschen Nonnenanlockmethode. *Zentrabl. Gesamte Forstwes. 66*:197-206, 252-67.

Nordin, G. L. and J. V. Maddox. 1972. Effects of simultaneous virus and microsporidian infections on larvae of *Hyphantria cunea. J. Invertebr. Pathol. 20*:66-9.

Nuorteva, M. 1972. Use of the nuclear polyhedrosis virus in the control of the European pine sawfly (*Neodiprion sertifer* (Geoffr.)). *Silva Fenn. 6*:172-86. (In Finn.).

Odier, F. and C. Vago. 1973. Mise en évidence d'une immunité antivirale chez les insectes. *C. R. Hebd. Seances Acad. Sci. Paris (Ser. D) 277*:1257-60.

Ohba, M. 1975a. Studies on the pathogenesis of *Chilo* iridescent virus. 3. Multiplication of CIV in the silkworm, *Bombyx mori* L., and field insects. *Sci. Bull. Fac. Agric., Kyushu Univ. 30*:71-81.

Ohba, M. 1975b. Studies on the pathogenesis of *Chilo* iridescent virus. 4. Simultaneous infection of CIV and a nuclear polyhedrosis virus. *Sci. Bull. Fac. Agric., Kyushu Univ. 30*:83-6.

Oliver, C. D. 1975. "The Development of Northern Red Oak in Mixed Species, Even-aged Stands in Central New England." Ph. D. Thesis, Yale Univ., New Haven, Conn. 223 pp.

Olmsted, C. E. 1937. Vegetation of certain sand plains of Connecticut. *Bot. Gaz. 99*:209-300.

Olofsson, E. 1973. Evaluation of a nuclear polyhedrosis virus as an agent for the control of the balsam fir sawfly, *Neodiprion abietis* Harr. Insect Pathol. Res. Inst., Dep. Environ. Can. For. Serv. Sault Ste. Marie, Ont. Inf. Rep. IP-X-2. 30 pp.

Ono, M. and M. Fukaya. 1969. The juvenile-hormone-like effect of *Chilo* iridescent virus (CIV) on the metamorphosis of the silkworm, *Bombyx mori* L. *Appl. Entomol. Zool.* 4:211-2.

Ono, M., S. Yagi, and M. Fukaya. 1972. Infectivity of *Chilo* iridescent virus on the silkworm, *Bombyx mori. Bull. Seric. Exp. Stn. 25*:77-102.

Orlovskaya, S. V. 1964. Infection of gypsy moth larvae with the virus of nuclear polyhedrosis and its effect on the fertility of the moth and survival of the progeny. (Transl. from Russ.). *Biol. Control Agric. For. Pests, Proc. of Symp. 17-20 Nov.* pp. 54-6.

Ossowski, L. L. J. 1960. Variation in virulence of a wattle bagworm virus. *J. Insect Pathol.* 2:35-43.

Ostrander, M. D. and C. H. Foster. 1957. Weevil-red rot associations in eastern white pine. *Northeast. For. Exp. Stn., For. Res. Note 68.* 2pp.

Otvos, I. S. and D. G. Bryant. 1972. An extraction method for rapid sampling of eastern hemlock looper eggs, *Lambdina fiscellaria fiscellaria* (Lepidoptera: Geometridae). *Can. Entomol. 104*:1511-4.

Otvos, I. S., D. M. MacLeod, and D. Tyrrell. 1973. Two species of *Entomophthora* pathogenic to the eastern hemlock looper (Lepidoptera: Geometridae) in Newfoundland. *Can. Entomol. 105*:1435-41.

Parker, D. L. 1933. The interrelations of two hymenopterous egg parasites of the gipsy moth, with notes on larval instars of each. *J. Agric. Res. 46*:23-34.

Parker, D. L. 1935. *Apanteles solitarius* (Ratzeburg), an introduced braconid parasite of the satin moth. *U.S. Dep. Agric. Tech. Bull. 477.* 17 pp.

Parmeter, J. R., Jr., J. E. Kuntz, and A. J. Riker. 1956. Oak wilt development in bur oaks. *Phytopathology 46*:423-36.

Parrott, P. J., H. E. Hodgkiss, and W. J. Schoene. 1906. The apple and pear mites. *N. Y. Agric. Exp. Stn. Geneva Bull. 283.* pp. 281-318.

Pasquill, F. 1962. "Atmospheric Diffusion: The Dispersion of Windborne Material from Industrial and Other Sources." D. Van Nostrand Co., Ltd., London. 297 pp.

Patric, J. H. and D. W. Smith. 1975. Forest management and nutrient cycling in eastern hardwoods. *U.S. For. Serv. Res. Pap. NE 324.* 12 pp.

Patterson, J. E. 1929. The pandora moth, a periodic pest of western pine forests. *U.S. Dep. Agric. Tech. Bull. 137.* 19 pp.

Pavan, M. and G. Ronchetti. 1971/72. Le formiche del gruppo *Formica rufa* in Italia nell'assestamento ecologico forestale. *Waldhygiene 9*:223-38.

Peacock, J. W., A. C. Lincoln, J. B. Simeone, and R. M. Silverstein. 1971. Attraction of *Scolytus multistriatus* (Coleoptera: Scolytidae) to a virgin-female-produced pheromone in the field. *Ann. Entomol. Soc. Am. 64*:1143-9.

Peacock, J. W., R. M. Silverstein, A. C. Lincoln, and J. B. Simeone. 1973. Laboratory investigations of the frass of *Scolytus multistriatus* (Coleoptera: Scolytidae) as a source of pheromone. *Environ. Entomol. 2*:355-9.

Peacock, J. W., R. A. Cuthbert, W. E. Gore, G. N. Lanier, G. T. Pearce, and R. M. Silverstein. 1975. Collection on Porapak Q of the aggregation pheromone of *Scolytus multistriatus* (Coleoptera: Scolytidae). *J. Chem Ecol. 1*:149-60.

Pearce, G. T., W. E. Gore, R. M. Silverstein, J. W. Peacock, R. A. Cuthbert, G. N. Lanier, and J. B. Simeone. 1975. Chemical attractants for the smaller European elm bark beetle *Scolytus multistriatus* (Coleoptera: Scolytidae). *J. Chem. Ecol. 1*:115-24.

Pearce, G. T., W. E. Gore, and R. M. Silverstein. 1976. The synthesis and absolute configuration of multistriatin. *J. Org. Chem.* in press.

Peck, M. D. 1817. On the insects which destroy the young branches of the pear-tree, and the leading shoot of the Weymouth-pine. *Mass. Agric. J. 4*:205-11.

Peck, O. 1963. "A Catalog of the Nearctic Chalcidoidea (Insecta: Hymenoptera)." Can. Entomol. Suppl. 30. 1092 pp.

Pemberton, C. E. 1948. History of the entomology department experiment station, H.S.P.A., 1904-1945. *Hawaii. Plant. Rec. 52*:90.

Persoons, C. J., A. K. Minks, S. Voerman, W. Roelofs, and F. Ritter. 1974. Sex pheromones of *Archips podana* (Lepidoptera: Tortricidae): isolation, identification and field evaluation of two synergistic geometrical isomers. *J. Insect Physiol. 20*:1181-8.

Peterson, A. 1931. Refrigeration of *Trichogramma minutum* Riley and other notes. *J. Econ. Entomol. 24*:1070-4.

Pimentel, D. 1963. Introducing parasites and predators to control native pests. *Can. Entomol. 95*:785-92.

Pimentel, D. and M. Shapiro. 1962. The influence of environment on a virus-host relationship. *J. Insect Pathol. 4*:77-87.

Pirone, P. P. 1970. "Diseases and Pests of Ornamental Plants." Ronald Press Co., N.Y. 546 pp.

Plumb, G. H. and R. B. Friend. 1939. An outbreak of the elm spanworm in Connecticut, 1938. *Conn. Agric. Exp. Stn. Bull. (New Haven) 428.* pp. 98-102.

Plummer, E. L., T. E. Stewart, K. Byrne, G. T. Pearce, and R. M. Silverstein. 1976. Determination of the enantiomeric composition of several insect pheromone alcohols. *J. Chem. Ecol.* in press.

Podgwaite, J. D. and R. W. Campbell. 1972. The disease complex of the gypsy moth. II. Aerobic bacterial pathogens. *J. Invertebr. Pathol. 20*:303-8.

Polson, A. and H. Gitay. 1972. A possible role of the cattle egret in the dissemination of the granulosis virus of the boll-worm. *Ostrich 43*:231-2.

Porter, B. A. 1924. The bud moth. *U.S. Dep. Agric. Bull. 1273.* 20 pp.

Prebble, M. L. 1951. Forest entomology in relation to silviculture in Canada. Part 1. A review of general principles. *For. Chron. 27*:1-32.

Prell, H. 1915. Zur Biologie der Tachinen *Parasetigena segregata* Rdi. und *Panzeria rudis* Fall. *Z. Angew. Entomol. 2*:57-148.

Prentice, R. M. 1965. Forest Lepidoptera of Canada recorded by the Forest Insect Survey. Vol. 4. Microlepidoptera. *Can. Dep. For. Publ. 1142.* pp. 545-840.

Price, P. W. 1970. Trail odors: recognition by insects parasitic on cocoons. *Science (Wash. D.C.) 170*:546-7.

Price, P. W. 1971. Niche breadth and dominance of parasitic insects sharing the same host species. *Ecology 52*:587-96.

Price, P. W. 1972a. Methods of sampling and analysis for predictive results in the introduction of entomophagous insects. *Entomophaga 17*:211-22.

Price, P. W. 1972b. Behavior of the parasitoid *Pleolophus basizonus* (Hymenoptera: Ichneumonidae) in response to changes in host and parasitoid density. *Can. Entomol. 104*:129-40.

Price, R. 1954. "Johnny Appleseed, Man and Myth." Indiana Univ. Press, Bloomington, Ind. 320 pp.

Prokopy, R. J. and G. L. Bush. 1972. Apple maggot infestation of pear. *J. Econ. Entomol. 65*:597.

Pschorn-Walcher, H. 1974. Gypsy moth (*Porthetria dispar*): work in Europe in 1974. Annual project statement. *Commonw. Inst. Biol. Control, Switzerland.* 17 pp.

Purrington, F. F. and J. S. Uleman. 1972. Brood size of the parasitic wasp *Hyssopus thymus* (Hymenoptera: Eulophidae): functional correlation with the mass of a cryptic host. *Ann. Entomol. Soc. Am. 65*:280.

Pyenson, L. 1943. A destructive apple sawfly new to North America. *J. Econ. Entomol.* *36*:218-21.

Quaintance, A. L. 1908. The lesser apple worm. *U.S. Dep. Agric. Bur. Entomol. Bull. 68.* pp. 49-60.

Quednau, F. W. 1967. Notes on mating behavior and oviposition of *Chrysocharis laricinellae* (Hymenoptera: Eulophidae), a parasite of the larch casebearer (*Coleophora laricella*). *Can. Entomol. 99*: 326-31.

Quednau, F. W. 1970. Notes on life-history, fecundity, longevity, and attack pattern of *Agathis pumila*, a parasite of the larch casebearer. *Can. Entomol. 102*:736-45.

Radovan, M. 1975. Activity of synthetic and natural sex attractants of the gypsy moth (*Lymantria dispar* L.) in the field trials. *8th Int. Plant Prot. Congr. Moscow. Sec V*:140-8.

Ramoska, W. A., G. R. Stairs, and W. F. Hink. 1975. Ultraviolet light activation of insect nuclear polyhedrosis virus. *Nature (Lond.) 253*:628-9.

Rao, V. P. 1966. Survey for natural enemies of gypsy moth. Report for the period July 1961 to July 1966. U.S. PL-480 Project (A7FS-8). *Commonw. Inst. Biol. Control, Bangalore, India.* 50 pp.

Rauschenberger, J. L. and R. L. Talerico. 1967. Egg parasitism of the fall cankerworm *Alsophila pometaria* by *Telenomus alsophilae. J. Econ. Entomol. 60*:881-2.

Raynor, G. S. 1971. Wind and temperature structure in a coniferous forest and a contiguous field. *For. Sci. 17*:351-63.

Raynor, G. S., J. V. Hayes, and E. C. Ogden. in press. Particulate dispersion from sources within a forest. *Boundary-Layer Meterorol.*

Reardon, R. C., M. W. Statler, and W. H. McLane. 1973. Rearing techniques and biology of five gypsy moth parasites. *Environ. Entomol. 2*:124-7.

Reed, D. K. 1974. Effects of temperature on virus-host relationships and on activity of the noninclusion virus of citrus red mites, *Panonychus citri. J. Invertebr. Pathol. 4*:218-23.

Reed, D. K. and I. M. Hall. 1972. Electron microscopy of a rod-shaped noninclusion virus infecting the citrus red mite. *J. Invertebr. Pathol. 20*:272-8.

Reed, D. K., J. E. Rich, and J. J. Shaw. 1974. Inhibition of formation of birefringent crystals by high humidity in citrus red mites infected with virus. *J. Invertebr. Pathol. 23*:285-8.

Reed, D. K., H. Tashiro, and J. B. Beavers. 1975. Determination of mode of transmission of the citrus red mite virus. *J. Invertebr. Pathol. 26*:239-46.

Reed, E. M. 1971. Factors affecting the status of a virus as a control agent for the potato moth (*Phthorimaea operculella*) (Zell.) (Lep., Gelechiidae). *Bull. Entomol. Res. 61*:207-22.

Reichelderfer, C. F. and C. V. Benton. 1973. The effect of 3-methyl-cholanthrene treatment on the virulence of a nuclear polyhedrosis virus of *Spodoptera frugiperda. J. Invertebr. Pathol. 22*:38-41.

Reichelderfer, C. F. and C. V. Benton. 1974. Some genetic aspects of the resistance of *Spodoptera frugiperda* to a nuclear polyhedrosis virus. *J. Invertebr. Pathol. 23*:378-82.

Reiff, W. 1911. The "wilt disease" or "flacherie" of the gypsy moth. *Contrib. Entomol. Lab., Bussey Inst., Harv. Univ. 36.* 60 pp.

Remington, C. L. 1968. The population genetics of insect introduction. *Annu. Rev. Entomol. 13*:415-27.

Retnakaran, A. and F. T. Bird. 1972. Apparent hormone imbalance syndrome caused by an insect virus. *J. Invertebr. Pathol. 20*:358-60.

Rice, R. E. 1968. Observations on host selection by *Tomicobia tibialis* Ashmead (Hymenoptera: Pteromalidae). *Contrib. Boyce Thompson Inst. 24*:53-6.

Rice, R. E. 1969. Response of some predators and parasites of *Ips confusus* (Lec.) (Coleoptera: Scolytidae) to olfactory attractants. *Contrib. Boyce Thompson Inst. 24*:189-94.

Richardson, L. F. 1926. Atmospheric diffusion shown on a distance-neighbor graph. *Proc. R. Soc. Lond. Ser. A. 110*:709-37.

Richerson, J. V. and J. H. Borden. 1971. Sound and vibration are not obligatory host finding stimuli for the bark beetle parasite, *Coeloides brunneri* (Hymenoptera: Braconidae). *Entomophaga 16*:95-9.

Richerson, J. V. and J. H. Borden. 1972a. Host finding behavior of *Coeloides brunneri* (Hymenoptera: Braconidae). *Can. Entomol. 104*:1235-50.

Richerson, J. V. and J. H. Borden. 1972b. Host finding by heat perception in *Coeloides brunneri* (Hymenoptera: Braconidae). *Can Entomol. 104*:1877-81.

Richerson, J. V. and E. A. Cameron. 1974. Differences in pheromone release and sexual behavior between laboratory-reared and wild gypsy moth adults. *Environ. Entomol. 3*:475-81.

Richerson, J. V., E. A. Brown, and E. A. Cameron. 1976a. Pre-mating sexual activity of gypsy moth males in small plot field tests (*Lymantria (= Porthetria) dispar* L.: Lymantriidae). *Can. Entomol. in press.*

Richerson, J. V., E. A. Cameron, and E. A. Brown. 1976b. Sexual activity of the gypsy moth. *Am. Midl. Nat.* in press.

Rinderer, T. E., W. C. Rothenbuhler, and J. M. Kulinčević. 1975. Responses of three genetically different stocks of the honeybee to a virus from bees with hairless-black syndrome. *J. Invertebr. Pathol. 25*:297-300.

Rivers, C. F. 1959. Virus resistance in larvae of *Pieris brassicae* (L.). *Trans. 1st. Int. Conf. Insect Pathol. Biol. Control, Prague, 1958.* pp. 205-10.

Roberts, D. W. and W. G. Yendol. 1973. Some recent advances in insect pathology. *Misc. Publ. Entomol. Soc. Am. 9*:51-119.

Roelofs, W. L. 1975. Insect communication-chemical. Pages 79-99 in D. Pimentel, ed. "Insects, Science, and Society." Academic Press, N.Y. 284 pp.

Roelofs, W. L. and R. T. Cardé. 1974. Sex pheromones in the reproductive isolation of lepidopterous species. Pages 96-114 in M. C. Birch, ed. "Pheromones." North-Holland Publ. Co., Amsterdam. 495 pp.

Roelofs, W. L. and A. Comeau. 1971. Sex attractants in Lepidoptera. Pages 91-114 in A. Tahori, ed. "Chemical Releasers in Insects." Vol. III. Gordon and Breach, N.Y. 227 pp.

Roelofs, W. and J. Tette. 1970. Sex pheromone of the oblique-banded leaf roller. *Nature (Lond.) 226*:1172.

Roelofs, W., A. Hill, and R. Cardé. 1975. Sex pheromone components of the redbanded leafroller moth, *Argyrotaenia velutinana. J. Chem. Ecol. 1*:83-9.

Roelofs, W., A. Hill, R. Cardé, J. Tette, H. Madsen, and J. Vakenti. 1974. Sex pheromones of the fruittree leafroller moth, *Archips argyrospilus. Environ. Entomol. 3*:747-51.

Roelofs, W., R. Cardé, E. Taschenberg, and R. Weires, Jr. 1976a. Pheromone research for control of lepidopterous species in New York. In M. Beroza, ed. "On Prospects for Insect Pest Management with Sex Attractants and Other Behavior-controlling Chemicals." Amer. Chem. Soc. Symp. In press.

Roelofs, W., A. Hill, A. Cardé, R. Cardé, H. Madsen, and J. Vakenti. 1976b. Sex pheromone of the European leafroller, *Archips rosanus. Environ. Entomol. 5*: ms. submitted.

Rogers, D. J. 1972. Random search and insect population models. *J. Anim. Ecol. 41*:369-83.

Rohwer, S. A. 1940. Fifty years of entomological progress, Part V, 1929 to 1939. *J. Econ. Entomol. 33*:58-65.

Rollinson, W. D., F. B. Lewis, and W. E. Waters. 1965. The successful use of a nuclear-polyhedrosis virus against the gypsy moth. *J. Invertebr. Pathol.* 7:515-7.

Romanova, Yu. S. and V. A. Lozinskij. 1958. Experiments on the practical use of egg parasites of *Malacosoma neustria* in forest conditions. *Zool. Zh.* 37:542-7. (In Russ., Engl. summ.)

Rose, A. H. 1958. The effect of defoliation on foliage production and radial growth of quaking aspen. *For. Sci.* 4:335-42.

Rudinsky, J. A., V. Novak, and P. Švihra. 1971. Attraction of the bark beetle *Ips typographus* L. to terpenes and a male-produced pheromone. *Z. Angew. Entomol.* 67:179-88.

Ruggles, A. G. 1913. Notes on a chestnut tree parasite. *Science (Wash. D.C.)* 38:852.

Rumbold, C. 1920a. The injection of chemicals into chestnut trees. *Am. J. Bot.* 7:1-20.

Rumbold, C. 1920b. Effect on chestnuts of substances injected into their trunks. *Am. J. Bot.* 7:44-56.

Růžička, J. 1924. Die neuesten Erfahrungen über die Nonne in Böhmen. *Zentralbl. Gesamte Forstwes.* 50:33-68.

Ryan, R. B. 1971. Interaction between two parasites, *Apechthis ontario* and *Itoplectis quadricingulatus.* 1. Survival in singly attacked, super-, and multiparasitized greater wax moth pupae. *Ann. Entomol. Soc. Am.* 64:205-8.

Ryan, R. B. 1974. Reduced oviposition by *Ephialtes ontario* and *Itoplectis quadricingulatus* in a humid environment. *Ann. Entomol. Soc. Am.* 67:928-30.

Ryan, R. B. and R. D. Medley. 1972. Interaction between two parasites, *Apechthis ontario* and *Itoplectis quadricingulatus.* 2. F_1 progeny production in light-stratified population cages. *Ann. Entomol. Soc. Am.* 65:172-7.

Ryan, R. B. and J. A. Rudinsky. 1962. Biology and habits of the Douglas-fir beetle parasite, *Coeloides brunneri* Viereck (Hymenoptera: Braconidae) in western Oregon. *Can. Entomol.* 94:748-63.

Ryvkin, B. V. 1959. The biology and economic importance of *Trichogramma embryophagum* (Htg) (Hymenoptera, Trichogrammatidae). *Entomol. Rev.* 38:344-54.

Sabrosky, C. W. and R. C. Reardon. 1976. Tachinid parasitoids of the gypsy moth, *Lymantria dispar* L., with keys to adults and puparia. *Misc. Publ. Entomol. Soc. Am.* in press.

Safranyik, L., D. M. Shrimpton, and H. S. Whitney. 1974. Management of lodgepole pine to reduce losses from the mountain pine beetle. *For. Tech. Rep., Pac. For. Res. Cent., Can. For. Serv. 1.* 24 pp.

Sager, S. M. 1960. On the transtadial transmission of insect viruses. *J. Insect Pathol.* 2:307-9.

Salman, K. A. and J. W. Bongberg. 1942. Logging high risk trees to control insects in pine stand of northeastern California. *J. For.* 40:533-9.

Sandquist, R. E., J. V. Richerson, and E. A. Cameron. 1973. Flight of North American female gypsy moths. *Environ. Entomol.* 2:957-8.

Sartwell, C. and R. E. Stevens. 1975. Mountain pine beetle in ponderosa pine, prospects for silvicultural control in second growth stands. *J. For.* 73:136-40.

Scepetil'nikova, V. A. 1970. Perspektiven der Kenntnis und Anwendung von Eiparasiten der Gattung *Trichogramma* zur Bekämpfung land-und forstwirtschaftlicher Schädlinge. *Dtsch. Akad. Landwirtschaftswiss Tagungsber. 110:*117-36.

Schaefer, C. W. 1974. Rise and fall of the apple redbugs. Pages 101-16 in R. L. Beard, ed. "25th Anniversary Memoir Connecticut Entomological Society." Conn. Entomol. Soc., New Haven, Conn. 322 pp.

Schaffner, J. V. 1927. Dispersion of *Compsilura concinnata* Meig. beyond the limits of the gipsy and brown-tail moth infestation. *J. Econ. Entomol.* 20:725-32.

Schaffner, J. V. 1934. Introduced parasites of the brown-tail and gipsy moths reared from native hosts. *Ann. Entomol. Soc. Am. 27*:585-92.

Schaffner, J. V. and C. L. Griswold. 1934. Macrolepidoptera and their parasites reared from field collections in the northeastern part of the United States. *U.S. Dep. Agric. Misc. Publ. 188.* 160 pp.

Schallau, C. H. 1975. Response to future needs for land to produce timber, perspectives on prime lands. *U.S. Dep. Agric. Seminar Retention of Prime Lands.* pp. 92-6.

Schedl, K. E. 1936. Der Schwammspinner (*Porthetria dispar* L.) in Eurosaien, Afrika, und Neuengland. *Monogr. Angew. Entomol. 12.* 242 pp.

Schiëferdecker, H. 1969. Zur Vermehrung von *Ooencyrtus kuwanae* (Howard, 1910) unter Laborverhaltnissen. *Beitr. Entomol. 19*:803-15.

Schindler, U. 1971. Changes in the use and choice of insecticides against forest insects in central Europe. *Proc. 6th Br. Insecticide Fungicide Conf. (1971).* pp. 463-6.

Schmid, A. 1974a. Untersuchungen zur *Trans-ovum*-Uebertragung des Granulosisvirus des Grauen Laerchenwicklers, *Zeiraphera diniana* (Lep.: Tortricidae) und Ausloesung der akuten Virose durch Stressfaktoren. *Entomophaga 19*:279-92.

Schmid, A. 1974b. Untersuchungen über die Umweltpersistenz des Granulosisvirus des Grauen Lärchenwicklers *Zeiraphera diniana* (Gn.) und die Schutzwirkung verschiedener Stoffe. *Z. Angew. Entomol. 76*: 31-49.

Schneider, D. 1964. Insect antennae. *Annu. Rev. Entomol. 9*:103-22.

Schneider, D., R. Lange, F. Schwartz, M. Beroza, and B. A. Bierl. 1974. Attraction of male gypsy and nun moths to disparlure and some of its chemical analogues. *Oecologia (Berl.) 14*:19-36.

Schock, O. D. 1914. Final report of the Pa. Chestnut Tree Blight Commission. *W. S. Ray, State Printer, Harrisburg, Pa.* 3 pp.

Schoene, W. J., L. R. Cagle, M. L. Bobb, and R. N. Jefferson. 1937. The oriental peach moth in Virginia apple and peach orchards. *Va. Agric. Exp. Stn. Bull. 308.* 23 pp.

Schoeneweiss, D. F. 1967. Susceptibility of weakened cottonwood stems to fungi associated with blackstem. *Plant Dis. Rep. 51*:933-5.

Schönherr, J. 1969. Freilandversuch zur biologischen Bekämpfung des Tannentriebwicklers *Choristoneura murinana* (Hübn.) mit Granuloseviren. *Entomophaga 14*:251-60.

Schönherr, J. 1970. Evidence on an aggregating pheromone in the ash-bark beetle *Leperisinus fraxini* (Coleoptera: Scolytidae). *Contrib. Boyce Thompson Inst. 24*:305-7.

Schönherr, J. 1972a. Die Wirkung von Disparlure auf die Nonne. *Z. Angew. Entomol. 71*:260-3.

Schönherr, J. 1972b. Pheromon beim Kiefern-Borkenkafer "Waldgärtner", *Myelophilus piniperda* L. (Coleopt., Scolytidae). *Z. Angew. Entomol. 71*:410-3.

Schread, J. C. and P. Garman. 1933. Studies on parasites of the oriental fruit moth. *Conn. Agric. Exp. Stn. Bull. (New Haven) 353.* pp. 691-756.

Schröder, D. 1974. A study of the interactions between the internal larval parasites of *Rhyacionia buoliana* (Lepidoptera: Olethreutidae). *Entomophaga 19*:145-71.

Schröter, H. J. and R. Lange. 1975. Untersuchungen über den Einflub des weiblichen Sexual pheromons auf die Flugaktivität der Männchen von *Lymantria monacha* L. in Freiland. *Z. Angew. Entomol. 77*:337-41.

Schuh, J. and D. C. Mote. 1948. The oblique-banded leaf roller on red raspberries. *Oreg. Agric. Exp. Stn. Tech. Bull. 13.* 43 pp.

Schultz, D. E. and D. C. Allen. 1975. Biology and descriptions of the cherry scallop shell moth, *Hydria prunivorata* (Lepidoptera: Geometridae), in New York. *Can. Entomol. 107*:99-106.

Schuster, M. F., J. C. Boling, and J. J. Marony, Jr. 1971. Biological control of rhodesgrass scale by airplane releases of an introduced parasite of limited dispersing ability. Pages 227-50 in C. B. Huffaker, ed. "Biological Control." Plenum Press, N.Y. 511 pp.

Schütte, F. and J. M. Franz. 1961. Untersuchungen zur Apfelwicklerbekämpfung (*Carpocapsa pomonella* (L.)) mit Hilfe von *Trichogramma embryophagum* Hartig. *Entomophaga* 6:237-47.

Schwalbe, C. P., E. A. Cameron, D. J. Hall, J. V. Richerson, M. Beroza, and L. J. Stevens. 1974. Field tests of microencapsulated disparlure for suppression of mating among wild and laboratory-reared gypsy moths. *Environ. Entomol.* 4:589-92.

Schwenke, W. 1958. Local dependence of parasitic insects and its importance for biological control. *Proc. 10th Int. Congr. Entomol. (Montreal)* 4:851-4.

Schwerdtfeger, F. 1932. Die Forleule in Neuendorf 1932. Untersuchungen über ihre Oekologie, Epidemiologie und Bekämpfung. *Mitt. Forstwirtsch. Forstwiss.* 3:342-404.

Schwerdtfeger, F. 1935. Studien über den Massenwechsel einiger Forstschädlinge. *Z. Forst-Jagdwesen.* 67:15-38, 85-104, 449-82, 513-40.

Schwerdtfeger, F. 1973. Forest entomology. Pages 361-86 in R. F. Smith, T. E. Mittler, and C. N. Smith, eds. "History of Entomology." Annu. Rev. Inc., Palo Alto, Calif. 517 pp.

Schwinck, I. 1954. Experimentelle Untersuchungen über Geruchssin und Strömungswahrnehmung in der Orientierung bei Nachtschmetterlingen. *Z. Vgl. Physiol.* 37:19-56.

Schwinck, I. 1955. Weitere Untersuchungen zur Frage der Geruchsorientierung der Nachtschmetterlinge: Partielle Fühleramputationen bei Spinnermännchen, insbesondere am Seidenspinner, *Bombyx mori* L. *Z. Vgl. Physiol.* 37:439-58.

Schwinck, I. 1958. A study of olfactory stimuli in the orientation of moths. *Proc. 10th Int. Congr. Entomol. (Montreal)* 2:577-82.

Seaton, F. A., M. Clawson, R. Hodges, Jr., S. Spurr, and D. Zinn. 1973. "Report of the President's Advisory Panel on Timber and the Environment." U.S. Gov. Printing Office, Wash. D.C. 541 pp.

Shaw, J. G., H. Tashiro, and E. J. Dietrick. 1968. Infection of the citrus red mite with virus in central and southern California. *J. Econ. Entomol.* 61:1492-5.

Shaw, R. H., R. H. Silversides, and G. W. Thurtell. 1974. Some observations of turbulence and turbulent transport within and above plant canopies. *Boundary-Layer Meteorol.* 5:429-49.

Shervis, L. J., G. M. Boush, and C. F. Koval. 1970. Infestation of sour cherries by the apple maggot: confirmation of a previously uncertain host status. *J. Econ. Entomol.* 63:294-5.

Shinn, J. H. 1969. Analysis of wind data from a South Carolina coastal forest. *ECOM-6036. U.S. Army Electronics Command, Fort Huachuca, Ariz.* 23 pp.

Shorey, H. H. 1970. Sex pheromones of Lepidoptera. Pages 249-84 in D. L. Wood, R. M. Silverstein, and M. Nakajima, eds. "Control of Insect Behavior by Natural Products." Academic Press, N.Y. 345 pp.

Shorey, H. H. 1973. Behavioral responses to insect pheromones. *Annu. Rev. Entomol.* 18:349-80.

Shorey, H. H. 1974. Environmental and physiological control of insect sex pheromone behavior. Pages 62-80 in M. C. Birch, ed. "Pheromones." North-Holland Publ. Co., Amsterdam. 495 pp.

Shorey, H. H. and L. K. Gaston. 1970. Sex pheromones of noctuid moths. XX. Short-range visual orientation by pheromone-stimulated males of *Trichoplusia ni. Ann. Entomol. Soc. Am.* 63:829-32.

Shorey, H. H. and R. L. Hale. 1965. Mass-rearing of the larvae of nine noctuid species on a simple artificial medium. *J. Econ. Entomol.* 58:522-4.

Shvetsova, O. I. 1950. The polyhedrosis disease of the greater wax moth (*Galleria mellonella* L.) and the role of the nutritional factor in virus diseases of insects. *Mikrobiologiia 19*:532-42.

Sicker, W., A. Magnoler, and A. Huger. 1965. Über ein verzögertes Absterben von viruskranken Raupen des Ringelspinners, *Malacosoma neustria* (L.), nach Behandlung mit einem *Bacillus thuringiensis*-Präparat. *Z. Pflanzenkr. Pflanzenschutz. 72*:599-605.

Sidor, C. 1959. Susceptibility of larvae of the large white butterfly (*Pieris brassicae* L.) to two virus diseases. *Ann. Appl. Biol. 47*:109-13.

Sikorowski, P. P., G. L. Andrews, and J. R. Broome. 1973. Trans-ovum transmission of a cytoplasmic polyhedrosis virus of *Heliothis virescens* (Lepidoptera: Noctuidae). *J. Invertebr. Pathol. 21*:41-5.

Sikura, A. I., I. V. Babchuk, V. Yu. Dulo, E. I. Fuchko, and R. S. Krasnitskaya. 1971. Entobakterin against *Hyphantria cunea. Zashch. Rast. 16*:48. (In Russ.).

Silverstein, R. M. 1970. Attractant pheromones of Coleoptera. Pages 21-40 in M. Beroza, ed. "Chemicals Controlling Insect Behavior." Academic Press, N.Y. 170 pp.

Simmonds, F. J. 1960. Biological control of the coconut scale, *Aspidiotus destructor* Sign. in Principe, Portuguese West Africa. *Bull. Entomol. Res. 51*:223-37.

Simmonds, F. J. 1963. Genetics and biological control. *Can. Entomol. 95*:561-7.

Simmons, G. A., D. E. Leonard, and C. W. Chen. 1975. Influence of tree species density and composition on parasitism of the spruce budworm. *Choristoneura fumiferana* (Clem.). *Environ. Entomol. 4*:832-6.

Simonova, E. Z. and M. D. Fufaeva. 1974. Adaptation of *Yponomeuta malinellus* Zell. nuclear polyhedrosis virus to a new host. *Zh. Obshch. Biol. 35*:289-96.

Skatulla, U. 1975. Über die Wirkung des Entwicklungshemmers Dimilin auf Forstinsekten. *Anz. Schädlingskd. Pflanzen-Umweltschutz. 48*:145-7.

Skilling, D. D. 1964. Ecological factors associated with maple blight. Part V. Pages 115-128 in "Studies of Maple Blight." Univ. Wis. Res. Bull. 250. 128 pp.

Skuhravý, V. 1973. Field control of the larch case-bearer moth, *Coleophora laricella*, with a juvenoid. *Acta Entomol. Bohemoslav. 70*:313-22.

Skuhravý, V. and R. Hochmut. 1975. Fangergebnisse von *Lymantria monacha* L. (Lepid., Lymantriidae) bei Verwendung von verschiedenen Pheromon-Lockfallen. *Anz. Schädlingskd. Pflanzen-Umweltschutz. 48*:52-5.

Skuhravý, V., M. Čapek, and R. Hochmut. 1974. Verwendung von *Lymantria dispar*-Pheromon zur Kontrolle des Vorkommens und der Flugdauer von *Lymantria monacha* L. und *Lymantria dispar* L. *Anz. Schädlingskd. Pflanzen-Umweltschutz. 47*:59-62.

Slobodkin, L. B. 1961. "Growth and Regulation of Animal Populations." Holt, Rinehart and Winston, N.Y. 184 pp.

Sluss, R. L. 1967. Population dynamics of the walnut aphid *Chromaphis juglandicola* (Kalt.), in northern California. *Ecology 48*:41-58.

Smirnoff, W. A. 1961. A virus disease of *Neodiprion swainei* Middleton. *J. Insect Pathol. 3*:29-46.

Smirnoff, W. A. 1962. Trans-ovum transmission of virus of *Neodiprion swainei* Middleton (Hymenoptera, Tenthredinidae). *J. Insect Pathol. 4*:192-200.

Smirnoff, W. A. 1965. The occurrence of *Nosema* and *Plistiphora* microsporidians on *Archips cerasivoranus* (Fitch) in Quebec. *Ann. Soc. Entomol. Que. 10*:121-3.

Smirnoff, W. A. 1967a. Effects of some plant juices on the ugly-nest caterpillar, *Archips cerasivoranus*, infected with microsporidia. *J. Invertebr. Pathol. 9*:26-9.

Smirnoff, W. A. 1967b. Influence of temperature on the development of a virus disease of *Neodiprion swainei* (Hymenoptera: Tenthredinidae). *Can. Entomol. 99*:244-9.

Smirnoff, W. A. 1968. Microorganisms isolated from *Malacosoma americanum* and *Malacosoma disstria* in the province of Quebec. *Can. For. Serv. Bi-mon. Res. Notes. 24*(1):4.

Smirnoff, W. A. 1971a. Adaptation de *Thelohania pristiphorae* Smir. chez *Arge pectoralis* (Leach) et sa dissémination dans les populations de cet insecte. *Ann. Soc. Entomol. Que. 16*:86-8.

Smirnoff, W. A. 1971b. Effect of chitinase on the action of *Bacillus thuringiensis*. *Can. Entomol. 103*:1829-31.

Smirnoff, W. A. 1972. Promoting virus epizootics in populations of the Swaine jack pine sawfly by infected adults. *Bioscience 22*:662-3.

Smirnoff, W. A. 1974. Three years of aerial field experiments with *Bacillus thuringiensis* plus chitinase formulation against the spruce budworm. *J. Invertebr. Pathol. 24*:344-8.

Smirnoff, W. A. and P. M. Hutchison. 1965. Bacteriostatic and bacteriocidal effects of extracts of foliage from various plant species on *Bacillus thuringiensis* var. *thuringiensis* Berliner. *J. Invertebr. Pathol. 7*:273-80.

Smirnoff, W. A., J. J. Fettes, and W. Haliburton. 1962. A virus disease of Swaine's jack pine sawfly, *Neodiprion swainei* Midd. sprayed from an aircraft. *Can. Entomol. 94*:477-86.

Smirnoff, W. A., J. J. Fettes and R. Desaulniers. 1973. Aerial spraying of a *Bacillus thuringiensis*-chitinase formulation for control of the spruce budworm (Lepidoptera: Tortricidae). *Can. Entomol. 105*:1535-44.

Smith, D. M. 1975. Dangers in over-simplifying forestry. *J. For. 73*:404-5.

Smith, H. S. 1929. Multiple parasitism: its relation to the biological control of insect pests. *Bull. Entomol. Res. 20*:141-9.

Smith, H. S. 1935. The role of biotic factors in the determination of population densities. *J. Econ. Entomol. 28*:873-98.

Smith, J. B. 1911. Miscellaneous shade and forest insects. *N.J. Agric. Exp. Stn. Rep. 1910*. pp. 346-50.

Smith, K. M. 1967. "Insect Virology." Academic Press, N.Y. 256 pp.

Smith, K. M. 1971. The viruses causing the polyhedroses and granuloses of insects. Pages 479-507 in K. Maramorosch and E. Kurstak, eds. "Comparative Virology." Academic Press, N.Y. 584 pp.

Smith, K. M. 1973. Insect viruses. Pages 14-25 in A. J. Gibbs, ed. "Viruses and Invertebrates." North-Holland Publ. Co., Amsterdam. 673 pp.

Smith, O. J., K. M. Hughes, P. H. Dunn, and I. M. Hall. 1956. A granulosis virus disease of the western grape leaf skeletonizer and its transmission. *Can. Entomol. 88*:507-15.

Society of American Foresters. 1958. "Forestry Terminology." Soc. Am. For., Wash. D.C. 84 pp.

Solomon, M. E. 1949. The natural control of animal populations. *J. Anim. Ecol. 18*:1-35.

Southwood, T. R. E. 1962. Migration of terrestrial arthropods in relation to habitat. *Biol. Rev. 37*:171-214.

Sower, L. L., R. S. Kaae, and H. H. Shorey. 1973. Sex pheromones of Lepidoptera. XLI. Factors limiting potential distance of sex pheromone communication in *Trichoplusia ni. Ann. Entomol. Soc. Am. 66*:1121-2.

Speare, A. T. and R. H. Colley. 1912. "The Artificial Use of the Brown-tail Fungus in Massachusetts." Wright and Potter Printing Co., Boston. 31 pp.

Spradbery, J. P. 1968. The biology of *Pseudorhyssa sternata* Merrill (Hym., Ichneumonidae), a cleptoparasite of siricid woodwasps. *Bull. Entomol. Res. 59*:291-7.

Spradbery, J. P. 1970. Host finding by *Rhyssa persuasoria*, an ichneumonid parasite of siricid woodwasps. *Anim. Behav. 18*:103-14.

Spring, S. N. 1911. Report of the state forester. Pages 775-84 in *33rd and 34th Annu. Rep. Conn. Agric. Exp. Stn. (New Haven)*. 842 pp.

Spring, S. N. 1913. Forest planting in Connecticut. Pages 485-507 in *36th Annu. Rep. Conn. Agric. Exp. Stn. (New Haven)*. 531 pp.

Spurr, S. H. and B. V. Barnes. 1973. "Forest Ecology." 2nd ed. Ronald Press, N.Y. 571 pp.

Stairs, G. R. 1964. Dissemination of nuclear polyhedrosis virus against the forest tent caterpillar, *Malacosoma disstria* (Hübner) Lepidoptera: Lasiocampidae. *Can. Entomol.* 96:1017-20.

Stairs, G. R. 1965a. Artificial initiation of virus epizootics in forest tent caterpillar populations. *Can. Entomol.* 97:1059-62.

Stairs, G. R. 1965b. The effect of metamorphosis on nuclear-polyhedrosis virus infection in certain Lepidoptera. *Can. J. Microbiol.* 11:509-12.

Stairs, G. R. 1966. Transmission of virus in tent caterpillar populations. *Can. Entomol.* 98:1100-4.

Stairs, G. R. 1968. Inclusion-type insect viruses. pages 1-23 in K. Maramorosch, ed. "Insect Viruses." Curr. Top. Microbiol. Immunol. Vol. 42. Springer-Verlag, N.Y. 192 pp.

Stairs, G. R. 1970. The development of nuclear-polyhedrosis virus in ligatured larvae of the greater wax moth, *Galleria mellonella. J. Invertebr. Pathol.* 15:60-2.

Stairs, G. R. 1971. The use of viruses for microbial control of insects. Pages 97-124 in H. D. Burges and N. W. Hussey, eds. "Microbial Control of Insects and Mites." Academic Press, N.Y. 861 pp.

Stairs, G. R. 1972. Pathogenic microorganisms in the regulation of forest insect populations. *Annu. Rev. Entomol.* 17:355-72.

Stairs, G. R. 1973. Means for regulation: viruses. Pages 58-64 in L. A. Bulla, Jr., ed. "Regulation of Insect Populations by Microorganisms." Ann. N.Y. Acad. Sci. 217. 243 pp.

Stairs, G. R. and F. T. Bird. 1962. Dissemination of viruses against the spruce budworm *Choristoneura fumiferana* (Clemens). *Can. Entomol.* 94:966-9.

Staley, J. M. 1965. Decline and mortality of red and scarlet oaks. *For. Sci.* 11:2-17.

Stambaugh, W. J., C. L. Fergus, F. C. Craighead, and H. E. Thompson. 1955. Viable spores of *Endoconidiophora fagacearum* from bark and wood-boring beetles. *Plant Dis. Rep.* 39:867-71.

Stark, R. W. 1971. Integrated control, pest management, or protective population management? Pages 111-26 in Toward integrated control. *U.S. For. Serv. Res. Pap. NE-194, Northeast. For. Exp. Stn.* 129 pp.

Stark, R. W. and R. F. Smith. 1971. Systems analysis and pest management. Pages 331-45 in C. B. Huffaker, ed. "Biological Control." Plenum Press, N.Y. 511 pp.

Stearns, F. W. 1949. Ninety years change in a northern hardwood forest in Wisconsin. *Ecology* 30:350-8.

Stehr, F. W. 1974. Release, establishment and evaluation of parasites and predators. Pages 124-36 in F. G. Maxwell and F. A. Harris, eds. "Proceedings of the Summer Institute on Biological Control of Plant Insects and Diseases." Univ. Press Miss., Jackson, Miss. 647 pp.

Stehr, F. W. and E. F. Cook. 1968. A revision of the genus *Malacosoma* Hübner in North America (Lepidoptera: Lasiocampidae): systematics, biology, immatures and parasites. *U.S. Natl. Mus. Bull.* 276. 321 pp.

Stein, W. 1960. Versuche zur Biologischen Bekämpfung des Apfelwicklers (*Carpocapsa pomonella* (L.)) durch Eiparasiten der Gattung *Trichogramma* (1-2). *Entomophaga* 5:237-59.

Steiner, P. 1931. Zur Kenntnis der Parasiten des Kiefernspanners. *Z. Angew. Entomol.* 17:601-30.

Steinhaus, E. A. 1948. Polyhedrosis ("wilt disease") of the alfalfa caterpillar. *J. Econ. Entomol.* 41:859-65.

Steinhaus, E. A. 1949. "Principles of Insect Pathology." McGraw-Hill Book Co., N.Y. 757 pp.

Steinhaus, E. A. 1954. The effects of disease on insect populations. *Hilgardia* 23:197-261.

Steinhaus, E. A. 1957. Microbial diseases of insects. *Annu. Rev. Microbiol.* 11:165-82.

Steinhaus, E. A. 1958a. Stress as a factor in insect disease. *Proc. 10th Int. Congr. Entomol. (Montreal)* 4:725-30.

Steinhaus, E. A. 1958b. Crowding as a possible stress factor in insect disease. *Ecology* 39:503-14.

Steinhaus, E. A. 1960a. Notes on polyhedroses in *Peridroma, Prodenia, Colias, Heliothis,* and other Lepidopera. *J. Insect Pathol.* 2:327-33.

Steinhaus, E. A. 1960b. Selected topics in microbial ecology. II. The importance of environmental factors in the insect-microbe ecosystem. *Bacteriol. Rev.* 24:365-73.

Steinhaus, E. A. 1963. "Insect Pathology, an Advanced Treatise." Academic Press, N.Y. Vol. 1. 661 pp., Vol. 2. 689 pp.

Steinhaus, E. A. 1964. Microbial diseases of insects. Pages 515-47 in P. DeBach, ed. "Biological Control of Insect Pests and Weeds." Reinhold Publ. Corp., N.Y. 844 pp.

Stelzer, M. J. 1967. Control of a tent caterpillar, *Malacosoma fragile incurva*, with an aerial application of a nuclear-polyhedrosis virus and *Bacillus thuringiensis. J. Econ. Entomol.* 60:38-41.

Stelzer, M. J., J. Neisess, and C. G. Thompson. 1975. Aerial applications of a nucleopolyhedrosis virus and *Bacillus thuringiensis* against the Douglas fir tussock moth. *J. Econ. Entomol.* 68:269-72.

Stephens, G. R. 1971. The relation of insect defoliation to mortality in Connecticut forests. *Conn. Agric. Exp. Stn. Bull. (New Haven)* 723. 16 pp.

Stephens, G. R. and P. E. Waggoner. 1970. The forests anticipated from 40 years of natural transitions in mixed hardwoods. *Conn. Agric. Exp. Stn. Bull. (New Haven)* 707. 58 pp.

Stern, V. M. 1973. Economic thresholds. *Annu. Rev. Entomol.* 18:259-80.

Stevens, L. J. and M. Beroza. 1972. Mating-inhibition field tests using disparlure, the synthetic gypsy moth sex pheromone. *J. Econ. Entomol.* 65:1090-5.

Stevens, R. E. 1966. The ponderosa pine tip moth, *Rhyacionia zozana*, in California (Lepidoptera: Olethreutidae). *Ann. Entomol. Soc. Am.* 59:186-92.

Stewart, F. C. 1912. Can the chestnut bark disease be controlled. Pages 40-5 in *Pa. Chestnut Tree Blight Comm. Publ., W. S. Ray, State Printer, Harrisburg (1915)*. (The bound volume of publications of The Pa. Chestnut Tree Blight Comm. 1911-1913).

Stewart, T. E., E. L. Plummer, L. McCandless, J. R. West, and R. M. Silverstein. 1976. Determination of the enantiomeric composition of several bicyclic ketal insect pheromone components. *J. Chem. Ecol.* in press.

Steyermark, J. A. 1959. "Vegetational History of the Ozark Forest." Univ. of Missouri Studies, Columbia, Mo. 138 pp.

Stoltz, D. B. and M. D. Summers. 1971. Pathway of infection of mosquito iridescent virus. I. Preliminary observations on the fate of ingested virus. *J. Virol.* 8:900-9.

Stone, E. 1973. The impact of timber harvest of soils and water. Pages 427-67 in F. A. Seaton et al., eds. "Report of President's Advisory Panel on Timber and the Environment." Gov. Printing Office, Wash. D.C. 541 pp.

Stultz, H. T. 1955. The influence of spray programs on the fauna of apple orchards in Nova Scotia. VIII. Natural enemies of the eye-spotted bud moth, *Spilonata ocellana* (D & S) (Lepidoptera: Olethreutidae). *Can. Entomol.* 87:79-85.

Sullivan, C. R. 1961. The effect of weather and the physical attributes of white pine leaders on the behaviour and survival of the white pine weevil, *Pissodes strobi* Peck, in mixed stands. *Can. Entomol.* 93:721-41.

Summers, M. D. 1972. Mechanism of infection of insect viruses. *Monogr. Virol.* 6:16-20.

Sutton, O. G. 1947. The problem of diffusion in the lower atomosphere. *Q. J. R. Meteorol. Soc.* 73:257-81.

Sweetman, H. L. 1936. "The Biological Control of Insects." Comstock Publ. Co. Inc., Ithaca, N.Y. 461 pp.

Swingler, W. S. 1959. Keeping forest insects in their place. *Am. For. Feb.* 11 pp.

Syme, P. D. 1970. Discrimination by *Hyssopus thymus* (Hymenoptera: Eulophidae) against *Orgilus obsecurator* (Hymenoptera: Braconidae), an internal parasite of the European pine shoot moth, *Rhyacionia buoliana* (Lepidoptera: Olethreutidae). *Can. Entomol. 102*:1523-7.

Syme, P. D. 1971. *Rhyacionia buoliana* (Schiff.), European pine shoot moth (Lepidoptera: Olethreutidae). *Tech. Commun. Commonw. Inst. Biol. Control (Trinidad). 4*:194-205.

Syme, P. D. 1975. The effects of flowers on the longevity and fecundity of two native parasites of the European pine shoot moth in Ontario. *Environ. Entomol. 4*:337-46.

Tabata, S. and K. Tamanuki. 1940. On the hymenopterous parasites of the pine caterpillar, *Dendrolimus sibiricus albolineatus* Mats in southern Sakhalin. *Cent. Exp. Stn. Sakhalin Rep. 33 Forest.* 50 pp. (in Japanese) (Abstr. in *Rev. Appl. Entomol. A 29*:95).

Tadic, M. D. 1961. A contribution to the knowledge of the diapause of the gypsy moth egg parasite *Anastatus disparis* R. on the island Hvar. *Zast. Bilja. No. 63-64*:13-9. (In Serb.-Kroat., Engl. summ.).

Talalaev, E. V. 1958. Induction of epizootic septicemia in the caterpillars of Siberian silkworm moth, *Dendrolimus sibiricus* Tschtv. (Lepidoptera, Lasiocampidae). *Entomol. Rev. 37*:557-67.

Talalayeva, G. B. 1967. A case of bacterial epizooty in a larval population of *Selenephera lunigera* Esp. (Lepidoptera, Lasiocampidae). *Entomol. Rev. 46*:191-2.

Tamaki, Y., H. Noguchi, T. Yushima, and C. Hirano. 1971a. Two sex pheromones of the smaller tea tortrix: isolation, identification, and synthesis. *Appl. Entomol. Zool* 6:139-41.

Tamaki, Y., H. Noguchi, T. Yushima, C. Hirano, K. Honma, and H. Sugawara. 1971b. Sex pheromone of the summerfruit tortrix: isolation and identification. *Konchu 39*:338-40.

Tanada, Y. 1959. Synergism between two viruses of the armyworm, *Pseudaletia unipuncta* (Haworth) (Lepidoptera, Noctuidae). *J. Insect Pathol. 1*:215-31.

Tanada, Y. 1961. The epizootiology of virus diseases in field populations of the armyworm, *Pseudaletia unipuncta* (Haworth) *J. Insect Pathol. 3*:310-23.

Tanada, Y. 1963. Epizootiology of infectious diseases. Pages 423-75 in E. A. Steinhaus, ed. "Insect Pathology, an Advanced Treatise." Vol. 2. Academic Press, N.Y. 689 pp.

Tanada, Y. 1964. Epizootiology of insect diseases. Pages 548-78 in P. DeBach, ed. "Biological Control of Insect Pests and Weeds." Reinhold Publ. Corp., N.Y. 844 pp.

Tanada, Y. 1967. Effect of high temperatures on the resistance of insects to infectious diseases. *J. Seric. Sci. Jap. 36*:333-9.

Tanada, Y. 1971a. Recent advances in insect virology. *Proc. Hawaii. Entomol. Soc. 21*:113-27.

Tanada, Y. 1971b. Persistence of entomogenous viruses in the insect ecosystem. Pages 367-79 in S. Asahina, J. L. Gressitt, Z. Hidaka, T. Nishida, and K. Nomura, eds. "Entomological Essays to Commemorate the Retirement of Professor K. Yasumatsu." Hokuryukan Publ. Co. Ltd., Tokyo. 389 pp.

Tanada, Y. 1971c. Interactions of insect viruses, with special emphasis on interference. Pages 185-200 in H. Aruga and Y. Tanada, eds. "The Cytoplasmic-polyhedrosis Virus of the Silkworm." Univ. Tokyo Press, Tokyo. 234 pp.

Tanada, Y. 1973. Environmental factors external to the host. Pages 120-30 in L. A. Bulla, Jr., ed. "Regulation of Insect Populations by Microorganisms." Ann. N.Y. Acad. Sci. 217. 243 pp.

Tanada, Y. 1975. Epizootics of virus diseases of insects. *Proc. 1st Intersection. Congr. Int. Assoc. Microbiol. Soc. 2*:621-39.

Tanada, Y. and G. Y. Chang. 1964. Interactions of two cytoplasmic-polyhedrosis viruses in three insect species. *J. Insect Pathol.* 6:500-16.

Tanada, Y. and S. Hara. 1975. Enzyme synergistic for insect viruses. *Nature (Lond.)* 254:328-9.

Tanada, Y. and T. Hukuhara. 1968. A nonsynergistic strain of a granulosis virus of the armyworm, *Pseudaletia unipuncta. J. Invertebr. Pathol.* 12:263-8.

Tanada, Y., and E. M. Omi. 1974a. Epizootiology of virus diseases in three lepidopterous insect species of alfalfa. *Res. Popul. Ecol.* 16:59-68.

Tanada, Y. and E. M. Omi. 1974b. Persistence of insect viruses in field populations of alfalfa insects. *J. Invertebr. Pathol.* 23:360-5.

Tanada, Y., T. Hukuhara, and G. Y. Chang. 1969. A strain of nuclear-polyhedrosis virus causing extensive cellular hypertrophy. *J. Invertebr. Pathol.* 13:394-409.

Tanada, Y., M. Himeno, and E. M. Omi. 1973. Isolation of a factor, from the capsule of a granulosis virus, synergistic for a nuclear-polyhedrosis virus of the armyworm. *J. Invertebr. Pathol.* 21:31-40.

Tanada, Y., R. T. Hess, and E. M. Omi. 1975. Invasion of a nuclear polyhedrosis virus in midgut of the armyworm, *Pseudaletia unipuncta*, and the enhancement of a synergistic enzyme. *J. Invertebr. Pathol.* 26:99-104.

Tanaka, S. 1971. Cross transmission of cytoplasmic-polyhedrosis viruses. Pages 201-7 in H. Aruga and Y. Tanada, eds. "The Cytoplasmic-polyhedrosis Virus of the Silkworm." Univ. Tokyo Press, Tokyo. 234 pp.

Tang, W. 1970. Study of air flow in and above a forest over different terrain. *U.S. Army Contract No. DAAD09-70-C-0008. Desert Test Center, Fort Douglas, Utah.* 63 pp.

Taylor, G. I. 1920. Diffusion by continuous movements. *Proc. Lond. Math. Soc.* 20:196-212.

Taylor, O. R. 1967. Relationship of multiple mating in *Atteva punctella* (Lepidoptera: Yponomeutidae). *Ann. Entomol. Soc. Am.* 60:583-90.

Taylor, T. H. C. 1935. The campaign against *Aspidiotus destructor* Sign. in Fiji, *Bull. Entomol. Res.* 26:1-102.

Taylor, T. H. C. 1937. "The Biological Control of an Insect in Fiji. An Account of the Coconut Leaf-mining Beetle and its Parasite Complex." Imp. Inst. Entomol. London. 239 pp.

Tennekes, H. and J. L. Lumley. 1972. "A First Course in Turbulence." The MIT Press, Cambridge, Mass. 300 pp.

Thatcher, R. W. 1926. Studies on apple insects. *Annu. Rep. N.Y. State Agric. Exp. Stn.* 45:36-8.

Thomas, E. D., C. F. Reichelderfer, and A. M. Heimpel. 1972. Accumulation and persistence of a nuclear polyhedrosis virus of the cabbage looper in the field. *J. Invertebr. Pathol.* 20:157-64.

Thomas, E. D., C. F. Reichelderfer, and A. M. Heimpel. 1973. The effect of soil pH on the persistence of cabbage looper nuclear polyhedrosis virus in soil. *J. Invertebr. Pathol.* 21:21-5.

Thomas, H. A. 1966. Parasitism by *Trichogramma minutum* (Hymenoptera: Trichogrammatidae) in the spruce budworm outbreak in Maine. *Ann. Entomol. Soc. Am.* 59:723-5.

Thomas, M. D. 1961. Effects of air pollution on plants. Pages 223-78 in "Air Pollution." Columbia Univ. Press, N.Y. 442 pp.

Thompson, C. G. and E. A. Steinhaus. 1950. Further tests using a polyhedrosis virus to control the alfalfa caterpillar. *Hilgardia* 19:411-45.

Thompson, W. R. 1946. A catalogue of the parasites and predators of insect pests. *Parasites of the Lepidoptera, Sec. 1, Part 8.* pp. 386-523.

Thompson, W. R. 1950. A catalogue of the parasites and predators of insect pests. *Index of parasites of the Lepidoptera, Sec. 1. Part 10.* 107 pp.

Thomson, H. M. 1958. Some aspects of the epidemiology of a microsporidian parasite of the spruce budworm, *Choristoneura fumiferana* (Clem.). *Can. J. Zool. 36*:309-16.

Thorpe, W. H. 1930. Observations on the parasites of the pine shoot moth. *Rhyacionia buoliana* Schiff. *Bull. Entomol. Res. 21*:387-412.

Thorpe, W. H. and H. B. Caudle. 1938. Study of the olfactory responses of insect parasites to the food plant of their host. *Parasitology 30*:523-8.

Ticehurst, M. and D. C. Allen. 1973. Notes on the biology of *Telenomus coelodasidis* (Hymenoptera: Scelionidae) and its relationship to the saddled prominent, *Heterocampa guttivitta* (Lepidoptera: Notodontidae). *Can. Entomol. 105*:1133-43.

Tigner, T. C. 1974. Gypsy moth parasitism in New York State. A manual for field personnel. *State Univ. N.Y. College Environ. Sci. For., Appl. For. Res. Inst. Res. Rep. 21.* 34 pp.

Tigner, T. C., C. E. Palm, and J. J. Jackson. 1974. Gypsy moth parasitism under and outside burlap skirts at two heights. *Appl. For. Res. Inst. Res. Rep. 20.* 7 pp.

Tinsley, T. W. and P. F. Entwistle. 1974. The use of pathogens in the control of insect pests. Pages 115-29 in D. P. Jones and M. E. Solomon, eds. "Biology in Pest Disease Control." Blackwell Sci. Publ., Oxford, England. 398 pp.

Tinsley, T. W. and K. A. Harrap. 1972. "Moving Frontiers in Invertebrate Virology." Monogr. Virol. Vol. 6. S. Karger, Basel, Switzerland. 66 pp.

Tooke, F. G. C. 1953. The eucalyptus snout-beetle, *Gonipterus scuterellatus* Gyll. A study of its ecology and control by biological means. *Union S. Afr. Dep. Agric. Entomol. Mem. 3*:1-282.

Torgersen, T. R. 1970. Parasites of the blackheaded budworm, *Acleris gloverana* (Lepidoptera: Tortricidae) in southeast Alaska. *Can. Entomol. 102*:1294-9.

Tothill, J. D. 1922. The natural control of the fall webworm (*Hyphantria cunea* Drury) in Canada. *Can. Dep. Agric. Bull 3. n.s. (Tech.).* 107 pp.

Tothill, J. D. and L. S. McLaine. 1919. The recovery in Canada of the brown-tail moth parasite *Compsilura concinnata* (Diptera, Tachinidae). *Annu. Rep. Entomol. Soc. Ont. 49*:35-9.

Tothill, J. D., T. H. C. Taylor, and R. W. Paine. 1930. "The Coconut Moth in Fiji. A History of its Control by Means of Parasites." Publ. Imp. Bur. Entomol. London. 269 pp.

Townes, H. 1958. Some biological characteristics of the Ichneumonidae in relation to biological control. *J. Econ. Entomol. 51*:650-2.

Townsend, J. F. 1943. Life history studies on the red-banded leaf roller in Connecticut. *Conn. Agric. Exp. Stn. Bull. (New Haven) 472.* pp. 241-8.

Traynier, R. M. M. 1968. Sex attraction in the Mediterranean flour moth, *Anagasta kuhniella*: location of the female by the male. *Can. Entomol. 100*:5-10.

Trullinger, R. W. 1937. The policies and procedure involved in the Hatch Act from the standpoint of efficiency in administering productive research. *Proc. 51st Annu. Conv., Assoc. Land-Grant Colleges and Univ.* pp 144-7.

Turner, N. 1963. The gypsy moth problem. *Conn. Agric. Exp. Stn. Bull. (New Haven) 655.* 36 pp.

Ullyett, G. C. 1936. Host selection by *Microplectron fuscipennis*, Zett. (Chalcididae, Hymenoptera). *Proc. R. Soc. Lond. B Biol. Sci. 120*:253-91.

Ullyett, G. C. 1953. Biomathematics and insect population problems. *Entomol. Soc. S. Afr. Mem. 2*:1-89.

Underhill, G. W. 1943. Some insect pests of ornamental plants. *Va. Agric. Exp. Stn. Bull. 349.* 38 pp.

Vago, C. 1956. Actions virusales indirectes. *Entomophaga 1*:82-7.

Vago, C. 1963. Predispositions and interrelations in insect diseases. Pages 339-79 in E. A. Steinhaus, ed. "Insect Pathology, an Advanced Treatise." Vol. 1. Academic Press, N.Y. 661 pp.

Vago, C. 1968. Non-inclusion virus diseases of invertebrates. Pages 24-37 in K. Maramorosch, ed. "Insect Viruses." Curr. Top. Microbiol. Immunol. Vol. 42. Springer-Verlag, N.Y. 192 pp.

Vago, C. 1975. Recent observations in the study of insect pathogens in *in vitro* cultured cells. *Proc. 1st Intersection. Congr. Int. Assoc. Microbiol. Soc. Tokyo, Japan. 2*:640-9.

Vago, C., and M. Bergoin. 1968. Viruses of invertebrates. *Adv. Virus Res. 13*:247-303.

Vail, P. V. and D. Gough. 1970. Effects of cytoplasmic-polyhedrosis virus on adult cabbage loopers and their progeny. *J. Invertebr. Pathol. 15*:397-400.

Vail, P. V. and D. L. Jay. 1973. Pathology of a nuclear polyhedrosis virus of the alfalfa looper in alternate hosts. *J. Invertebr. Pathol. 21*:198-204.

Vail, P. V., I. M. Hall, and D. Gough. 1969. Influence of a cytoplasmic polyhedrosis on various developmental stages of the cabbage looper. *J. Invertebr. Pathol. 14*:237-44.

Vail, P. V., G. Sutter, D. L. Jay, and D. Gough. 1971. Reciprocal infectivity of nuclear polyhedrosis viruses of the cabbage looper and alfalfa looper. *J. Invertebr. Pathol. 17*:383-8.

Vail, P. V., D. L. Jay, and D. K. Hunter. 1973. Infectivity of a nuclear polyhedrosis virus from the alfalfa looper, *Autographa californica,* after passage through alternate hosts. *J. Invertebr. Pathol. 21*:16-20.

Van Alfen, N. K., R. A. Jaynes, S. L. Anagnostakis, and P. R. Day. 1975. Chestnut blight: biological control by transmissible hypovirulence in *Endothia parasitica. Science (Wash. D.C.) 189*:890-1.

Van den Berg, M. A. 1971. Studies on the egg parasites of the mopani emperor moth *Nudaurelia belina* (Westw.) (Lepidoptera: Saturniidae). *Phytophylactica 3*:33-6.

Van den Berg, M. A. 1974. Natural enemies and diseases of the forest insects *Pseudobunaea irius* (F.) and *Holocerina similax* (Westw.) (Lepidoptera: Saturniidae). *Phytophylactica 6*:69-71.

van den Bosch, R. and P. S. Messenger. 1973. "Biological Control." Intext Educational Publ., N.Y. 180 pp.

Varley, G. C. and G. R. Gradwell. 1958. Oak defoliators in England. *Proc. 10th Int. Congr. Entomol. (Montreal). 4*:133-6.

Varley, G. C. and G. R. Gradwell. 1968. Population models for the winter moth. *Symp. R. Entomol. Soc. London. 4*:132-42.

Varley, G. C., G. R. Gradwell, and M. P. Hassell. 1974. "Insect Population Ecology–An Analytical Approach." Univ. Calif. Press, Berkeley. 212 pp.

Vasiljević, L. 1957. Share of the polyhedry and other disease in the reduction of the gypsy moth gradation in the PR of Serbia in 1957. *Zašt. Bilja. No. 41-42*:123-37. (In Yugo.).

Vasiljević, L. 1961. Susceptibilité des chenilles du Bombyx disparate (*Lymantria dispar* L.) envers la polyédrie dans les diverses phases de gradation de leur dévelopment dans la nature. *Entomophaga 6*:269-76.

Vasiljević, L. 1973. Lutte microbiologique contre *Lymantria dispar* L. 9-12 Septembre– Belgrade. *Zašt. Bilja 24* (124-125):159-293.

Vaughn, J. L., J. R. Adams, and T. Wilcox. 1972. Infection and replication of insect viruses in tissue culture. *Monogr. Virol. 6*:27-35.

Vité, J. P. 1970. Symposium on population attractants. *Contrib. Boyce Thompson Inst. 24*:249-350.

Vité, J. P., A. Bakke, and P. R. Hughes. 1974. Ein Populationslockstoff des zwölfzähnigen Kiefernborkenkäfers *Ips sexdentatus. Naturwissenschaften 61*:365-6.

Vité, J. P., R. Lühl, B. Gerken, and G. N. Lanier. 1976. Ulmensplintkäfer: Anlockversuche mit synthetischen Pheromonen im Oberrheintal. *Z. Pflanzenkr. Pflanzenschutz. 83*: in press.

von Finck, E. 1939. Untersuchungen über die Lebensweise der Tachine *Parasetigena segregata* Rond. in der Rominter Heide. *Z. Angew. Entomol. 26*:104-42.

Vorontsov, A. I. 1975. Basic principles of integrated protection of forest plantations. *8th Int. Congr. Plant Prot. Moscow. Sec. III*:82-7.

Voûte, A. D. 1964. Harmonious control of forest insects. *Int. Rev. For. Res. 1*:325-83.

Wagner, G. W., S. R. Webb, J. D. Paschke, and W. R. Campbell. 1974. A picornavirus isolated from *Aedes taeniorhynchus* and its interaction with mosquito iridescent virus. *J. Invertebr. Pathol. 24*:380-2.

Wahlenberg, W. G. 1946. "Longleaf Pine." C. L. Pack Forestry Foundation, Wash. D.C. 429 pp.

Walgenbach, D. D. and D. M. Benjamin. 1963. Natural controlling factors affecting the pine tussock moth. *Proc. North Cent. Branch Entomol. Soc. Am. 18*:15-6.

Wallace, P. P. 1945. Certain effects of defoliation of deciduous trees. *Conn. Agric. Exp. Stn. Bull. (New Haven) 488.* pp. 358-73.

Wallis, R. C. 1957. Incidence of polyhedrosis of gypsy-moth larvae and the influence of relative humidity. *J. Econ. Entomol. 50*:580-3.

Wallis, R. C. 1959. Factors affecting larval migration of the gypsy moth. *Entomol. News 70*:235-40.

Wallis, R. C. 1962. Environmental factors and epidemics of polyhedrosis in gypsy moth larvae. *Proc. 11th Int. Congr. Entomol. Vienna. 2*:827-9.

Wargo, P. M. 1972. Defoliation induced chemical changes in sugar maple roots stimulate growth of *Armillaria mellea. Phytopathology 62*: 1278-83.

Wargo, P. M., J. Parker, and D. R. Houston. 1972. Starch content in roots of defoliated sugar maple. *For. Sci. 18*:203-4.

Warren, L. O. and M. Tadic. 1970. The fall webworm, *Hyphantria cunea* (Drury). *Arkansas Agric. Exp. Stn. Bull. 759.* 106 pp.

Watanabe, C. 1958. Review of biological control of insect pests in Japan. *Proc. 10th Int. Congr. Entomol. (Montreal) 4*:414-517.

Watanabe, H. 1967. Development of resistance in the silkworm, *Bombyx mori* to peroral infection of a cytoplasmic-polyhedrosis virus. *J. Invertebr. Pathol. 9*:474-9.

Watanabe, H. 1968. Development of resistance in the silkworm to peroral infection of the cytoplasmic polyhedrosis virus. *Proc. Joint U.S.-Japan Seminar Microbial Control Insect Pests, Fukuoka, Apr. 21-23, 1967.* pp. 13-14.

Watanabe, H. 1971. Resistance of the silkworm to cytoplasmic-polyhedrosis virus. Pages 169-84 in H. Aruga and Y. Tanada, eds. "The Cytoplasmic-polyhedrosis Virus of the Silkworm." Univ. Tokyo Press, Tokyo. 234 pp.

Watanabe, H. and H. Aruga. 1970. Susceptibility of dauerpupa of the silkworm, *Bombyx mori* L. (Lepidoptera: Bombycidae), to a nuclear-polyhedrosis virus. *Appl. Entomol. Zool. 5*:118-20.

Watanabe, H. and Y. Tanada. 1972. Infection of a nuclear-polyhedrosis virus in armyworm, *Pseudaletia unipuncta* Haworth (Lepidoptera: Noctuidae), reared at a high temperature. *Appl. Entomol. Zool. 7*:43-51.

Watanabe, H., S. Tanaka, and T. Shimizu. 1974. Interstrain difference in the resistance of the silkworm, *Bombyx mori* to a flacherie and a cytoplasmic-polyhedrosis virus. *J. Seric. Sci. Jap. 43*:98-100.

Watanabe, H., Y. Aratake, and T. Kayamura. 1975. Serial passage of a nuclear polyhedrosis virus of the silkworm, *Bombyx mori*, in larvae of rice stem borer, *Chilo suppressalis. J. Invertebr. Pathol. 25*:11-7.

Waters, W. E. 1971. Ecological management of forest insect populations. *Proc. Tall Timbers Conf. Ecol. Anim. Control Habitat Manage. 3*:141-53.

Watt, K. E. F. 1970. Discussion remark to Baltensweiler. *W. Proc. Adv. Study Inst. Dynamics Numbers Popul. (Oosterbeck.).* pp. 217-8.

Webber, R. T. 1932. *Sturmia inconspicua* Meigen, a tachinid parasite of the gipsy moth. *J. Agric. Res. 45*:193-208.

Webber, R. T. and J. V. Schaffner. 1926. Host relations of *Compsilura concinnata* Meigen, an important tachinid parasite of the gipsy moth and the brown-tail moth. *U.S. Dep. Agric. Bull. 1363.* 31 pp.

Webster, R. L. 1909. The lesser apple leaf-folder *Peronea minuta* Rob. *Iowa Agric. Exp. Stn. Bull. 102.* pp. 181-212.

Wehner, R. 1972. "Information Processing in the Visual Systems of Arthropods." Springer-Verlag, Berlin. 334 pp.

Weiser, J. 1957. Možnosti bioligického boje s přástevníčkem americkým (*Hyphantria cunea* Drury)–III. *Cesk. Parasitol. 4*:359-67.

Weiser, J. 1961. Protozoan diseases of the gipsy moth. *Proc. 1st Int. Conf. Protozool. Prague.* pp. 497-9.

Weiser, J. and J. Verber. 1957. Die Mikrosporidie *Thelohania hyphantriae* Weiser des weissen Bärenspinners und anderer Mitglieder seiner Biocönose. *Z. Angew. Entomol. 40*:55-70.

Wellenstein, G. 1942a. Zum Massenwechsel der Nonne. Pages 207-78 in "Die Nonne in Ostpreussen (1933-1937)." Monogr. Angew. Entomol. Nr. 15. 682 pp.

Wellenstein, G. 1942b. Überwachung der Nonne und Vorhersage ihrer Massenvermehrung. Pages 478-534 in "Die Nonne in Ostpreussen (1933-1937)." Monogr. Angew. Entomol. 15. 682 pp.

Wellenstein, G. 1973a. The use of insect viruses for the protection of forests. *EPPO Bull. No. 9*:43-52.

Wellenstein, G. 1973b. The development of artificially founded colonies of hill-building red wood ants of the *Formica rufa*-group in southwestern Germany. *EPPO Bull. No. 9*:23-34.

Wellenstein, G. and K. Fabritius. 1973. Beobachtungen am Schlehen=spinner (*Orgyia antiqua* L.) und seinen parasiten. *Anz. Schaedlingskd. Pflanzenumweltschutz. 46*:24-30.

Wellenstein, G. and R. Lühl. 1972. Bekämpfung schädlicher Räupen mit insekten-pathogenen Polyederviren und chemischen Stressoren. *Naturwissenschaften 59*:517.

Wellhouse, W. H. 1920. Wild hawthorns as hosts of apple, pear and quince pests. *J. Econ. Entomol. 13*:388-91.

Wellhouse, W. H. 1922. The insect fauna of the genus *Crataegus. N.Y. Agric. Exp. Stn. Ithaca Mem. 56.* pp. 1045-136.

Wellington, W. G. 1962. Population quality and maintenance of nuclear polyhedrosis between outbreaks of *Malacosoma pluviale* (Dyar). *J. Insect. Pathol. 4*:285-305.

Wellington, W. G. 1974a. Changes in mosquito flight associated with natural changes in polarized light. *Can. Entomol. 106*:941-8.

Wellington, W. G. 1974b. Bumblebee ocelli and navigation at dusk. *Science (Wash. D.C.) 183*:550-1.

Wellington, W. G. 1974c. A special light to steer by. *Nat. Hist. 83*:46-53.

Wellington, W. G. and W. R. Henson. 1947. Notes on the effects of physical factors on the spruce budworm *Choristoneura fumiferana* (Clem.). *Can. Entomol. 79*:168-70, 195.

Wellington, W. G., J. J. Fettes, K. B. Turner, and R. M. Belyea. 1950. Physical and biological indicators of the development of outbreaks of the spruce budworm, *Choristoneura fumiferana* Clemens. *Can. J. Res. Dev. 28*:308-31.

Wellington, W. G., P. J. Cameron, W. A. Thompson, I. B. Vertinsky, and A. S. Landsberg. 1975. A stochastic model for assessing the effects of external and internal heterogeneity on an insect population. *Res. Popul. Ecol. 17*:58-85.

Weseloh, R. M. 1971. Behavioral responses of the gypsy moth egg parastoid *Ooencyrtus kuwanai* to abiotic environmental factors. *Ann. Entomol. Soc. Am. 64*:1050-7.

Weseloh, R. M. 1972a. Influence of gypsy moth egg mass dimensions and microhabitat distribution on parasitization by *Ooencyrtus kuwanai. Ann. Entomol. Soc. Am. 65*:64-9.

Weseloh, R. M. 1972b. Diel periodicities of some parasitoids of the gypsy moth and noctuid cutworms. *Ann. Entomol. Soc. Am. 65*:1126-31.

Weseloh, R. M. 1972c. Spatial distribution of the gypsy moth (Lepidoptera: Lymantriidae) and some of its parasitoids within a forest environment. *Entomophaga 17*:339-51.

Weseloh, R. M. 1972d. Field responses of gypsy moths and some parasitoids to colored surfaces. *Ann. Entomol. Soc. Am. 65*:742-6.

Weseloh, R. M. 1974a. Host recognition of the gypsy moth larval parasitoid, *Apanteles melanoscelus. Ann. Entomol. Soc. Am. 67*:583-7.

Weseloh, R. M. 1974b. Host-related microhabitat preferences of the gypsy moth larval parasitoid, *Parasetigena agilis. Environ. Entomol. 3*:363-4.

Weseloh, R. M. 1976. Discrimination between parasitized and non-parasitized hosts by the gypsy moth larval parasitoid, *Apanteles melanoscelus. Can. Entomol.* in press.

Westveld, M. 1945. A suggested method for rating vulnerability of spruce-fir stands to budworm attack. *U.S. For. Serv. Northeast. For. Exp. Stn.* 4 pp.

Westveld, M. 1946. Forest management as a means of controlling the spruce budworm. *J. For. 44*:949-53.

Westveld, M., R. I. Ashman, H. I. Baldwin, R. P. Holdsworth, R. S. Johnson, J. H. Lambert, H. J. Lutz, L. Swain, and M. Standish. 1956. Natural forest vegetation zones of New England. *J. For. 54*:332-8.

Wiackowska, I. 1965. Utilisation of *Trichogramma cacoeciae* March. Hym. Trichogrammatidae in control of the plum moth Lep. Tortricidae depending on the numbers used and time of introduction. *Entomophaga 10*:151-7.

Wiackowski, S. K. and I. Wiackowska. 1966. Biological, microbiological and chemical control of the plum moth *Laspeyresia funebrana* Tr. (Lep. Tortricidae) in Poland. *Entomophaga 11*:261-7.

Wilkes, A., H. C. Coppel, and W. C. Mathers. 1948. Notes on the insect parasites of the spruce budworm *Choristoneura fumiferana* (Clem.) in British Columbia. *Can. Entomol. 80*:138-55.

Wilkinson, D. S. 1926. The Cyprus processionary caterpiller (*Thaumetopoea wilkinsoni,* Tams). *Bull. Entomol. Res. 17*:163-82.

Wilkinson, D. S. 1945. Description of Palearctic species of *Apanteles* (Hymenoptera: Braconidae). *Trans. R. Entomol. Soc. Lond. 95*:35-226.

Wilson, F. 1965. Biological control and the genetics of colonizing species. Pages 307-29 in H. G. Baker and G. L. Stebbins, eds. "The Genetics of Colonizing Species." Academic Press, N.Y. 588 pp.

Wilson, L. F. 1961. Variable oak leaf caterpillar. *U. S. For. Serv. For. Pest Leafl. 67.* 4 pp.

Winer, H. I. 1955. "History of the Great Mountain Forest, Litchfield County, Connecticut." Ph. D. Thesis, Yale Univ., New Haven, Conn. 278 pp.

Witter, J. A. and H. M. Kulman. 1972. A review of the parasites and predators of tent caterpillars (*Malacosoma* spp.) in North America. *Minn. Agric. Exp. Stn. Tech. Bull. 289.* 48 pp.

Witter, J. A., H. M. Kulman, and A. C. Hodson, 1972. Life tables for the forest tent caterpillar. *Ann. Entomol. Soc. Am. 65*:25-31.

Woods, F. W. and R. E. Shanks. 1959. Natural replacement of chestnut by other species in the Great Smokey Mountains National Park. *Ecology 40*:349-61.

Wright, R. H. 1958. The olfactory guidance of flying insects. *Can. Entomol. 90*:81-9.

Yadava, R. L. 1971. On the chemical stressors of nuclear-polyhedrosis virus of gypsy moth, *Lymantria dispar* L. *Z. Angew. Entomol. 69*:303-11.

Yasumatsu, K. 1958. An interesting case of biological control of *Ceroplastes rubens* Maskell in Japan. *Proc. 10th Int. Congr. Entomol. (Montreal). 4*:771-5.

Yates, H. O., III. 1966. *Rhyacionia* egg parasitism by *Trichogramma minutum* Riley. *J. Econ. Entomol. 59*:967-9.

Yearian, W. C., S. Y. Young, and J. M. Livingston. 1973. Field evaluation of a nuclear polyhedrosis virus of *Neodiprion taedae linearis*. *J. Invertebr. Pathol. 22*:34-7.

Yendol, W. G. 1975. Effectiveness of a baculovirus against the gypsy moth, *Porthetria dispar* L. *8th Int. Plant Prot. Congr., Moscow. Sec. V*:217-23.

Yendol, W. G. and R. A. Hamlen. 1973. Ecology of entomogenous viruses and fungi. Pages 18-30 in L. A. Bulla, Jr., ed. "Regulation of Insect Populations by Microorganisms." Ann. N.Y. Acad. Sci. 217. 243 pp.

Yendol, W. G., R. A. Hamlen, and S. B. Rosario. 1975. Feeding behavior of gypsy moth larvae on *Bacillus thuringiensis*-treated foliage. *J. Econ. Entomol. 68*:25-7.

Young, E. C. 1974. The epizootiology of two pathogens of the coconut palm rhinoceros beetle. *J. Invertebr. Pathol. 24*:82-92.

Young, J. R., J. W. Snow, J. J. Hamm, W. D. Perkins, and D. G. Haile. 1975. Increasing the competitiveness of laboratory-reared corn earworm by incorporation of indigenous moths from the area of sterile release. *Ann. Entomol. Soc. Am. 68*:40-2.

Young, S. Y. and W. C. Yearian. 1974. Persistence of *Heliothis* NPV on foliage of cotton, soybean, and tomato. *Environ. Entomol. 3*:253-5.

Younghusband, H. B. and P. E. Lee. 1969. Virus-cell studies of *Tipula* iridescent virus in *Galleria mellonella* (L.) I. Electron microscopy of infection and synthesis of *Tipula* iridescent virus in hemocytes. *Virology 38*:247-54.

Zak, B. 1961. Aeration and other soil factors affecting southern pines as related to littleleaf disease. *U.S. Dep. Agric. Tech. Bull. 1248*. 30 pp.

Zarin, I., I. Rituma, and R. Vitola. 1974. Nuclear polyhedrosis against *Malacosoma neustria* and *Neodiprion sertifer. Lesn. Khoz. No. 10*:79-83. (In Russian).

Zelazny, B. 1973a. Studies on *Rhabdionvirus oryctes*. II. Effect on adults of *Oryctes rhinoceros. J. Invertebr. Pathol. 22*:122-6.

Zelazny, B. 1973b. Studies on *Rhabdionvirus oryctes*. III. Incidence in the *Oryctes rhinoceros* population of Western Samoa. *J. Invertebr. Pathol. 22*:359-63.

Zimmerman, G. A. 1936. A further report on induced immunity to chestnut blight. *Annu. Rep. Northern Nut Growers Assoc. 27*:90-4.

Zinov'yev, G. A. 1962. The Siberian silkworm moth, *Dendrolimus sibiricus* Tschetv. (Lepidoptera, Lasiocampidae) and its parasites in the middle Urals. *Entomol. Rev. 41*:28-9. *41*:28-9.

Zivnuska, J. A. and H. J. Vaux. 1975. Future needs for land to produce timber, perspectives on prime lands. *U.S. Dep. Agric. Seminar Retention of Prime Lands*. pp. 69-90.

Zwölfer, H. and M. Kraus. 1957. Biocoenotic studies on the parasites of two fir and two oak tortricids. *Entomophaga 2*:173-96.

Author Index

Subject Index

A

Abies
  alba Miller, 304
  balsamea (L.) Mill., *see* Balsam fir
Ablerus clisiocampae (Ashm.), 238-239
Acer, 315
  pensylvanicum L., 69
  rubrum L., *see* Red maple
  saccharum Marsh, *see* Sugar maple
12-acetoxy-1-hydroxy-9-octadecene, 128
Acleris
  chalybeana (Fernald), 316
  gloverana (Wals.), 241
  minuta (Robinson), 316
  nivisellana (Walsingham), 316
  variana (Fernald), 241
Acronicta
  americana (Harris), 318
  distans (Grote), 318
  interrupta Guen., 318
  oblinita (J. E. Smith), 318
Acronycta aceris L., 108
Aculus schlechtendali (Nalepa), 314
Adelocera oculatus Lec., 82
Adjuvants, 282-283
Adoxophyes
  fasciata Walsingham, 119
  orana (Fischer von Roeslerstamm), 119
Aedes
  sollicitans (Wlkr.), 275-276
  taeniorhynchus (Wiedemann), 275-276
Aesculus hippocastanum L., 69
Agathis pumila (Ratzeburg), 100, 104
Agrilus
  anxius Gory, *see also* Bronze birch borer, 75-76, 78
  bilineatus (Weber), *see also* Twolined chestnut borer, 30, 73-83
  bilineatus var. *carpini* Knull, 75
  granulatus liragus Barter and Brown, 78
  vittaticolis (Randall), 315
Agrypon flaveolatum (Grav.), 208, 210

Albizia julibrissin Durazz., 69
Aleurocanthus
  spiniferus (Quaint.), 209
  woglumi Ashby, 209
Aleurothrixis flocossus (Mask.), 209
Alfalfa caterpillar, *see Colias eurytheme*
Alfalfa looper, *see Autographa californica*
Allotropa utilis Mues., 209
Almond moth, *see Cadra cautella*
Alsophila pometaria (Harris) *see also* Fall cankerworm, 27, 240, 244, 253, 318
Amelanchier, 313, 321
  canadensis (L.) Medic, 69
American beech, 12, 23, 75, 77, 106, 243, 321
American chestnut, *see also* Chestnut blight, 10-11, 16, 22, 24, 29-30, 61-70, 73, 75, 77-78, 81
American elm, 12, 23, 30, 32, 149, 160-175, 315, 321
Amitus spiniferus (Brethes), 209
Amorbia humerosana Clemens, 319
Amphicerus bicaudatus (Say), 317
Amsacto moorei Butler, 268
Amylostereum, 102
Anagasta kuehniella (Zeller), 129-131, 133
Anagyrus sp. near *kivuensis*, 209
Anaphoidea nitens Gir., 209
Anastatus, 236, 238-240, 248
  bifasciatus Fons., 216, 237, 244
  disparis Ruschka, 216-217, 220, 237, 244-248
  semiflavidus Gah, 244
Anchylopera
  fuscociliana (Clemens), 316
  nubeculana (Clemens), 316
Ancylis apicana Walker, 316
Anemotaxis, 129-130, 133-134
Angoumois grain moth, 331
Anicetus beneficus Ish. & Yam., 209
Anisota senatoria (J. E. Smith), 27, 236, 259
Anopheles, 332